Fundamentals of Psychological Research

Gordon Wood
Michigan State University

Fundamentals of Psychological Research

LITTLE, BROWN AND COMPANY Boston

Library of Congress Catalog Card Number: 73-16695

SECOND PRINTING

Published simultaneously in Canada
by Little, Brown & Company (Canada) Limited

Printed in the United States of America

TO JOAN AND DANA

Preface
Acknowledgments

CHARACTERISTICS OF THE TEXT

This text has three characteristics that set it apart from most other methodology texts. First, research methodology and statistics are presented by using examples from many different research areas. No attempt has been made to present all the findings in a particular area. This approach was adopted because presenting methodology within the context of one area is not very satisfactory for those individuals who have little or no interest in the subject considered. The advantage of using examples from many research areas is that the text does not restrict the options of instructors and students for emphasizing preferred content areas. Also, this text is suitable for general methodology courses, in which no particular research area is emphasized. Instructors who prefer to consider a particular content area to show how research is conducted can use this text along with a paperback text that presents research findings in the area of interest. Instructors of upper-level undergraduate courses who want to avoid spending time on methodology and statistics, but are usually unable to do so because many of their students have "forgotten" the basics of research, can offer this text as a review and reference. Although this text is intended primarily for courses in psychological research, it should also be suitable for general methodology courses in the social sciences.

The text can be used both by instructors who plan experiments for their students and by instructors who have students plan their own experiments. All the major steps of experimentation are considered, and the information in the text should be sufficient to enable the student to successfully test a research idea. If the students are required to share the methodological difficulties they encounter, it should be possible to cover a wide range of methodological problems.

A second characteristic of this text is that research methodology has been integrated with statistics. Although research methodology and statistics are frequently taught in separate courses, there are a number of advantages to presenting them together. The major reason for joint presentation is that they are highly related. A knowledge of methodology is useful for an understanding of statistics and vice versa. Including statistics and methodology in the same text makes it possible to more clearly indicate the relationship and thus present a more comprehensive view of the research enterprise in the social sciences. Unfortunately, it is not uncommon for students to leave statistics courses without an appreciation of the important role of statistics in research. I believe this problem is solved by integrating statistics and methodology in the same text.

A third characteristic is that the practical use of statistics is emphasized. The goal is to enable students to use statistical techniques that function as tools for researchers in psychology. By emphasizing the tool function of statistics, it is possible to present very useful statistical tests at a level that can be understood by students lacking a background in mathematics or statistics. However, there is some danger that potential users of this text will mistakenly think that the statistics section is too difficult for students who have not had mathematical training or a prior course in statistics. This is not the case. The text has been used in an introductory statistics and methodology class and found to be appropriate for students taking their second course in psychology. The reader who can add, subtract, multiply, and divide should have little or no difficulty with the statistics section of this text.

In summary, the text is intended for use by instructors who want to emphasize methodology without restricting their teaching options. The text can be used for a general methodology course, for a methodology course in which a specific research area is considered, or for a course in which students are required to conduct experiments. The text should be particularly welcome for instructors who share the author's view that methodology and statistics should be integrated so that students can attain a more comprehensive view of psychological research. Statistics instructors who believe that, on the introductory level, the tool function of statistics should be emphasized and the mathematical aspects minimized, should also find this text useful.

PLAN OF THE TEXT

The plan of the text is to consider the different stages of research, starting with the rationale for understanding research methodology and ending with the reporting of research findings. The first section is devoted primarily to methodological considerations, but statistical concepts are discussed whenever necessary. The major purpose of Section I is to discuss the problems involved in obtaining evidence to test theories. Topics include selecting a phenomenon for investigation, proposing explanations for the phenomenon, designing tests for the proposed solutions, and collecting evidence. Instructors who choose to emphasize methodology can assign all of Section I and use Section II for reference. (Section II will be very useful for analyzing experiments.) The major purpose of Section II is to consider the description and evaluation of evidence, so that the validity of the proposed explanation can be determined. Instructors who choose to emphasize statistical techniques can assign Chapter 4 and all of Section II. The non-assigned portion of Section I can serve as a reference. Statistical proofs, additional examples, research topics, and a more detailed discussion of probability have been included in appendixes. A glossary is also included, so that definitions of terms used in the text can be readily obtained.

ACKNOWLEDGMENTS

A number of people contributed to this text. Christopher Hunter, editor for Little, Brown and Company, made helpful suggestions. James V. Hindrichs, Eugene A. Lovelace, and two anonymous reviewers played an important role in shaping the final version of the manuscript by providing numerous constructive criticisms. Terrence M. Allen provided useful criticisms of a portion of the manuscript. Carl P. Duncan, Albert Erlebacher, and Benton J. Underwood contributed indirectly, in that they were largely responsible for my formal training in methodology and statistics. A number of my former students helped by indicating the sections in earlier drafts which were unclear or incomplete. LeAnn Slicer assisted in the preparation of the manuscript.

I am indebted to the Literary Executor of the late Sir Ronald A. Fisher, F.R.S., to Dr. Frank Yates, F.R.S., and to Oliver and Boyd, Edinburgh, for their permission to reprint material from Tables III and VI from their books *Statistical Methods for Research Workers* and *Statistical Tables for Biological, Agricultural and Medical Research.*

Special thanks are due Joyce Pennington for her numerous readings and detailed criticisms, and for her help in preparing the manuscript. Her assistance was invaluable.

Contents

APPENDIX A
PROOFS AND EXAMPLES 263

APPENDIX B
RESEARCH TOPICS 271

APPENDIX C
TABLES 285

Fundamentals of Psychological Research

section I

RESEARCH METHODOLOGY

introduction

The chapter begins with a discussion of some of the reasons why the informed citizen should have an understanding of how knowledge is accumulated in the social sciences. Additional reasons for understanding research methodology are offered for potential majors in psychology. Aspects of the scientific approach are discussed, including the assumptions of this approach, the goals of science, the importance of theories, the need to test theories, and measurement.

RESEARCH METHODOLOGY AND THE CITIZEN

The reader who has completed a course in introductory psychology or who is reasonably well informed about current events is aware that a vast amount of research is being conducted in the social sciences; he should also become aware of *how* such research is conducted. An understanding of research methodology makes it possible to evaluate the claims, ideas, theories, and new research findings of investigators and "experts" in the social sciences. There is little question that the public is confronted with numerous claims and findings which have important implications.

One approach is to accept passively what the experts say without evaluating their statements critically. If you do not choose to believe what one investigator says, you may be able to find another who agrees with you. A more satisfactory approach is to evaluate critically the statements of experts. There is good reason to be skeptical of their claims because the conclusions reached are not always justified by the evidence obtained. The individual who wants to see evidence before deciding what to believe needs an understanding of research methodology.

A few examples should help to demonstrate the usefulness of a knowledge of psychological research methods. Since it is safe to assume that interested citizens are likely to keep informed of current events by reading newspapers, as well as other publications, I selected a newspaper and looked for articles discussing the results of research. The October 22, 1972, edition of *The State Journal,* serving the greater Lansing, Michigan, area, was selected — simply because it happened to be on my breakfast table and not because it carried any more articles about psychological research than other Sunday papers.

One of the front page stories reported the results of a presidential preference poll conducted between October 11 and October 17, 1972. A sample of 2,696 voters was taken from six communities in six different states. In the Lansing, Michigan, sample, 56 percent were for Nixon, 19 percent for McGovern, and 25 percent for other candidates or undecided. The results of such a political poll can be of considerable importance to many citizens. For example, people may be less willing to work for or send money to a candidate who has little chance of winning. If this is the case, then it is important to know whether the results of the poll truly represent voter sentiment at the time the poll was taken. More specifically, is the result of the Lansing, Michigan, sample an accurate reflection of the preferences of Lansing voters who will actually vote on election day? In order to answer this question it is necessary to know more about the way the poll was conducted and also to know what is meant by "an accurate reflection." Some readers would consider an accurate prediction to be within one percentage point of the actual vote; others would settle for a prediction within 2, 4, 6, 8, or perhaps even 10 percentage points. What is needed in this case is an indication of the margin of error claimed for the prediction, the size of the sample for Michigan, the way the sample was selected, and whether those not likely to vote were screened from the sample.

In this case the pollsters may have used techniques to assure that their samples were representative of the larger population, but there is no way for the reader of the article to know. In the absence of more information about procedures, there is little reason to place more weight on the results of this poll than on the results of an Ice Cream Poll reported in a story on page 3 of the paper. The Ice Cream Poll, taken by tallying customer preference for "Dick's Double Dip Delight" or "George's Grand Gourmet Sundae," found Nixon leading McGovern by 250 scoops. In neither poll, however, is there any way to know whether the sample selected was representative of the population (i.e., voters in Lansing, Michigan) being considered.

Since the results of the election provide a check on the accuracy of political polls, most independent pollsters (i.e., those not working for a political party) are motivated to obtain representative samples. For example, any polling organization that did not predict Nixon's overwhelming victory would lose credibility. However, in most other types of surveys there is no final check on accuracy, so the motivation to be accurate may not be as great. In the absence of a final check the validity of the results can only be evaluated by examining the procedures used. The reader who has an understanding of what constitutes acceptable sampling techniques is equipped to evaluate the procedures. In some cases he may want to withhold judgment because insufficient information is presented. The informed reader should be able to decide whether the information presented is adequate; the uninformed reader will have no basis for an intelligent assessment of the facts.

Although some newspaper reporters do an excellent job of presenting the evidence on which their conclusions are based, there is usually a marked difference in the way newspapers and professional journals present research findings. The reports in journals typically include a detailed account of how the evidence was obtained, making it unnecessary for a reader to withhold judgment for lack of information. Thus, newspaper articles are usually not the best source for information about recent scientific advances. A person who prefers to evaluate the evidence to determine whether the conclusions are justified will often want more information than he can get from the newspaper. Fortunately, there are publications specifically intended for those who want to see detailed reports. And, although many newspaper accounts of research findings may be incomplete, a knowledge of research methodology should still be useful for understanding and evaluating these accounts.

The problem of students dropping out of school was discussed in another front page story in the same newspaper. In this case a number of factual statements were made. One of every four students drops out of school; some inner-city schools have more dropouts than graduates; in Chicago over 70 percent of the Puerto Rican students never graduate; and 1,000 students drop out of New York City schools each month. The dropout appears likely to die young; a black man who fails classes and is truant is eight times as likely to be dead at an early age as a black who does not have problems in school. The dropout is also more likely to be an alcoholic or a heroin addict, or to end up in jail.

The solution offered by the president of the United Federation of Teachers is to provide more teachers in order to establish closer personal relationships between teachers and students. The director of Chicago's Dropout Prevention Program thinks that the unions should be opened to the dropout and public service jobs provided. It is argued that it is cheaper to handle the problem in the community than to spend three to six thousand dollars a year to maintain the dropout in a health or penal institution.

Once again, there is no information about how the evidence was obtained, but let us accept the data as accurate. How, then, should the data be interpreted? If dropouts tend to have more difficulty than nondropouts, does this mean that dropping out of school is a *cause* of the subsequent difficulty? Or is it, instead, a *result* of difficulties already encountered? Unfortunately, no evidence is reported to support either interpretation. If dropping out of school is, in fact, a cause, then reducing the number of dropouts should also reduce the number of individuals who experience difficulty.

The reader who is concerned with the plight of the dropout should be interested in the effectiveness of the suggested solutions. For example, will the problem be solved by providing more teachers? Possibly not, particularly if being a dropout is the *result* of other difficulties. Will it be solved by obtaining jobs for the dropout? Once again, possibly this measure will have no effect on the rate of alcoholism, drug addiction, or early death. In short, there are two very important questions: Is the relationship between being a dropout and having subsequent difficulty a causal relationship? Are the recommended solutions effective? Someone with an understanding of research methodology in the social sciences would know how to obtain the necessary evidence to answer these questions.

A number of other articles in the same newspaper raise questions about how knowledge is accumulated in the social sciences and medicine. In one article Adelle Davis, a nutritionist, argues for the importance of obtaining forty nutrients daily from various foods: milk products; meat, fish, and fowl; fruits and vegetables; and breads and cereals. She claims that missing breakfast causes a drop in blood sugar, lack of energy, failure of the brain to work well, and problems in thinking clearly. The critical reader will ponder how one obtains evidence to support the view that missing breakfast affects the brain. How does one determine whether or not the brain is working well and how does one link any improper functioning of the brain to a specific antecedent condition such as missing breakfast?

One article asks whether consumers are taking more drugs than necessary because of the effectiveness of advertisements. For example, does advertising nonprescription sleeping pills through the mass media result in the use of such pills by people who do not really need them? Another article discusses the effectiveness of different tooth-brushing techniques. Another claims that smoking causes crows-feet (wrinkles around the eyes). Yet another argues that polluted air speeds nylon deterioration. There are also articles discussing the noise level in different subways, pollution in the Caribbean and Hawaii, the investigation of Congress by consumer advocate Ralph Nader, the effect of a changed environment on the mentally retarded, and alternatives to the usual practice of sending convicted men to jail. In short, it is unlikely that you will be able to find a metropolitan newspaper that does not contain articles making claims for particular products, techniques, or courses of action. The concerned reader should be able to evaluate such claims, and in order to do so he must understand the methods used to test ideas.

Although to understand and to judge research in some areas of the social sciences requires specific technical knowledge, numerous research findings can be thoroughly understood, and in many cases critically evaluated, through a knowledge of general research methodology. Moreover, the methodology presented in this text is frequently applicable to the evaluation of research outside of the social sciences. For example, the evaluation of birth control pills, of gun control legislation and violence, and of monosodium glutamate in baby food are disparate problems which are nevertheless likely to involve the use of similar methodologies.

The primary reason for studying research methodology, then, is to develop critical judgment. But there are two additional reasons. One is that the student's view of the social sciences may change drastically as he absorbs the scientific approach to generating and testing ideas. Simply stated, the evaluation of ideas, people, and events may be subjective or may be based on empirical evidence. Since it does not require any training to make subjective judgments, this method is readily available to all individuals. But since effort and training are necessary to understand the empirical method, some students opt to avoid it entirely. This is unfortunate because a knowledge of the empirical approach may have an influence on how ideas are evaluated, what is considered interesting and important, and what is learned from experience. Some students may be so impressed with the scientific approach that they will decide to pursue a career in the social sciences. It is extremely important that those who decide to major in psychology or the social sciences have a thorough understanding of methodology.

A second reason is that research can be fun. For most students, conducting research is a marked change from the typical educational experience. It gives them the opportunity to test ideas rather than to function primarily as sponges for the thoughts of others. This does not mean, of course, that students cannot examine ideas without doing research. It simply means that, for many of them, conducting research will be a new and exciting way to evaluate ideas critically.

RESEARCH METHODOLOGY AND MAJORS IN PSYCHOLOGY

A casual reading of almost any introductory psychology text should convince most readers that our knowledge is limited. For example, we still do not have an adequate understanding of brain functioning, psychotherapy, the effects of viewing violence on television, drug and alcohol addiction, or learning and retention. Yet, even though there are many unsolved problems, we know much more about behavior and mental activity than we did a decade ago. If we are to continue to extend our knowledge in psychology, we have little choice but to encourage individuals to construct and test theories about behavior and mental activity.

It is reasonable to expect psychology students to acquire the ability to understand and evaluate the research in their discipline. In the less advanced areas of knowledge, such as the social sciences, this may be the most important ability the student can develop. The state of knowledge in any given field changes with new research findings, but research methodology remains relatively constant over the years. The student who is familiar with methodology should have a much easier time weighing new findings. The student who does not know methodology will be taking the risk of knowing far less than the informed layman about psychology.

Some undergraduate psychology majors and minors will continue their formal education as graduate students in psychology. It is common for them to be surprised by the emphasis on statistics and methodology. As an undergraduate the student may have taken one or two methodology courses, but methodology was probably not emphasized. Rather, it was probably viewed by the undergraduate as something to be tolerated only in order to achieve the bachelor's degree. Many undergraduates would prefer to learn about interesting psychological theories and findings without considering the steps by which knowledge is accumulated.

It *is* tempting, for the beginning student in particular, to take a dilettantish approach to psychology. Yet, advanced work in psychology requires a thorough understanding of the means by which psychologists accumulate knowledge. In addition, it is generally easier to understand the end results of an investigation if the intermediate steps are understood. A psychology major who masters research methods can spend the subsequent graduate years doing research, not merely learning how.

Fortunately, the student who is considering becoming a researcher can receive research training and still have the option of pursuing other careers in psychology. The relatively incomplete state of knowledge in psychology can be an advantage in that the formal training necessary to become a researcher is very similar to that necessary to become a practitioner or teacher. That is, in psychology the "distance" between the acquisition and dissemination of knowledge is frequently so small that the effective teacher or practitioner should be able to evaluate research. It is, therefore, possible to prepare for an applied and research career at the same time; the decision to emphasize one or the other can be made later.

THE SCIENTIFIC APPROACH

Assumptions of the Scientific Approach

Order and Determinism. Two assumptions are essential for the scientific approach. The first is that nature is ordered, not haphazard. The assumption of *order* is a simple assertion that events follow each other in regular sequences, that an overall pattern or scheme of events is discernible. This assumption is usually easy to accept since there are so many instances of order: a child crawls before walking; eclipses of the moon can be accurately predicted; and applying heat to ice causes it to melt. The second assumption is that events have causes which can be detected. A particular event is assumed to be caused by other events. This assumption is known as *determinism.* A scientist would argue, for example, that the relevant prior experiences which lead to heroin addiction can be determined, that there is a set (or sets) of conditions resulting in heroin addiction *and* that these conditions can be discovered. Although scientists accept both the order and determinism assumptions, some nonscientists are reluctant to accept the idea of determinism.

Determinism and Free Will. Some people are willing to acknowledge that the scientific approach is applicable to many areas of investigation, but they reject its application to the study of human behavior. They believe that it is possible to determine the lawful relations which explain phenomena (i.e., facts or events) of the physical sciences, and they are even willing to believe that it is possible to explain the behavior of lower animals. Yet, they balk at the scientific investigation of human behavior. Humans, they believe, have free will. Manipulations can have an effect only by choice of the person concerned. The individual is in control of the environment in the sense that he can overcome or offset environmental changes. For example, if your mate berates you for showing a complete lack of responsibility, you are not forced to give a set response to the attack. You have freedom of choice. You can leave, become responsible, beg for forgiveness, increase the volume setting on the television, discuss the problem, and so on. Therefore, one can argue that it is futile to try to determine causal relations among events, that the important thing is the freedom of humans to respond.

In general, scientists who study human behavior do not become very excited about the free will issue because there are numerous instances in which behavior has been satisfactorily explained as a consequence of the prior experiences of those involved. The fact that it is not always possible, given our present state of knowledge, to specify the reasons for a particular behavior does not preclude the possibility that the relevant antecedent conditions can be discovered. It is often difficult to specify those conditions because an event may be influenced by a number of different factors. The determinism assumption does not deny the possibility of multiple causes for a particular behavior; the existence of unknown determinants is irrelevant to the question of the validity of the determinism concept. Some theorists argue that humans only appear to have freedom of choice because investigators do not have adequate control over the environment (e.g., physical environment, social interactions, number of siblings). If investigators had complete control of the environment, humans might be revealed to have little or no freedom of choice (see Skinner, 1971). Although the indeterminancy-determinancy issue appears very difficult to settle, the success of psychologists in formulating many principles of human behavior indicates that the determinism view is a good *working* assumption.

The Goals of Science

Scientists have three general goals. The first is to describe phenomena accurately. Basically, the task of description involves determining whether a particular phenomena exists and, if it does exist, determining the degree to which it exists. Usually the acquisition of knowledge starts with a description, since it is easier to describe a phenomenon than to explain it. For example, one can observe that students placed in identical conflict situations differ markedly in aggressiveness, but it is quite a different matter to explain why this is so.

The second goal is to explain phenomena. A phenomenon is explained if the antecedent conditions necessary to obtain it have been specified. If there are a number of different, plausible reasons for a particular phenomenon, then a state of ignorance exists. On the other hand, if there is firm evidence to support only one explanation, then the phenomenon can be considered explained or understood. Scientists regard all explanations as tentative, however, because the gathering of additional evidence may reveal that a previously rejected or new explanation is better than the accepted one. The only adequate explanation is one that makes it possible to predict the occurrence of the phenomenon accurately.

The third goal is to organize the available evidence into a coherent body of knowledge. This process is analogous to solving a jigsaw puzzle. At the early stages of investigation it is likely that investigators will be concerned primarily with attempting to get a few pieces of the puzzle together. For example, scientists interested in how humans process information may study such problems as the mechanisms involved in the perception of printed material, the retention of information for short periods of time (e.g., remembering a telephone number long enough to dial it), the retention of information for long periods of time (e.g., material covered in methodology courses), and the subsequent use of stored information. As investigators gain a fuller understanding of the various components of human information processing, they should be able to determine how the components are related, that is, how the larger pieces of the jigsaw puzzle fit together.

Although the puzzle analogy is appropriate for emphasizing the point that scientists seek an overall picture of the relationships among their research findings, it is somewhat misleading to imagine that all the pieces of the puzzle are available. Since additional phenomena may be discovered, the reader should keep in mind that new pieces can be added to the puzzle.

The Importance of Theory

Definition of Theory. A theory is a set of principles used to explain a particular phenomenon or set of phenomena. Although the word *theory* can be used as a synonym for the words *idea, view, notion,* or *hypothesis,* researchers tend to use these latter words — to extend the jigsaw analogy — as labels for tentative explanations of how two or more small pieces of the puzzle go together, whereas they frequently reserve the word *theory* for a tentative explanation of how larger pieces of the puzzle go together. *Theory* is also more likely to be used if there is considerable evidence to support the explanation. Yet, since all of these words can refer to tentative explanations, the reader can expect to find them used interchangeably by some investigators.

Functions of Theory. There are two important functions of theory. One is to guide research. Given that one of the important goals of science is to explain phenomena, it is reasonable to start with tentative explanations of phenomena, explanations typically derived from opposing theories, and then to test these explanations in an effort to eliminate those that are unsatisfactory. By the gradual process of rejecting what is wrong, scientists are able to obtain a better estimate of the true state of affairs. Obviously, if numerous attempts to disprove a theory fail, then that theory is likely to be viewed as more plausible than one which has not been tested extensively. Theories are important to scientists because they stimulate inquiry by generating testable predictions.

A second function of theory is to organize facts — an important aid toward arriving at a systematic body of knowledge. Theories play a crucial role in clarifying knowledge by providing a basis for organization. If a theory has firm support, then research findings can be generated from it. The situation is analogous to remembering a rule instead of memorizing a vast number of specific instances. For example, it is considerably easier to remember the spelling rule "*i* before *e* except after *c*" than to memorize the ordering of *i* and *e* for all the words in which these letters appear consecutively.

Theories Are Tentative. It is important to recognize that theories are *tentative* explanations, and it is necessary to evaluate each theory by determining how well it accounts for the available research findings and how well it can predict new findings. A theory that cannot be used to make predictions about observable events is of no value to scientists. If the research findings do not support the theory, then it should be modified or discarded. Research findings should dominate the theory, not vice versa. The facts cannot be changed to accommodate the theory; the theory must be changed to accommodate the facts.

Testing Theories

A basic purpose of this text is to discuss the procedures that social scientists use in their attempt to test theories. To be testable, a theory must make predictions about observable events. It is important, of course, that the prediction follow logically from the theory and that evidence be obtainable which will either support or contradict it. This means that the prediction must be stated in clear and simple language and must be made about events which can be measured.

A few examples should clarify these assertions. The view that daily exercise will improve the mind is an unacceptable prediction because it is not clear what is meant by daily exercise or improving the mind. In contrast, the prediction that jogging two miles each day will result in higher scores on the Mednick Remote Associates Test (Mednick & Mednick, 1967) is acceptable because it is clear what operations have to be performed in order to test the prediction. (A phenomenon that has been defined in terms of the operations necessary in order to demonstrate it is said to be operationally defined.)

The assertion that the Freudian method of therapy is superior to other methods is meaningless unless a set of operations can be specified for each therapy (i.e., operational definitions provided) and a single set of criteria for evaluating the different therapies can be agreed upon. Unfortunately, it is difficult, if not impossible, to arrive at a single standard or set of evaluative criteria that would be acceptable to different therapists and to scientists. For the scientist, the standard would have to be stated in terms of observable, measurable behavior. The topic of measurement requires further consideration.

Measurement

Reliability. The importance of measurement is difficult to overemphasize. Psychologists, whether they are interested in conducting research or describing behavior, expend considerable effort measuring behavior. Two major problems in this task are obtaining reliable measures and valid measures. The important factor in assessing the reliability of a measuring instrument is *consistency*. The issue is whether consistent results are obtained if repeated measures are made. An example should help to clarify this point.

Let us assume that an investigator is interested in predicting success in medical school. He believes that stress tolerance is an important consideration, so he administers a stress tolerance test to 100 medical school students. The plan is to determine how the score on the test is related to success in medical school. In order to make sure that a good estimate of each student's stress tolerance is obtained, another test is administered to each student two weeks after the first test. Let us assume that the two tests of stress tolerance are equivalent. (In some cases it is possible to assess reliability by using the same test at two points in time provided there are no carry-over effects from the first to the second testing.) The dismayed experimenter finds that there is little relationship between the scores of each student on the two tests. Some of the individuals who scored high on the first test scored high on the second test, but just as many others who scored high on the first scored low on the second. It should be clear that stress tolerance, at least as it is defined by these tests, is an *unreliable* phenomenon. Obviously, if it is not possible to obtain a consistent (reliable) measure of stress tolerance, it is difficult to make any statement about the relationship between amount of stress tolerance and performance in medical school. Thus, in most cases, obtaining a reliable measure is a prerequisite to investigating the relationship between two or more measures.

Validity. Assuming that a reliable measure is obtained, it is then possible to consider the validity of the measure. There are different ways to assess validity, but the basic issue is whether the test measures what it is supposed to measure. Thus, if a test is supposed to predict success in medical school, it should do exactly that. In this case predictive validity can be assessed by comparing performance on the test and performance in medical school.

If the validity of a test has not been established, the label of the test may be misleading. For example, let us assume that you are interested in assessing altruism. You construct a test and demonstrate that it is reliable; you label it The Altruism Test. But a friend objects because she does not think the test is actually measuring *true* altruism. She decides to make her point by constructing her own test, which she demonstrates to be reliable and labels The *True* Altruism Test. You object because you believe your test is every bit as good a measure of true altruism as hers. You and your friend have 100 individuals take both tests and find that scores on one test are unrelated to scores on the other. Since the two tests are unrelated, it is apparent that they are measuring different things. If this is the case, who is measuring true altruism? There is nothing to be gained by arguing for entities such as true altruism, true anxiety, true intelligence, and so forth. Instead it is more useful to recognize that individuals may possess a relatively stable set of behaviors that may or may not be useful in predicting other behaviors.

The usefulness of such a test, assuming it is reliable, can be assessed by determining whether the results can be used to predict other behaviors. It is necessary to establish a criterion for altruism (e.g., donating blood, helping the poor) in order to assess the predictive validity of the test. The question of interest is whether the score on the *test* predicts performance on the *criterion* (e.g., whether the person whose test score indicates a high degree of altruism will in fact donate blood or help the poor). Many needless disputes arise because people do not bother to specify the criteria they use to evaluate success. For example, the problem of assessing the quality of instruction is complicated by the failure of many individuals to specify their criteria for evaluating instruction. A difficult problem encountered in assessing validity is establishing an acceptable criterion.

SUMMARY

The reader who learns how research is conducted in the social sciences is in a good position to evaluate the reports of research findings and the claims of investigators and so-called experts. A knowledge of research methodology can have an important influence on how you evaluate ideas, what you consider interesting and important, and what you learn from experience. Psychology majors, in particular, should have a clear understanding of how knowledge is obtained in their discipline.

The two assumptions of the scientific approach are *order* and *determinism. Order* refers to the assertion that events follow each other in regular sequences, *determinism* to the assertion that events have causes which can be detected. There are three basic goals of science. The first goal is to describe phenomena by determining whether they exist and, if so, the degree to which they exist. The second is to explain phenomena by specifying the antecedent conditions necessary to produce them. The third is to organize research findings into a coherent body of knowledge.

Theories guide research and serve as a basis for the organization of knowledge. They are tentative explanations which must be testable in order to be of any use to scientists. In order to be testable, a theory must make predictions about observable events. Measurement is a crucial aspect of research because in order to test theories it is necessary to develop objective standards. Two problems encountered in measuring phenomena are obtaining reliable and valid measures. *Reliability* refers to the consistency with which the same operations yield the same measurement. *Validity* refers to whether these operations actually measure what they are purported to measure.

QUESTIONS

1. Examine a recent issue of a newspaper for articles in which claims are made for a particular product, technique, or course of action. Select one of the claims not accompanied by supporting evidence and indicate how support for the claim could be obtained.
2. Select your area of special interest in psychology or the social sciences and make a list of the findings that you believe are important. That is, what facts or theoretical notions, if any, do you consider to be crucial? Are there studies or theories which opened up new lines of investigation or provided insight into previously baffling problems? Were these findings the result of the scientific approach? If not, what approach was used?
3. Defend or refute the view that theories are important for the accumulation of knowledge. Is it necessary to test theories in order to conduct research?
4. Do you believe social science researchers should attempt to influence legislation in the areas of their expertise (e.g., gun control legislation and violence, violence on television)? That is, should the researcher give up the role of impartial investigator to argue for particular courses of action?
5. In undergraduate courses the emphasis on methodology versus specific content varies greatly among the sciences. What factors do you believe should determine whether specific content or methodology is emphasized?
6. What is your position on the determinism issue? Do you believe that you are largely a product of your past experiences?
7. Distinguish between reliability and validity and indicate, by example, how you would determine each. Use an example other than the ones presented in the text.
8. Let us assume that you have developed a test to evaluate classroom instruction. Make a list of potential criteria that could be used to establish the predictive validity of the test.
9. Let us assume that you want to measure creativity. What kind of items would you use to assess creativity? How would you determine the reliability and validity of the test?

2 creativity, investigators, problems, and ideas

The chapter begins with a theory of creativity which argues against the view that we can wait for a select group of specially gifted, insightful investigators to solve the important problems that confront us. Some of the characteristics of active researchers are considered. Then suggestions are made for selecting a problem area, generating ideas, and evaluating ideas. Special emphasis is placed on the testability of ideas.

A THEORY OF CREATIVITY

A person's notions about creativity can have an important effect on his approach to psychological research. A common view is that there are people who have direct insights into baffling problems. Obviously, individuals differ in their problem-solving abilities, but it is questionable whether it is necessary to postulate some special ability to account for these differences. Rather one can argue, as Campbell (1960) does, that problem solving is better described as a trial-and-error process* than an insightful process.

There is no question that some people are better equipped than others to store information. To use a computer analogy, some people have better hardware. It is also obvious that people differ in the kind and amount of information they process and store. Contrast the student who spends his leisure time in the library with the one who spends his watching television. And, it is also true that people differ in their desire to find solutions to problems. A person who is highly motivated to solve a problem is likely to make more attempts to reach a solution and be more tolerant of failure; he is likely to generate ideas and continue to generate ideas even if the first several attempts are not very fruitful.

The major point is that there is no need to postulate a creativity mechanism to account for differences in problem-solving ability. If partial information is available — i.e., if several ideas have been tested and found lacking — the researcher who is aware of this information is more likely to solve the problem since a number of potential blind alleys can be eliminated. Without partial knowledge, attempts at problem solution can only reflect a trial-and-error process. The reader who finds this difficult to accept should attempt to specify the mechanism that would provide information about nature's secrets. Campbell points out that we are prone to postulate such a mechanism because of a tendency to conclude, falsely, that marvelous consequences have marvelous antecedents.

This view requires further comment. An example, similar to one offered by Campbell, may help clarify the issue. Let us assume that there are five prospectors who each have a theory about the location of a gold vein. They have "equal" abilities, and their theories are equally plausible. Let us further assume that one prospector happens to locate the gold vein. Would you be tempted to attribute special characteristics to the lucky prospector? Perhaps

* Professor Campbell describes problem solving as a process of blind variation and selective retention. The *successes* obtained through blind variation (trial-and-error) procedures are selectively retained.

you would be willing to conclude that the one prospector was just lucky. Would you reach the same conclusion if, instead of prospectors, the five individuals were cancer researchers, and one investigator found an effective cure?

The reader should not interpret this example to mean that the primary difference between a successful researcher and an unsuccessful one is luck. Although luck can certainly be a factor, it is probable that differences in encoding ability, amount and type of information encoded, and motivation to reach a solution provide better explanations of individual differences in problem solving. In any case there is no compelling reason to assume that the successful researcher has special creative abilities.

You may balk at accepting the trial-and-error view because you believe that great men such as Newton, Poincaré, and Einstein were indeed qualitatively different from others in the same field. Yet, it may be that you attribute special characteristics to successful individuals because you are ignorant of the antecedent conditions. If you were aware of the antecedent conditions, you would, I believe, be less likely to argue for a creative process. For example, the fact that I know a considerable amount about psychology and about the antecedents of important findings in this field, and know very little about such matters in physics, leads me to view the giants of these two fields differently. I am more likely to attribute special abilities to the giants in physics. I expect that someone very knowledgeable in physics, and not himself a recognized giant, would be less likely to do so. The introspective reports of scientists who have achieved great success are generally consistent with the trial-and-error view (see Campbell, 1960).

The trial-and-error view of creative endeavors has important implications for the potential researcher. It suggests that the reasonably bright individual who is willing to process a considerable amount of information, generate ideas, and then test these ideas has the best chance of success. It seems unreasonable to expect that we can wait for a select group of specially gifted, insightful people to solve the important problems that confront us. Readers who still prefer to believe in "creative abilities" will, hopefully, at least reject the view that only a select group possesses these abilities. This is important because conducting research would allow these readers to use their own "creative" ability.

INVESTIGATORS

A logical starting point for a consideration of psychological research is the experimenter. Since personal involvement is important in research, it makes good sense for the student to play the role of the experimenter. To take this role you should be curious, reasonably intelligent, independent, and motivated. Moreover, you should believe that important ideas can be empirically tested and that you can generate ideas worth testing.

You should not be too quick to conclude that you do not possess the characteristics of the active experimenter. For the most part, it is difficult to evaluate whether you have such characteristics until you have made a sincere effort to involve yourself in a research problem. There are many instances of apathetic, antiscientific individuals who have developed a fondness for the scientific approach to problem solving. I expect that most researchers were apathetic toward research until they became ego-involved in the conduct of *their* research. The first task for the experimenter is to select a problem. If you have already decided on a problem area, or if your instructor has provided you with one, you may elect to skip to the section entitled *Criteria for Evaluating Ideas.*

THE PROBLEM

Selecting a Problem Area

You should select a problem area that you consider to be interesting and important. If you select a dull or unimportant problem, it is unlikely that you will derive much satisfaction from your efforts. Moreover, if you cannot get excited about the research you are doing, it is improbable that you will continue doing research for any prolonged period. Choosing a research area is analogous to selecting a mate. You should choose a problem that you can live with, one that you find exciting.

Resolving to select an important problem is decidedly easier than finding one. You may rule out entire areas of study because of ignorance; you may not understand an area well enough to evaluate it. The well-read investigator has an obvious advantage when it comes to finding an interesting problem. The basic task is to make a value judgment about what you find appealing and valuable. Then you could examine an introductory psychology test or read Appendix B of this book, discuss your interests with your instructor, or read articles in the many psychology journals found in the library. By reading about the various areas and discussing them with others, you should be able to select one in which you would like to work. If no constraints are placed on your selection, you may prefer to choose an area in one of the other social sciences. Since the material presented in this text is applicable to many areas of social science, there is no compelling reason, from the author's point of view, why your selection has to be in the area of psychology.

Limiting the Scope of the Problem

In all probability you will find selecting a broad area of study a relatively easy task. You may decide that you are interested, say, in sociology, social psychology, clinical psychology, experimental psychology, or personality. However, deciding that you want to do research in one of these areas is analogous to deciding that you want to go to college; there are still many decisions to make. The task of narrowing your interests in order to isolate a researchable problem may prove to be difficult. It is a little like prospecting; the yield will depend upon the area selected for investigation. Unfortunately, there are no road signs directing researchers to rich areas. It is quite understandable, therefore, that many students experience some anxiety while attempting to narrow their interests.

You should not be timid about isolating your research problem for fear of making a poor decision. At this point there is little reason to be overly concerned about how others view your selection. It is more important to find a problem that *you* consider worthwhile. If you continue to do research, it is likely that you will experience a gradual shift in what you consider interesting and important. There will be ample time to worry about how others view your research if you continue with a research career. It is amazing how many students believe that they can only do research on dull projects. The reader who is skeptical about the large number of attractive areas for possible research is invited to examine a recent index of *Psychological Abstracts.* It is incredible how many problem areas investigators in the social sciences have unearthed. Out of the thousands of different problems, the reader should be able to find at least one that awakens his interest.

Laboratory versus Library Research

There is some question whether a student who has no research experience should spend the major portion of his time in the library trying to find a suitable problem or in the laboratory testing tentative solutions. The advantage of the laboratory is that it offers a greater likelihood of gaining personal involvement. The student who lacks a personal commitment is advised to become immersed in the testing of an idea as soon as possible. The excitement of conducting an experiment is likely to send him back to the library eventually to compare his results with those of others.

On the other hand, a researcher should not be *too* anxious to begin experimentation. Since it is likely that at least some aspect of the problem selected has been investigated by others, there are advantages to becoming aware of these findings before proceeding with your own investigation. The reason for this is obvious. If you are aware of the mistakes of others and the evidence obtained by others, you can avoid pitfalls and the testing of views already demonstrated to be incorrect. You can acquaint yourself with the partial knowledge available in your area of interest. This should enable you to do better research than the investigator who is ignorant of previous findings.

The importance of library research will depend on the reasons for doing the research and on what is already known. The investigator who is interested in extending the knowledge in a particular area would be foolish not to determine what knowledge has already been accumulated before starting his own investigation. It is, however, usually more enjoyable to do your own research than to read about the research of others. Therefore, if lack of motivation is a problem, the student who wants an introduction to research should probably opt to spend much of his time in the laboratory.

Generating Ideas

Given that a problem has been selected, the next step is to generate possible solutions and tests for the solutions. There is little to be said regarding how best to generate ideas because "discovering" explanations and tests for explanations seems to be a trial-and-error process. You may be unable to think of a possible solution while consciously attempting to solve the problem, but an idea may suddenly occur to you while you are engaged in some other activity. This phenomenon is akin to not being able to think of the name of an old friend while consciously trying to retrieve the name, and then having it "pop into awareness" a little later when you are otherwise occupied. It is very doubtful, however, that the name would have "popped into awareness" if a conscious search for it had not been made earlier. The same argument can be made about searching for a solution to a problem. Although some will argue that such a search involves vastly different processes than those involved in retrieving previously stored information, there is no good evidence to support the view that the processes are qualitatively different.

There is no way for an investigator to know beforehand whether his search will be successful. He may spend days, weeks, or even years in research before arriving at a solution. In some cases, it may not be possible to reach an acceptable solution. The investigator who is unable to generate a possible solution may elect to consider testing someone else's ideas. Investigators sometimes mention testable ideas in the discussion section of their articles. It is permissible to test someone else's ideas as long as he is given credit. What is important is that good ideas get tested — not who originates the ideas or who tests them.

CRITERIA FOR EVALUATING IDEAS

Testability and Operational Definitions

It is important to evaluate ideas according to several criteria. Often an idea which initially appears to be good turns out to be either unimportant or untestable. Many ideas are untestable because they cannot be reduced to specific operations. If it is not clear what has to be done, then it is not possible to test the idea. For example, an investigator interested in testing whether pornography has a deleterious effect on the moral fiber of youths is likely to encounter difficulty. First, it is difficult to decide what is pornographic and what is not. One person's pornography can be another person's art. Let us assume, however, that the investigator is able to find materials that most judges classify as hard-core pornography.

The crux of the experiment is to present the pornographic materials to one group of youths and to make sure that an "equivalent" group of youths does not see any such material. Then, the only task is to measure whether the groups differ with respect to moral fiber. This is the second rub. It is not clear how one would go about measuring differences in moral fiber. Thus, the idea, as stated, is not testable. However, if the statement was made in terms of specific operations, it could be tested. For example, one could investigate the influence of pornographic materials on the number of convictions for crimes involving sexual offenses. One would then have an operational definition of the idea previously expressed vaguely in the phrase "moral fiber." Although it would be difficult to obtain the necessary cooperation to do such a study, the idea is stated in such a way that, assuming agreement regarding what is pornographic, it could be tested.

It is essential to avoid the use of vague language that leaves it unclear what operations should be performed to test the proposed view. In one sense, there is an advantage to vaguely stated notions since it is not possible to refute them. By the same token, however, the vague language prevents the ideas from ever being supported by empirical evidence, and thus accepted by the scientific community.

Testability and Refutability

A testable idea is one that can be refuted. If a theory is so general that it can explain any possible outcome, then it is not testable. Many theories are not refutable because explanation is after the fact. One example is the Freudian view of personality structure. The id, ego, and superego vie for control, but the decision as to what structure has control tends to be after the fact. It is possible to describe behavior after the fact in terms of the interplay of the id, ego, and superego, but it is quite another matter to arrange a set of operations which would demonstrate that the notions about the id, ego, and superego are incorrect. A theory that cannot be refuted is of little use to the scientific community; there is no way to build a body of knowledge unless incorrect ideas can be rejected. By the gradual process of rejecting what is wrong, we gain a more accurate picture of the true state of affairs.

The reader should not conclude that vaguely stated theories are necessarily "bad." It is just that they are of no help to the investigator who is interested in empirically testing ideas in order to advance the knowledge of a field. If a vaguely stated, untestable theory is an aid to a practitioner in his efforts to help people solve their problems, then it is obviously of some worth. The interesting applied problem is whether the theory, *per se,* does prove to be a beneficial addition to the therapeutic process. Unfortunately, it is difficult to evaluate most personality theories since the criteria, i.e., the goals of therapy which follow from the theories, differ as a function of the theory considered. This brings us to another aspect of evaluating ideas.

Testability and Comparability

Many ideas are untestable because they involve a comparison of processes or events or things which are simply not comparable. For instance, it is not possible to compare the effectiveness of two therapies if the criteria for evaluating a "cure" differ for the two therapies. To take another example, you may be concerned with the effects of marihuana and alcohol. For personal reasons, you would like to demonstrate that the effects of marihuana are at least no worse than the effects of alcohol. The problem is that comparing marihuana and alcohol is like trying to compare apples and oranges. Is one apple equal to one orange? How much marihuana is equal to a six-pack of beer?

It should be clear that one cannot assess the "true" relative effects of marihuana and alcohol. However, it is possible to equate the two on dollar value and assess the relative effects. Thus, one might be able to conclude that the behavioral effects of smoking two dollars' worth of marihuana are no worse than the effects of drinking two dollars' worth of beer. Yet, since many factors determine price (supply and demand, taxes, greed), it is unlikely that many people would be impressed by this demonstration. Except for the propaganda value of such an investigation, the knowledge obtained could hardly be described as more than trivial. However, the methodological point is that, if an investigator is making a comparison between treatments, organisms, or whatever, it is important that he be aware of the danger of making apples-and-oranges comparisons.

The apples-and-oranges problem may appear in many different disguises. Consider the problem of studying cognitive development by devising tasks appropriate for the various age levels investigated. Or consider preparing tasks appropriate for mentally retarded and normal individuals, for males and females, or for primates and humans. The difficulty is that there is no way to determine whether the differences obtained should be attributed to the use of different subject populations or to the different tasks involved.

Testability and Practical Considerations

Many ideas are testable in theory but are not in practice because of ethical, financial, or other considerations. There may be many reasons why a particular experiment should not be conducted. Perhaps the investigator lacks facilities, animal or human subjects, or money for supplies. If an experimenter believes his ideas are worth testing in spite of the large costs involved in collecting the relevant data, he can request support from federal, state, or private granting agencies. One should be reluctant to conclude that an experiment cannot be conducted if the only difficulty is lack of resources. However, if the difficulty is an ethical consideration, one should seriously consider not conducting the experiment.

Testability and Ethical Considerations

Ethics and the Use of Animals. Concern for the proper care and treatment of animals used in research is great. Researchers who use animals must be aware of the laws and guidelines for their care and handling. An investigator who plans to use animals should contact the local humane society and the American Humane Association, P.O. Box 1266, Denver, Colorado, 80201. The animal health regulations for each state can be obtained from the state public health office or state veterinarian. Another essential publication, available from the United States Department of Health, Education, and Welfare, is entitled *Guide for Laboratory Animal Facilities and Care.* Or, the investigator can write to the American Psychological Association, Office of Scientific Affairs, 1200 Seventeenth Street, N.W., Washington, D.C., 20036, for the manual on the care of animals.

Additional regulations must be followed when laboratory animals are used by people not trained in their care and treatment. The American Psychological Association Committee on Precautions and Standards in Animal Experimentation has prepared guidelines on the use of animals in school science behavior projects. These are published in the *American Psychologist,* 1972, Volume 27, page 337. Although they were intended primarily for students in intermediate and secondary schools, they are also applicable to the use of animals by students in colleges and universities. The guidelines are briefly considered here, to give the reader an appreciation of the steps used to safeguard the welfare of animals.

The first four guidelines cover the proper planning and supervision of each project, the adherence to the laws of each state and to the recommendations of humane societies, and the use of small animals that are easy to maintain or of invertebrates whenever possible. The fifth guideline is that, "No student shall undertake an experiment which includes the use of drugs, surgical procedures, noxious or painful stimuli such as electric shock, extreme temperature, starvation, malnutrition, ionizing radiation, etc. except under extremely close and rigorous supervision of a researcher qualified in the specific area of study." The purpose of this restriction is, of course, to assure that there are sound reasons for any unusual treatment of animals. The sixth guideline directs researchers to make certain that the animals receive proper housing, food, water, exercise, gentle handling, and so forth. It is crucial that arrangements be made for the care of the animals over vacation periods.

The seventh guideline concerns the disposition of animals at the conclusion of the experiment. Sometimes the animals are maintained as pets. In some cases they are selected so that their normal life span corresponds to the duration of the experiment. In other cases it is necessary to perform euthanasia, which should be carried out only by a trained person. In connection with this, it should be pointed out that most of the animals used in experiments are bred solely for the purpose of research; they would not exist otherwise.

Ethics and the Use of Human Subjects. The task of determining ethical standards governing the use of human subjects is an immense undertaking. There are so many different kinds of research projects involving human subjects and so many different opinions on how the rights of these subjects should be protected that it is difficult to arrive at a set of principles to which all researchers can subscribe. In spite of the difficulty, the American Psychological Association appointed a Committee on Ethical Standards in Psychological Research to revise the Association's 1953 code of ethics for research using human subjects. The committee worked approximately three years. They polled thousands of researchers, held numerous discussions at professional meetings, reviewed earlier ethical standards, and invited members of the American Psychological Association to criticize each of the two drafts. The first draft appeared in July, 1971, the second in May, 1972. The adopted standards were published in the January, 1973, issue of the *American Psychologist* (p. 79). This list of Ethical Principles is as follows:

*The Ethical Principles in the Conduct of Research with Human Participants**

1. In planning a study the investigator has the personal responsibility to make a careful evaluation of its ethical acceptability, taking into account these Principles for research with human beings. To the extent that this appraisal, weighing scientific and humane values, suggests a deviation from any Principle, the investigator incurs an increasingly serious obligation to seek ethical advice and to observe more stringent safeguards to protect the rights of the human research participant.

2. Responsibility for the establishment and maintenance of acceptable ethical practice in research always remains with the individual investigator. The investigator is also responsible for the ethical treatment of research participants by collaborators, assistants, students and employees, all of whom however, incur parallel obligations.

3. Ethical practice requires the investigator to inform the participant of all features of the research that reasonably might be expected to influence willingness to participate, and to explain all other aspects of the research about

* The principles shown above were written by the Committee on Ethical Standards in Psychological Research. Copyright 1973 by the American Psychological Association, reprinted by permission.

The final version of the Committee report, entitled *Ethical Principles in the Conduct of Research with Human Participants,* has been published by the American Psychological Association (1200 Seventeenth Street, N.W., Washington, D.C. 20036) in booklet form. Except for a slight wording change in Principle 3, the principles presented here are identical to those in the final report. The booklet offers a detailed discussion of each principle, to help the reader place the issues in context. I would encourage all who plan to use human subjects in research to obtain a copy of this report.

which the participant inquires. Failure to make full disclosure increases the investigator's responsibility to maintain confidentiality, and to protect the welfare and dignity of the research participant.

4. Openness and honesty are essential characteristics of the relationship between investigator and research participant. When the methodological requirements of a study necessitate concealment or deception, the investigator is required to ensure the participant's understanding of the reasons for his action and to restore the quality of the relationship with the investigator.

5. Ethical research practice requires the investigator to respect the individual's freedom to decline to participate in research or to discontinue participation at any time. The obligation to protect this freedom requires special vigilance when the investigator is in a position of power over the participant. The decision to limit this freedom increases the investigator's responsibility to protect the participant's dignity and welfare.

6. Ethically acceptable research begins with the establishment of a clear and fair agreement between the investigator and the research participant that clarifies the responsibilities of each. The investigator has the obligation to honor all promises and commitments included in that agreement.

7. The ethical investigator protects participants from physical and mental discomfort, harm and danger. If the risk of such consequences exists, the investigator is required to inform the participant of that fact, to secure consent before proceeding, and to take all possible measures to minimize distress. A research procedure may not be used if it is likely to cause serious and lasting harm to participants.

8. After the data are collected, ethical practice requires the investigator to provide the participant with a full clarification of the nature of the study and to remove any misconceptions that may have arisen. Where scientific or humane values justify delaying or withholding information, the investigator acquires a special responsibility to assure that there are no damaging consequences for the participant.

9. Where research procedures may result in undesirable consequences for the participant, the investigator has the responsibility to detect and remove or correct these consequences, including, where relevant, long-term aftereffects.

10. Information obtained about the research participants during the course of an investigation is confidential. When the possibility exists that others may obtain access to such information, ethical research practice requires that this possibility, together with the plans for protecting confidentiality, be explained to the participants as a part of the procedure for obtaining informed consent.

The reader should note that informed consent is the basic notion embodied in these Ethical Principles. That is, the investigator has an obligation to inform the potential subject of all the features of the experiment which can reasonably be expected to influence the subject's willingness to participate. If this is impossible, then the investigator must take additional steps to insure that the rights of the subject are not violated.

The Stuart W. Cook Committee, the group responsible for drafting the

Ethical Principles, invited thousands of researchers to list incidents of research involving ethical issues. Some of the incidents were reported in the special issue of *The Monitor* (May, 1972) in which the second draft of the standards was presented and discussed. In order to give the reader an appreciation of some of the ethical problems researchers may confront, a number of these incidents have been paraphrased in the list of Examples of Research Involving Ethical Issues which follows:

*Examples of Research Involving Ethical Issues**

1. An investigator is interested in the effect of manipulating the level of initial self-esteem. The proposed research would involve having two people compete for the attention of a member of the opposite sex. The experimenter would arrange the situation in such a way that one competitor would experience an embarrassing defeat while the other would be victorious. In this case there is no way to inform the subjects about the factors which may influence their willingness to participate and still make the desired manipulation. Is it possible to do this research without violating the ethical standards?

2. An investigator observes people in situations in which they do not know they are being observed. A cost-benefit rationale is offered for the invasion of privacy. The value of the findings is weighed against the possible harm to the subjects (e.g., the extent to which their privacy is violated). In cases in which the investigator has any misgivings about the ethical issue, a decision is made not to conduct the research. Furthermore, the investigator consults his colleagues before starting any research of this nature and weighs their views in arriving at a decision. The plan is to inform the subjects in full about the nature of the experiment after it is completed. If the subjects object to the study or to aspects of it, the investigator would not publish the results. Is research of this nature ethical? Are there some situations in which it would be ethical and others in which it would be unethical?

3. An investigator who was studying procedures for reducing fear of snakes had his graduate students telephone undergraduates to determine their willingness to participate. The investigator was unaware that the graduate students told the undergraduates they had to participate. What standards are violated?

4. The subjects were informed correctly regarding the basic procedures that would be used, but they were misinformed about the purpose of the experiment. They were told the experiment was designed to test the speed of the visual system. Actually, the experimenter was interested in testing long-term memory. The subjects were not told the real purpose because the investigator was afraid this knowledge would influence their performance. The experimenter reasoned that a subject who would participate for the stated reason would also participate for the real reason. Is this an acceptable procedure?

5. A doctoral student was interested in factors influencing cheating. The

* Selected and adapted from the Special Issue of The American Psychological Association *Monitor* (May, 1972).

doctoral student administered an examination, collected the papers, and then photographed each one. The students were not informed about the photographing. The papers were returned unscored and the students were given the opportunity to cheat while scoring their papers. The papers were collected again and were compared with the photographs. Is this an ethical procedure?

6. A professor of psychology worked on the production line in a factory for one semester. He did not reveal his identity to his coworkers or his reasons for being there. His purpose was to study the interactions of his coworkers. The findings proved to be useful in his subsequent teaching and research. His coworkers, some of whom he became very close to, were not informed of his purpose until the observation session was completed. Is this type of data collection ethical?

7. An experimenter returned fake test scores to male college students in order to assess the effects of success and failure on a second task. The subjects were told that the test scores were related to I.Q. and grade point average. After the second test, the subjects were told that the scores were faked and why the false information was given. The entire experiment was executed in a single session so that any fears the subjects had could be quickly alleviated. Is this an acceptable procedure?

8. A kidney patient and his nearest relative were asked to consent to having the patient take some tests to determine cognitive functioning before and after hemodialysis. The investigators were interested in the effects of uremia on cognitive functioning. In this case there is some question whether the patient was coerced into participating since his life depended on his remaining in the program. Did the patient have a real choice? Is the procedure ethical?

9. An experiment was conducted to assess driver reaction to a stressful situation. The subject was asked to drive a car past a construction site. The experimenter rigged a human-looking dummy in such a way that it would be propelled in front of the car making it impossible for the subject to avoid it. The subjects reacted as one would expect. And, when they learned that the situation was rigged, they informed the experimenter of their displeasure. Despite their complaints, the experimenter continued testing subjects. Is this procedure ethical?

10. An investigator was interested in how children would perform a task after watching another child being punished for low performance in the task. The question of interest was whether observing a punishment scene would raise or lower the children's subsequent performance relative to children who did not observe punishment. The children were tested in pairs. The first member of each pair received a scolding for low performance. The child's task was to drop marbles through holes. Even though the children were doing their best, they were scolded for low performance for approximately three minutes of the six-minute session. It was clear to the experimenter that most of the children were very anxious. After the session was over, the experimenter explained that he was only fooling and praised each child extensively. Most of the children seemed to understand. Is it ethical to use psychological torment in research?

11. An investigator, who was using Galvanic Skin Responding procedures,

had a subject become extremely upset during a testing session. The eight-year-old subject discontinued the experiment and went home. The experimenter was unaware of the subject's reason for leaving. Later, it was determined that the subject thought that blood was being extracted from his body since the electrode wires had a red plastic covering and red ink was used in the recording pens. Was the experimenter's behavior unethical?

12. The respondents to a mailed questionnaire were told that they would not be identified with their responses. A self-addressed return envelope was included for the "convenience" of the responder. The type and location of the stamp were such that the investigator could identify 100 of the respondents to the questionnaire. Is this procedure unethical?

13. An investigator conducted a series of interviews with patients in a state mental institution. The investigator assured each patient that the taped interviews would not be heard by anyone but the other member of the research team. Under these circumstances many of the patients gave extremely candid responses. For the purpose of discussion, assume that one patient indicated a strong desire to escape from the institution for the purpose of committing sexual offenses on young children. What would you do if you were the investigator?

The reader can decide whether or not each of the above incidents violates the adopted standards presented in the Ethical Principles list. It should be kept in mind that researchers were specifically asked to provide examples of research involving ethical questions. The incidents presented are not representative of the research problems encountered by the "typical" investigator. The reader may want to have additional information before evaluating some of the incidents. Indeed, an important aspect of evaluation is deciding what additional information, if any, is needed.

A consideration of the list of Ethical Principles and the list of Examples of Ethical Issues should provide the reader with an awareness of some of the ethical problems that may be raised by research. If a proposed project is in violation of these ethical standards, the investigator must either abandon the project or change it to eliminate unethical procedures. In some cases there is likely to be disagreement about whether a research project is in violation of the standards. For instance, there will probably be disagreement regarding whether some of the incidents described in the Examples of Ethical Issues list should be placed in the unethical or ethical category. In some of these cases it is likely that procedural changes could be made which would eliminate the ethical problem.

If there is considerable difference of opinion about whether a particular procedure is in violation of the ethical standards and there is no change that can be made to eliminate the ethical problem, then the investigator is well advised to abandon the project. Fortunately, the vast majority of research projects do not pose serious ethical problems. Of course, this does not mean that ethical considerations can be taken lightly. Every investigator should evaluate his procedures carefully to determine whether they conform to the ethical standards.

Importance of Ideas

Students have been urged to select a problem area that they think is important and to evaluate their ideas according to the criterion of importance, but nothing has been said about what is meant by importance. Underwood (1966, pp. 260–264) discusses the meaning of the words *uninteresting* and *unimportant* in the context of psychological literature and cautions against the premature labeling of research with these terms. He states that a finding may be considered uninteresting because it is obvious or because it exists in isolation. Yet, the obvious prediction is not always supported by the facts. And the isolated finding may be justified as the starting point for new experimentation. *Unimportant* may be used in the same way that *uninteresting* is used, or it may mean that the research does not have worthwhile practical implications.

To label research that lacks immediate practical value as *unimportant* is most uninformed, according to Underwood. The accumulation of knowledge, even if it does not appear to have practical application, is important to many people because it reduces fears of the unknown and provides aesthetic pleasure. Underwood also points out that we cannot expect to judge the ultimate usefulness of an experimental discovery. Students of history are well aware that basic research can have unexpected uses. Investigators should be reluctant to apply the criterion of practical importance to all research findings. Without a relatively complete understanding of a phenomena it may be impossible to consider the practical implications.

The author is in general agreement with Underwood's assertions. There is little justification for regarding applied research as important and basic research as unimportant. It is more reasonable to consider applied and basic research as one continuum and importance as a separate continuum. Applied and basic research may be either important or unimportant depending on whether the findings make a contribution to knowledge.

A number of individuals usually participate in judging the contribution that a particular finding makes to knowledge. The investigator assesses the value of his work at various stages in the investigation, particularly the planning stage. Colleagues are usually asked to participate in this evaluation. If the results are submitted for publication, then the work is usually evaluated by specialists in the same area. Most journal editors insist that research findings pass a contribution to knowledge test as one step in determining whether the findings should be published.

At this point, the student does not have to be concerned about the contribution to knowledge criterion. He can test an idea of personal interest regardless of the potential importance of the results. The beginning researcher or one-time researcher can allow himself the luxury of testing an idea that may not be of particular interest to others but that serves as his vehicle for learning more about research methodology.

SUMMARY

There is little need to postulate a special mechanism such as creativity to account for differences in scientific accomplishments. The idea of a creative process has appeal because of the tendency to conclude, incorrectly, that marvelous consequences must have marvelous antecedents. It is recognized, of course, that people differ in encoding ability, the amount and kind of information stored, the motivation to reach a solution, and luck. The trial-and-error view which is offered here suggests that the reasonably bright individual who is willing to process a considerable amount of information, generate ideas, and then test these ideas has the best chance of success. Active researchers tend to be curious, reasonably intelligent, independent, and motivated.

It is difficult to make general statements about the relative importance of laboratory and library research. The investigator who is interested in extending the knowledge in a particular area would be foolish not to find out what knowledge has already been accumulated prior to starting his investigation. But since in most cases it is more interesting to do research than to read about it, the student who lacks motivation and is only interested in an introduction to research may elect to spend most of his time in the laboratory rather than in the library.

The important questions to consider when evaluating ideas are: Is it possible to specify the operations that should be performed to test the idea? Is the idea refutable? Are the processes or events to be compared actually comparable? Are the procedures used to test the idea practical and ethical? And, is the idea important? The ethical considerations involved in doing research are great regardless of whether animals or humans are tested.

QUESTIONS

1. Do you agree with Campbell's trial-and-error view of problem solving? Why or why not?
2. What research problem do you believe is of sufficient importance and interest to justify expending time and energy to arrive at a solution?
3. Select a proverb like: "A bird in the hand is worth two in the bush"; "Out of sight, out of mind"; "Too many cooks spoil the soup"; "One rotten apple spoils the bushel." Then indicate how you could evaluate the proverb. Be sure to consider any problems you are likely to encounter in testing it (e.g., specifying operations, ethical and practical considerations).

4. Why are only testable ideas of worth to the scientific community? Give examples, other than those mentioned in the text, of one testable and one non-testable idea.
5. If you have not already done so, evaluate each of the incidents presented in the list of Examples of Ethical Issues on page 26 in terms of the Ethical Principles listed on page 24.
6. Defend or refute the view that the most important ingredient in the research endeavor is good ideas. What other factors are necessary for successful research?
7. Do you believe experimenters should have to justify their research in terms of its practical importance? Why or why not?

3 methods of research

The plan of this chapter is to consider the three basic ways in which investigators test ideas about behavior and mental activity. The three approaches are through observational techniques, correlation, and the experimental method. The discussion of observational techniques includes consideration of the observer, of reactive measures, of nonreactive measures without intervention, and of nonreactive measures with intervention. The nature, uses, and limitations of the correlational approach are discussed. Then the nature, logic, and uses of the experimental method are considered. Experiments investigating characteristics of subjects are given special attention since the procedures to be used and the types of conclusions to be drawn are different for subject and nonsubject variable studies. Examples of the three basic methods are provided to give the reader practice in classifying research according to method. The chapter is concluded with a discussion of experiments that examine more than one variable. Special emphasis is placed on the interaction of variables.

To understand and evaluate research findings one needs a good grasp of research methods. Casual reading in the numerous psychological journals may lead the student to conclude that learning the methodology is a gigantic task. Fortunately, however, social scientists use primarily three basic methods in conducting their thousands of investigations of behavior and mental activity. The conclusions that can be drawn from research findings depend on the type of method used. A knowledge of these three approaches — observation, correlation, experimentation — provides a good foundation for understanding and evaluating research.

OBSERVATIONAL TECHNIQUES

It is important to distinguish between restricted and unrestricted observation. In unrestricted observation one makes an attempt to observe as much of the organism's behavior as possible with no preconceptions about what behaviors are important. It is difficult to overemphasize the value of such broad observation, particularly in the early stages of an investigation. Investigators are often too quick to use controlled observations or experiments to test their views, thereby taking the risk of failing to see the forest for the trees. The researcher who takes the time to view the organism in a number of situations gains a better overall picture of the interrelations among the various behaviors. A particular behavior may be understandable only in terms of other behaviors. The importance of unrestricted observation is not limited to the study of animals in their natural habitat, of course. It can be valuable in all areas of psychology with the possible exception of physiological psychology.

Restricted observations are made after the investigator has selected a particular phenomenon for study. Observations are then confined to those behaviors that are relevant for understanding the phenomenon. Usually this means that the investigator makes systematic observations and records them in detail. For example, if he is interested in territorial behavior, he may note the extent to which an animal will defend and mark its territory (e.g., urinating on the boundaries of its territory), and also the relationship between territorial and breeding behaviors. He may record the number of times an animal engages in each activity during a specified period such as one hour each day for a month.

Several different techniques can be used to observe behavior; they vary according to the nature of the situation and the relationship of the observer to the observee. For convenience in exposition, the observational techniques have been classified as: reactive measures, nonreactive measures without intervention, and nonreactive measures with intervention. Before considering the three classes, it is necessary to say a few words about the observer.

The Observer

The function of the observer is, of course, to record in some way the behavior that actually occurred. This, it turns out, is not an easy task. One danger is that the observer will introduce bias by reporting more than is observed. For example, you may see a rabbit eating dandelions and record that the hungry rabbit ate dandelions. However, it is not clear that the animal was hungry; perhaps it was eating because of boredom, to reduce anxiety, or because of an unresolved oral fixation. Another danger is that the observer may not be equipped to make the relevant observations. For example, someone interested in the speech sounds of infancy may not be able to recognize the wide variety of sounds emitted by infants and therefore may fail to record the relevant behaviors. Obviously, in some cases it is best to use mechanical recording equipment instead of, or in addition to, a human observer. One must analyze the situation to determine what kind of observations (e.g., tape recorder, movie camera, human observer) and what level of observation (e.g., behavioral or physiological) will be most useful.

There is ample reason to believe that human observers must be trained in order to minimize the number of recording errors. Untrained observers of the same event tend to disagree about what happened. This point can be demonstrated by staging an argument in front of a group of unsuspecting students. After the argument, the students are asked to record what happened. If the staged event is complicated, the reports are likely to express disagreement. We tend to be rather unobservant. (Can you recall the color of the outfit your companion was wearing yesterday?) Fortunately, it is possible to obtain reliable observations by deciding in advance what behaviors are to be observed and by training observers to respond to the appropriate features of the situation.

The reliability of observations can be checked by having observers independently record the same event. If they agree, the problem of reliability has been solved. The difficulty of obtaining agreement about the important aspects of a situation is not unique to the social sciences. It is well known, for example, that sports fans do not always agree about the occurrence of a rule infraction even though, presumably, they all have the same information.

Reactive Measures

Nature of Reactive Measures. If an investigator observes the behavior of an animal and the animal detects his presence, a reactive measure will be obtained. That is, the animal may react to the presence of the investigator, and its reaction will be a part of the record. Similarly, if an animal is removed from its natural environment and placed in a new one for the purpose of observation, a reactive measure will result. The animal may react to the new situation. Ethologists and comparative psychologists have long recognized that the behavior of an animal in its natural habitat can be markedly different from its behavior in an unnatural situation. They have also recognized that it is important to remain unobtrusive when observing animals in their natural habitat.

Again, if an investigator is monitoring the behavior of a human who recognizes that he is being observed, the result will be a reactive measure. For example (ethical questions aside), if a listening device placed in an apartment is detected, the behavior of the occupants will reflect the fact that they know they are being overheard. Many of the measures that psychologists obtain are reactive measures, including personality tests, intelligence tests, interviews, surveys, and questionnaires.

Psychologists are aware that their measures may be influenced by lack of candor in subjects who know they are being tested. For example, an individual taking a personality test may exaggerate in an effort to make a good impression. There is a lie scale for the *Minnesota Multiphasic Personality Inventory* which can be used to assess willingness to exaggerate. Those who respond that they never put off until tomorrow what they can do today are probably stretching the truth somewhat, as are those who indicate that they never do anything in private that they would not do in public. Items of this nature allow psychologists to estimate the veracity of the responses. Obviously, a reactive measure may be of little value if the testee's responses are not candid. About all that can be concluded is that he would like to make a good impression. Sometimes the real purpose of a test is disguised in order to prevent biasing of the results. And, although some reactive measures may have little value, others can be very useful.

Usefulness of Reactive Measures. Reactive measures have considerable usefulness because there are many times when it is necessary to assess performance with the full cooperation of the person being assessed. Achievement tests, intelligence tests, some personality tests, most skill tests, and most interviews are based on the assumption that very useful information can be obtained when the individual is fully aware that he is being evaluated. For example, if there is a large number of applicants for only a few open positions, it may be desirable to use a reactive measure to determine the "best" applicants. Such a measure can assure that each applicant will give his best effort.

It is true that some applicants may not perform at the highest level of their capabilities because of emotional considerations; still, a reactive measure usually provides a better way to assess achievement and intelligence than a nonreactive measure. The relative usefulness of the two approaches can be determined, of course, by comparing their reliability and validity. There are situations in which a nonreactive measure is preferable.

Nonreactive Measures Without Intervention

The need for nonreactive as well as reactive measures can perhaps best be indicated by an example. A man is driving his car on a four-lane interstate highway. The driving conditions are excellent: traffic is light, the road is dry, visibility is good. He checks the speedometer and notices that he is going slightly over the 70 mile per hour limit. He is unconcerned. He sees a police car ahead and slows down to 70. After passing the police car he gradually increases his speed over the speed limit. After about twenty minutes of driving, he sees two police cars with their warning lights flashing. The officers are slowing all traffic and requiring some drivers to pull their cars to the side of the road. Our driver was clocked by a helicopter going 81.12 miles per hour in a 70 mile per hour zone, so he receives a ticket for speeding. (The example is true; my fine was twenty-one dollars.) The point is, of course, that our behavior when we know we are under observation may differ considerably from our behavior when we do not know. Law enforcement agencies recognize this and, therefore, use nonreactive measures as an additional means to apprehend lawbreakers.

This particular approach may produce an undesirable result, however, if motorists, in an effort to outwit the men in blue, spend more time looking up in the air for helicopters than watching the road! That is, a nonreactive technique may become ineffective with continued use. It is probable, for example, that the use of one-way mirrors is no longer an effective way to obtain a nonreactive measure of adult human behavior. Many students who serve in psychological experiments are aware that there could be someone watching them from behind the "mirror." Yet, for many other nonreactive measures, there is little or no danger of discovery.

An investigator may conclude that reactive measures are unsatisfactory for a particular purpose because the behaviors which occur in a structured situation are much different from those that occur naturally. If the natural behavior is of interest, then nonreactive measures should be used. Observation of animals in their natural habitat is one way to obtain nonreactive measures without intervention. In order not to influence the behavior being observed, the investigator should refrain from making changes in the animal's habitat, and should make an effort to remain undetected.

A good source of information on nonreactive measures is an entertaining book by Webb, Campbell, Schwartz, and Sechrest (1966). It contains numerous examples of how such measures can be used for research in the social sciences. For example, alcohol consumption can be measured by counting the number of alcohol bottles in the garbage. Obviously, any form of bugging device, if undetected, would provide a nonreactive measure.

Public and private records may also provide useful nonreactive measures. An investigator may be interested in studying, say, the effect of a national disaster such as an earthquake in California on human migration to and from that state. If he contacts the major moving companies and obtains their records of moves in and out of California for the year preceding and the year following the earthquake, he can estimate its effect on migration. If there is "considerably more" movement out of California after the earthquake than there was before, *and* if the exodus is not attributable to other factors (e.g., industry moving out of California, weakness in the aerospace industry), then there is support for the view that the earthquake resulted in the exodus. Nonreactive measures can thus provide useful information, particularly if they are obtained at different points in time. If the occurrence of a particular event is *followed* by a marked change in the nonreactive measure, then there is some support for the view that the event caused the change. The weakness of this approach is that it is difficult to rule out other possible causes.

Nonreactive Measures with Intervention

The use of nonreactive measures without intervention may not be the most appropriate way to investigate a particular phenomenon because one may have to wait too long for it to occur. It may be necessary to modify the situation to produce the desired phenomenon. If so, the modification must be unsuspected. If the observee detects the intervention then, of course, the measure obtained will be reactive instead of nonreactive.

The observation that weaver finches build their nests after a rainfall may lead an investigator to conclude that rainfall is a necessary condition for nest building. Once this notion is formulated, it is then possible to intervene to assess its accuracy. Marshall and Disney (1957) demonstrated that if green grass is made available to weaver finches, they will initiate nest building in the absence of a preceding rainfall. Thus, the notion that rainfall is a necessary precondition is discounted. The intervention was important because it enabled the investigators to test their idea. If they had not intervened, it might have been a long time before an observer, a weaver finch, green grass, and dry weather occurred in such a way as to demonstrate that green grass and not rainfall is the necessary condition.

Intervention is also useful for studying human responses. For example, a social psychologist may want to observe the reactions of individuals to a person in distress; to this end, he may have a confederate fake a heart attack on a crowded subway. Since the "victim" is a confederate of the investigator, the procedure involves intervention. Or, several confederates could stage a fight in order to determine how bystanders will respond.

One could argue that there is little need to go to the trouble of staging a fight or faking a heart attack. To find out how people will react in a particular situation, all you have to do is ask them. In some cases this is probably true. Some people who claim that they would intervene would in fact do so. However, in other cases, the self-report procedure (reactive measure) would yield misleading results. That there are discrepancies between reactive and nonreactive measures is the reason for using both. The usefulness of each is likely to depend on the particular problem investigated.

The observational techniques are useful for describing behaviors and — provided the observer is more than a passive recorder of events — for suggesting ideas. For example, many therapists modify their methods as a result of observations made during therapy sessions. Yet, in order to test adequately the ideas generated during simple observation, it is usually necessary to go beyond it. Some sort of intervention may be required, or it may be necessary to use the correlational or the experimental method.

The reader should not conclude that only investigators in the social sciences use observational techniques. All sciences and many service professions use them extensively. The epidemiologist, for instance, frequently compares a current set of observations with an earlier set. It is possible to determine whether there is an epidemic of a particular disease by comparing the present incidence of the disease per 100,000 population with earlier observations of the incidence per 100,000. Or, the epidemiologist can evaluate the alleged side effects of a drug by comparing sets of observations. He can, for example, determine whether or not the number of deaths due to blood clotting per 100,000 is greater for women taking birth control pills than for women not taking them. Observational techniques are so useful in many different areas partly because of the sheer number and kinds of observations already recorded. Information that is already a matter of public record can be used to answer many questions.

In summary, the three observational techniques differ with respect to whether the observer remains undetected and whether he intervenes. Our next task is to consider the approach which allows specification of the degree of relationship between variables. The term *variable* refers to a thing or event which can be measured or manipulated.

CORRELATIONAL APPROACH

Nature of Correlation

The use of correlational techniques makes it possible to specify the degree of relationship between events. For the correlational methods considered in this text, the basic task is to determine to what extent a person who has a high, medium, or low score on one measure tends to have a high, medium, or low score on a second measure. For example, if there is a high positive correlation between the rate of pupil dilation and problem-solving ability, then people with rapid dilation should tend to be good problem solvers (e.g., solve many problems in a twenty-minute period), and people with slow dilation should tend to be poor problem solvers (e.g., solve few problems in a twenty-minute period). If there is a high negative correlation between the two measures, then those with rapid dilation should be poor problem solvers and those with slow dilation good problem solvers. Or, there may be little or no correlation between the two variables. The magnitude of a correlation can be any value from −1.00 to +1.00.

The reader should be careful not to misinterpret the adjectives *positive* and *negative* as used to modify *correlation.* They do not indicate a value judgment; a positive correlation is not better than a negative one. A positive correlation means only that high scores on one measure tend to go with high scores on the other, middle scores tend to go with middle scores, and low scores with low. A negative correlation means that high scores on one measure tend to go with low scores on the other, and middle scores with middle scores. In many cases the investigator determines whether the obtained correlation is positive or negative by using a particular measuring procedure. An example should help clarify this point.

Let us assume that our investigator is interested in the relationship between the aggressiveness of adult male seals and the number of seals in their harems. He and another investigator observe a group of twelve adult males for a month and independently rank order them on aggressiveness. The observers are in exact agreement regarding the rankings. The most aggressive seal is given the rank of one, the next most aggressive the rank of two, and so on. Then, the animals are observed during the mating season and the size of the harem of each adult male is determined. Our investigator computes a correlation between the aggressiveness rankings and the size of harem measure and obtains a high negative correlation. This means that the seals with low numbers on the aggressiveness scale (i.e., the more aggressive seals) have larger harems. The investigator could have made the correlation positive, without changing its magnitude (or its meaning), by assigning the rank of twelve to the most aggressive male, eleven to the next most aggressive, and so on.

Correlation and Prediction

One of the advantages to being able to specify the degree of relationship between two variables is that prediction is made possible. If two variables are highly correlated, and an individual's performance level on one variable is known, then his performance on the second can be predicted. For example, given a high correlation between aggressiveness and harem size among seals, it is possible to predict harem size accurately by assessing aggressiveness or vice versa. Or, if there is a high correlation between success in graduate school and performance on a particular test, the test can be used to predict success. If there are more applicants than can be accepted, it can be used to select the ones to be admitted. Whether or not such a selection procedure is justified would depend in part on the degree of relationship between the variables. In this case, success in graduate school would be the *criterion* on which to judge how well the test predicts.

If the correlation between the test and the criterion is perfect — i.e., if the person who gets the highest score is the best graduate student, the one who gets the second highest score is the second best, and so on — then it is possible to justify using the test to screen applicants. However, if the correlation is not close to +1.00 or −1.00, it is more difficult to justify the procedure, since the abilities that produce a high score on the test are not necessarily those that lead to academic success. If the actual correlation is .50, a person who does well on the test has a higher probability of doing well in graduate studies than one who does poorly on the test; however, some individuals who do well on the test will fail in graduate school and vice versa. In this case of an imperfect correlation between the test and the criterion, a person's decision as to whether the use of the test as a screening device is justified might well depend on his or her ability to perform well on written tests. An admissions office would, with reason, most likely be willing to accept the screening device in spite of its limitations, so long as the tests do predict academic success for a significant number of applicants.

Correlation and Causality

Interpreting a Correlation. Another advantage of correlation is that it can help support or refute notions about behavior. The reader has probably been warned to be careful not to infer a causal relationship from a correlation. Two variables can be related without being causally related. For example, although there may be a high correlation between the consumption of alcohol and the birth rate in the United States for the years 1947 to 1962, you would not want to conclude, necessarily, that the increased consumption of alcohol was responsible for the increased birth rate. Similarly, there may be a high correlation between height and weight, but it does not follow that the relationship is causal. However, it is important to note that highly correlated variables can be causally related. Many people are willing to conclude, for example, that smoking can cause lung cancer even though the evidence is almost entirely correlational. Also, many people accept the view that there is a causal relationship between the number of years spent in coal mines and black lung disease even though, once again, the evidence is largely correlational.

If it is necessary to make a decision about whether to stop smoking, it is reasonable to interpret the high correlation between smoking and lung cancer as evidence of a causal relationship. Although this interpretation may or may not be correct, one can hardly question the smoker's right to make it. After all, the concern is with his lungs! Besides, there does not seem to be any reasonable alternative explanation, at least at the present time, for this high correlation.

The heated arguments over how to interpret a correlation generally occur when a causal interpretation is likely to have public influence *and* when there are other credible interpretations. For example, there is a positive correlation between the number of handguns and the number of homicides involving the use of handguns. In areas where there are many handguns, there are many homicides. If one interprets this correlation as indicating a causal relationship, one is likely to favor the outlawing of handguns. Yet, it is also possible that a high incidence of violence may cause people to buy handguns in order to protect themselves, rather than the other way around. One is free to argue for either position because correlational evidence may or may not reflect an underlying causal relationship. And, even when causality *is* involved, knowledge of the correlation does not by itself tell you which variable is the cause of the other. There is a correlational technique that makes it possible to reach cause-effect conclusions about variables when the magnitude of the correlation changes over time, but a consideration of this approach is beyond the scope of this text (see Crano, Kenny, and Campbell, 1972).

Multiple Correlations and Causality. If a particular problem cannot be investigated by other methods, an investigator may elect to make extensive use of the correlational approach in an attempt to get "close" to a causal statement. The basic difficulty with this approach is that some variable other than the one being considered may be responsible for the obtained correlation. Let us assume, for instance, that an investigator is interested in the factors which contribute to a successful marriage. He elects to correlate the degree of childhood happiness and marital happiness and obtains a high positive correlation. A critic points out that childhood happiness may not be the important variable. He believes, rather, that the important variable may be the number of siblings of each marital partner, that the number of siblings is related both to happiness in childhood and to marital success.

In order to test this notion, correlations can be computed separately for all subjects having the same number of siblings. That is, the correlation between childhood happiness and marital success for people having no siblings is computed, then that for people having one sibling, and so on. If high correlations are still obtained regardless of the number of siblings, then it is possible to discount the critic's position. By the same process, other explanations can be tested. If the relationship cannot be accounted for as a consequence of other variables, then it is reasonable to place more confidence in the initial interpretation. It does not follow necessarily that there is a causal relationship between happiness in childhood and success in marriage, but this is a good possibility.

The person who is in the process of selecting a mate may decide not to consider members of the opposite sex who had unhappy childhoods. There is little reason for one to ignore the correlational evidence when making a decision because the correlation may, in fact, be due to a causal relationship between the two variables. Even if a third variable is responsible, it is still possible to use the correlation to predict marital success. Although it is important theoretically to determine whether two highly correlated variables are causally related, it may not make any practical difference.

Correlation and Discovery. The correlational method, like the observational method, can lead to the discovery of possible causal relationships, which may then become the subject of experimental investigation. The correlational technique is somewhat better than the observational in that it specifies the degree of the relationship.

One should consider the amount of influence a variable has on behavior when selecting variables for experimental investigation. For example, if correlations of fifty different variables with the incidence of lung cancer lead to the discovery that some variables have high correlations with lung cancer whereas others have very low or zero correlations, then the investigator who wants to select some variables and manipulate them experimentally to assess whether they *cause* lung cancer would be well advised to select those that have high correlations.

EXPERIMENTAL METHOD — BASIC PROPERTIES

Logic of the Experimental Method

The experimental method differs from the observational and correlational approaches in that the experimenter manipulates one or more independent variables in an attempt to influence the behavior of the subjects. The logic of the method is straightforward. If two groups of "equivalent" subjects are treated identically in all respects except one *and* if the performance of the two groups differs, it follows that the one respect in which the groups varied (i.e., the independent variable) is the cause of the performance difference.

Independent and Dependent Variables

We use the label *variable* to refer to a thing or event which can be measured or manipulated. The manipulation can be qualitative (e.g., two or more instructional techniques) or quantitative (e.g., the amount of protein in a diet). It can involve comparing the presence of a thing or event with its absence (instruction versus no instruction, or protein versus no protein). Whatever can be manipulated can be used as an *independent variable.* For example, if a farmer varies systematically the amount of fertilizer that he uses on each of four plots, the amount of fertilizer is an independent variable.

It is *independent* of other variables since it is manipulated by the farmer. The yield from the four plots (e.g., number of bushels of corn) is also a variable, but the amount of it is *dependent* on other variables such as the amount of rainfall, the amount of fertilizer, and the temperature; it is, therefore, a *dependent variable*. The crux of experimentation is to manipulate independent variables and assess the effect on one or more dependent variables. That is, one conducts experiments to determine whether the level of the dependent variable does, in fact, depend on the level of the independent variable. The independent variable is what is manipulated; the dependent variable is what is measured.

Experimental and Control Groups. Experimenters test ideas by making predictions that can be checked experimentally. Sometimes ideas are tested by comparing the relative effectiveness of two or more treatments. In other cases, the experimenter may be interested in comparing a particular treatment with no treatment. In such a treatment–no treatment manipulation, the treated group is called the *Experimental Group*, and the untreated group is called the *Control Group*. The Experimental Group consists of all the subjects who are given the treatment, the Control Group of a similar set of subjects who are not. The two groups are treated differently by the experimenter in order to assess the effect of the treatment manipulation on the dependent measure.

Examples of Independent and Dependent Variables. A particular variable may be used as either an independent or a dependent variable, according to whether it is controlled by the experimenter or is determined by other variables. A few examples can be used to make this distinction.

Let us assume that you are interested in the effect of the amount of rainfall on wheat production. You decide to manipulate the "rainfall" by varying the amount of time that you turn on a sprinkling system in an experimental wheat field, protected from natural rainfall. In this case the amount of rainfall is the independent variable because you have control over the sprinkling system. Yet, rainfall can also be used as the dependent variable. You could conduct an experiment to assess whether salting the clouds or doing a rain dance results in greater rainfall than normally occurs. First, the thirty days of September are randomly divided into three groups of ten days each. The rain dance is done for one set of ten days; the clouds are salted on the second set; and nothing is done for the third set. The effect of the independent variable (rain dance, salting clouds, nothing) is assessed by measuring the amount of rainfall for each of the three sets of days. In this case rainfall is the dependent variable.

In some cases the same thing can be used as an independent and dependent variable in the same experiment. One can manipulate the level of punishment given to subjects and then give them the opportunity to punish others. The amount of punishment they receive is the independent variable, the amount they administer is the dependent variable. Or, if an investigator is interested in the social effects of laughing, he can use the amount of laughing as both an independent and dependent variable. He can have a confederate remain quiet, giggle slightly, or give a hearty belly laugh according to a prearranged sequence. This is, of course, the independent variable. Then the effect of the confederate's laughter on the laughter of the subjects can be assessed. The laughing behavior of the subjects is the dependent variable.

SUBJECT VARIABLES AND THE EXPERIMENTAL METHOD

Definition of a Subject Variable

A subject variable is a characteristic of the subject that can be measured. For example, height, weight, age, intelligence, anxiety level, number of siblings, beauty, hostility, and self-esteem are all subject variables. Research in which such variables are manipulated requires special attention because these manipulations do not fit neatly into either the correlational or experimental method category. It is not possible to manipulate a subject variable in the same way as a nonsubject variable, such as instructional technique or incentive.

When a nonsubject variable is manipulated, the experimenter is free to determine what level of the independent variable each subject will receive; however, when a subject variable is used as the independent variable, its level has already been determined for each subject. The experimenter can only *select* subjects who have particular characteristics and compare them. For example, he can select some who are tall and some who are short and compare them on a dependent measure (e.g., strength), but he cannot decide who will be tall and who will be short. A subject variable can be manipulated only in the sense that the experimenter is free to *select* and compare subjects who differ on a characteristic of interest.

This distinction is an important methodological consideration. With a nonsubject variable manipulation, it is possible to arrive at a cause-effect conclusion; however, with a subject variable manipulation, it is extremely difficult, if not impossible, to do so. Manipulating a subject variable is, for interpretational purposes, the same as correlating it with the dependent variable. One has to be careful *not* to conclude that a subject variable manipulation is the *cause* of group differences in performance on the dependent measure. A few examples should help clarify this point.

Subject Variables and Causality

The Correlation of Subject Variables. An investigator is interested in the relationship between intelligence, a subject variable, and classroom performance. One approach is to obtain an I.Q. score and a classroom performance score for each subject and then compute a correlation between the two sets of scores. The obtained correlation would provide an index of the extent to which high I.Q. scores go with high classroom performance scores, middle scores go with middle scores, and low scores with low. Even if a high positive correlation were obtained, the investigator would still be unwilling to conclude that intelligence was the cause of classroom performance, because he would realize that other subject variables might be responsible. For example, it may be that people with high I.Q.'s are more highly motivated to do well. Perhaps motivation level is the important variable.

The Experimental Manipulation of Subject Variables. The fact that one should be reluctant to infer causality from correlational data, but not from experimental data, may lead this investigator to convert his correlational study into an "experimental" study. Instead of correlating intelligence with classroom performance, he decides to form two groups, one of high I.Q. subjects and one of low I.Q. subjects, and to assess their classroom performance. The I.Q. manipulation (i.e., the *selection* of subjects who differ on I.Q.) is the independent variable and classroom performance is the dependent variable.

Now, in this experimental version of the study, if the High I.Q. Group does better than the Low I.Q. Group, is it possible to conclude that intelligence caused the difference in performance? No! The "experimental" manipulation of a subject variable does not allow the investigator to arrive at a cause-effect conclusion. Performance and intelligence are related, but not necessarily causally related. High and low intelligence groups are likely to differ in more ways than intelligence; therefore, it is not possible to manipulate only intelligence through selection of subjects. Thus the experiment is *confounded* in that some correlate of intelligence (e.g., motivation level) may have been responsible for the difference in performance. An experiment is said to be *confounded* when two or more variables could be responsible for the obtained difference in performance of two groups.

Suppose an investigator wants to test a theory which predicts that blonde college girls are likely to have more dates. The procedure could be very simple. The investigator *selects* thirty natural blondes and thirty natural redheads and tabulates the number of dates each girl has for a given period. Let us assume that blondes had significantly more dates. Can this difference be attributed to hair color? No. All one can say is that the blondes had more dates. It is unreasonable to conclude that hair color was the reason; other factors such as aggressiveness, beauty, or morals may have been responsible. One can only conclude that hair color is related to having dates, *not* that the relationship is causal.

Subject Variables and Equivalent Groups. The selection of subjects according to hair color in the foregoing example is a subject variable manipulation. All experiments in which subject variables are manipulated are confounded since it is not possible to form equivalent groups and then introduce the independent variable. This point is very important and bears repeating. For nonsubject variable manipulations it is possible to establish equivalent groups. After such groups have been formed, the independent variable can be introduced. This makes it possible to assure that the independent variable is the *only* one that is systematically varied so that differences in performance between groups can be attributed to it. It is reasonable to conclude that the *nonsubject* variable is the *cause* of the difference in performance on the dependent measure.

However, when a subject variable manipulation is made, one cannot form equivalent groups because the characteristics of the subject determine the group in which the subject will be placed. If it is not possible to form equivalent groups prior to the introduction of the independent variable, then there is no way to assess its effect accurately since there is no way to manipulate just *one* independent variable. It is unreasonable to reach a cause-effect conclusion when a subject variable manipulation is made. Again, correlational studies and subject variable manipulations are similar in that it is only possible to assess whether the variables are related, not whether they are causally related.

A few words need to be said about the special meaning of *equivalent groups* in psychological research. Equivalent groups are not identical or equal in an absolute sense; rather, they are groups whose differences in performance can be attributed solely to chance fluctuations. The subjects in two groups can differ somewhat in performance and still be equivalent in this sense. Chance fluctuations are always present. A central question in analyzing the results of experiments is whether the performance differences between groups are due solely to chance or to chance *plus* the effect of the independent variable. The procedures used to answer this question will be discussed later. For the present it is only necessary to note that it is reasonable to assume that equivalent groups are formed (prior to the introduction of a *nonsubject* independent variable) when procedures are used which assure that any differences between groups are due solely to chance.

Classification of Subject Variable Manipulations

The fact that subject variable manipulations are similar to correlational studies with regard to causality statements, and similar to the experimental method with regard to *some* procedures, makes it difficult to arrive at a simple, completely satisfactory classification. Some investigators classify subject variable manipulation as an instance of the experimental method. The subject variable is treated as the independent variable and the performance measure is the dependent measure. There is no harm in doing this as long as one remembers that the results of such experiments should not be interpreted in cause-effect terms. In this text, we will treat subject variable manipulation as a special case of the experimental method, applying the label of independent variable to subject variables as well as to nonsubject variables. The advantage to such a classification is that it is frequently useful to combine subject variable and nonsubject variable manipulations in the same experiment. Before returning to this point, it is necessary to give the reader some practice in classifying research according to the method employed.

CLASSIFYING RESEARCH ACCORDING TO METHOD

In the beginning of this chapter we noted that social scientists use three basic methods to accumulate knowledge, namely, observational techniques, the correlational approach, and the experimental method. It is important that the student be able to classify research according to method, because the method employed determines, in large part, what conclusions are justified. The following examples will give the student some practice in classification. He should attempt to classify each example before reading the discussion of it. (The label for each example is the title of the article discussed.)

Example 1 — Children's Reactions to Second-Hand Smoke

A study was conducted (Cameron, 1972) in which 2,365 children between the ages of seven and fifteen were interviewed to determine their reaction to smoking by others. The general finding was that the children did not like being exposed to tobacco smoke. They tended to disapprove of their parents' smoking and indicated some loss of respect for their parents because they smoked.

Discussion. It should be clear to the reader that the above study is an example of the use of an observational technique. A reactive measure was obtained. It might be that the responses of the children were influenced by the fact that they knew the investigator was interested in their reaction to smoking. For example, a child who wanted to please may have concluded that the interviewer had a negative attitude toward smoking and may have responded accordingly. There is usually some danger that the results obtained with a reactive measure may be influenced by the subject's awareness of the evaluation. The investigator's task is to determine whether the advantages of the method outweigh the bias which may result if some subjects modify their responses in an effort to please or displease him.

Example 2 — Marital Agreement as a Function of Status-Related Agreement

Married couples of higher social status tend to agree with each other more than married couples of lower social status. The investigator (Bennett, 1971) interviewed ninety-six couples to assess whether the differences in agreement were due to marital interaction or to status-related factors. The spouses were interviewed separately to measure their attitude toward radioactive-fallout shelters. The degree of agreement of each couple was found to be directly related to status; the high status couples agreed more than the lower status couples. Yet, if individuals were artificially paired (i.e., couples were re-paired), the pairs of high status still agreed more than the pairs of lower status. The results suggest that status and not marital interaction is responsible for the differences in agreement.

Discussion. The above study demonstrates the point that more than one method can be used in a single study. An observational technique is used in virtually every study because a performance measure is needed in order to use the correlational or experimental methods. Usually a reactive measure is obtained, because the subjects are aware that their performance is being assessed. In this study a reactive measure was used to assess each subject's attitude toward radioactive-fallout shelters, but subjects did not know that the investigator's principal interest was in the degree of marital agreement and its relation to social status. The reader should recognize that the investigator also used the correlational approach. The issue was whether high scores on the social status variable would go with high scores on the agreement variable.

Example 3 — Racial Discrimination in Apartment Rentals

The investigators (Johnson, Porter, and Marteljan, 1971) performed a study in southern California to determine whether minority groups were discriminated against by apartment landlords. The investigators had male-female couples from Mexican-American, Negro, or Caucasian ethnic groups visit twenty-five apartment houses. Each couple inquired about the availability of an apartment, rent, and other fees. The results revealed that Mexican-Americans were discriminated against more than Caucasians, and Negroes more than either of the others.

Discussion. This study is an example of the experimental method. The independent variable is the ethnic group of the potential tenants, and the dependent variables are the information on availability, on rent, and on miscellaneous fees provided by the landlords. This is a nonsubject variable manipulation, because the ethnic group membership of the potential tenants, and not some characteristic of the landlords, was manipulated. The subjects in this experiment were the twenty-five landlords. Subject variable manipulations are made by assigning subjects to groups on the basis of a particular characteristic; there was no such assignment in this experiment. The only variable manipulated was the characteristics of the potential tenants, so it is possible to conclude that these characteristics were responsible for the differences in the information obtained.

Some readers may prefer to consider the independent variable any differences between the potential tenants and not just ethnic group differences. That is, although it is probable that the ethnic group membership of the potential tenants was responsible for the differences in the information provided by the landlords, it is also possible that other characteristics, such as differences among the couples in dress or manner, were responsible. In some cases, there may be disagreement regarding the exact nature of the independent variable.

Example 4 — Effects of Early Social Deprivation on Emotionality in Rats

The investigators (Koch and Arnold, 1972) assigned ninety-five newborn rats to four different rearing conditions to assess the effect of social deprivation on emotionality. One group was reared with mother and peers, a second group with mother but without peers; a third group was reared in incubators with peers; a fourth group in incubators in isolation. A number of measures of emotionality (e.g., heart rate, frequency of urination) were obtained when the rats were 65 and 113 days of age. The general finding was that maternally deprived rats showed higher emotionality.

Discussion. This study is an example of the use of the experimental method. The assignment of subjects to groups was such that the investigators could be confident that the groups were equivalent prior to the introduction of the independent variable. The independent variable was the type of early social experience, a nonsubject variable. Although early social experience is a characteristic of the subject, this is not a subject variable manipulation in the sense used in this text, because the manipulation is under the control of the experimenter. He decides which rat gets a particular early experience and which doesn't. Thus, it is possible to manipulate just one "subject" variable — not merely to *select,* as in a typical subject variable case. It is reasonable, therefore, to conclude from this experiment that the maternal deprivation *caused* the higher emotionality.

Example 5 — Sex, Setting, and Reactions to Crowding on Sidewalks

The investigator (Dabbs, 1972) studied how people reacted to having someone stand very close to them at stoplights and bus stops. The basic procedure consisted of having a male or female confederate of the investigator approach and stand very close to a pedestrian waiting for a bus or for a traffic light to change. There were 643 pedestrians, both males and females. The extent to which each pedestrian moved away from the confederate was recorded. One finding was that male confederates induced more movement than female confederates, and female pedestrians tended to move more than male pedestrians.

Discussion. The above study can be classified as an example of a nonreactive measure with intervention. A nonreactive measure was obtained in that the pedestrians were not given any reason to suspect that their movement, relative to a confederate, was being recorded. The intervention is, of course, the presence of the confederate. It is likely that the investigator would have had to wait a long time to determine how pedestrians react to crowding if he had waited for the crowding to occur naturally. By using confederates, it is possible to arrange the situation of interest and then observe how subjects react.

Some readers may object to the above classification because they believe the study is more accurately classified as an example of the experimental method, with sex of the confederate, sex of the pedestrian, and location of the encounter (bus stop or stoplight) as the three independent variables. Sometimes it is possible to make a case for more than one classification, because the study has the properties of more than one method. Nonreactive measures with intervention and the experimental method are especially likely to overlap. It is frequently possible to decide between these two classifications by considering how the subjects were assigned to conditions. If no attempt is made to assure that the subjects tested in each condition are equivalent prior to obtaining the dependent measure, it is usually more appropriate to view the research as an instance of an observational technique. If an effort *is* made to assure such equivalence, then the study may be regarded as an example of the experimental method. If the investigator had used a procedure to assure that the pedestrians approached by male confederates were equivalent to the pedestrians approached by female confederates, this study would have been a good example of the experimental method — provided that the sex of the confederate was the only variable manipulated.

Example 6 — The Physical Attractiveness of Dating versus Married Couples

The investigators (Cavior and Boblett, 1972) were interested in whether there is a higher correlation between the physical attractiveness of married partners or of dating partners. The correlations were obtained by having judges independently rate each person on physical attractiveness. The subjects were unaware that they were being so rated. Then a correlation was computed to assess the extent to which people with high scores on physical attractiveness marry people with high scores, middle scores go with middle scores, and low scores with low. A similar procedure was used for the people who were dating partners. The major finding was that the correlation was considerably higher for married partners than for dating partners.

Discussion. It should be clear to the reader that this study involved obtaining a nonreactive measure without intervention and then the correlational approach. The measure was nonreactive in that the subjects were not given any reason to believe they were being judged on their physical attractiveness. There are some obvious ethical problems in obtaining nonreactive measures on human subjects. However, the reader should also realize that there would be numerous methodological difficulties to overcome if a study of this type were performed by obtaining reactive measures. The partners who would give their informed consent to participate in a study on physical attractiveness might not be representative of married or dating partners. For example, consider the likelihood of a couple giving their informed consent if both members were physically attractive. Now consider the likelihood if one member were attractive and the other unattractive.

Example 7 — Social Rehabilitation of Isolate-Reared Monkeys

The investigators (Suomi and Harlow, 1972) attempted to rehabilitate four male rhesus monkeys that had been reared in total social isolation for the first six months of life. Previous isolation studies indicated that monkeys so reared have defects in play, sex, and aggression behaviors which appear to be permanent. The six-month-old male isolates in the present study were allowed to interact with three-month-old females. The isolates gradually developed normal social responses. After six months with the younger females, the isolate group was indistinguishable from the control group. (The controls were monkeys that had not been isolated.)

Discussion. The above study can be classified as an example of the experimental method. There is room for disagreement on this classification, however, because it is necessary to assume that these isolates would not have recovered without the rehabilitation treatment. This is a reasonable assumption, since earlier work had indicated that the effects of isolation are permanent. The reader who is willing to accept this assumption can then consider the presence or absence of the younger females as the independent variable. The fact that the isolates recovered when allowed to interact with the younger females *and* that isolates in previous studies, who were not allowed to play with younger females, did not recover suggests that the younger females were responsible for the recovery.

From a methodological point of view, it would have been better to have a group of isolates who were not given rehabilitation, to be compared with the rehabilitation group. Yet, the decision not to have another group is understandable, given the previous data on the effects of isolation and the practical and ethical considerations involved in isolating animals for a six-month period.

Hopefully, the reader now has an understanding of the three basic methods used in accumulating knowledge in the social sciences. It should be clear from the examples that many investigators use a combination of research techniques in a single study. It is also true that they may study the effect of more than one independent variable in a single study. It is frequently necessary to do so, since the effect of one independent variable may be influenced by the level of a second. Thus, although the previous discussion should have provided the reader with a general understanding of the scope of the three methods, it is necessary to consider the experimental method in greater detail.

EXPERIMENTAL METHOD — ADDITIONAL PROPERTIES

Experiments with Two Independent Variables

Experiments can be conducted in which equivalent groups are formed and two or more independent variables are then introduced. Experiments can also be conducted in which two or more subject variables are manipulated. (In this case, of course, since the nature of the independent variables determines group composition, the groups cannot be formed prior to the introduction of these variables — nor can cause-effect conclusions be reached.) One can also perform experiments in which both subject and nonsubject variables are manipulated. Let us consider such an experiment.

For the purposes of illustration, assume that an investigator has developed a new method of instruction to motivate students academically. He believes the method will increase academic performance as assessed by grades. He wants to establish whether the method is successful and whether its success depends on the characteristics of the students. To accomplish this end, 200 natural science students and 200 social science students are recruited for the experiment. The subject variable is the type of student, natural science or social science. The investigator is not interested in comparing the performance of the two types of students, but rather in the effectiveness of the new method with each type.

The next step is to divide the social science students into two equivalent groups of 100 each, and the natural science students in the same way. A procedure can be used to assign the students to groups so that it is highly likely that equivalent groups will be formed. Following the formation of the two sets of equivalent groups, the investigator gives the new method to one group of natural science and one group of social science students. The other two groups are treated identically except they are not given the new method. It is important to note that if there is a large difference in the performance of the two groups of social science students after the method manipulation, the difference can be attributed to the method, since the two social science groups were previously equivalent. The same thing is true for the natural science students.

The results of the experiment are clear. The method facilitated the academic performance of the social science students but not of the natural science students. Specifically, the social science students who received the method were far superior academically to the social science students who did not receive it for two successive school terms following its introduction. Yet, the two natural science groups did not differ during the same period. A comparison of the performance of the social science students to that of the natural science students is of little interest, since these subjects differ in many respects. The important point is that the method was effective for the social science students only. If the investigator had used only natural science students in the experiment, he would have concluded that the method does not have any effect. If he had used only social science students, he would have concluded that it does have an effect, but would perhaps have remained unaware of its limitations.

If the effect of one independent variable (e.g., the method) is influenced by the level of another independent variable (in this case a subject variable), then the variables are said to *interact.* The study of *interactions* between variables is extremely important. It would, of course, be much easier to understand behavior if the effect of each independent variable was the same regardless of the situation. However, it is abundantly clear that this is not so. Variables can interact, so understanding the effect of a particular independent variable also involves knowing what other variables, if any, interact with it. A *factorial design* was used in the preceding example. In a factorial design, each level of each independent variable occurs with each level of all other independent variables. In this case each type of student (natural science or social science) equally often received the new method or did not.

Interaction of Independent Variables

It is important to note that independent variables interact, not dependent variables. Thus, in order to obtain an interaction it is necessary to manipulate two or more independent variables; the effect of any one of them is assessed by performance on the dependent variable. In order to simplify the task of discussing interactions, let us assume that all subjects who receive a particular treatment attain the same level of performance on the dependent variable. That is, for the purposes of illustration, we will assume that all individuals are of identical ability. Any difference between groups can be attributed to the effect of the treatment manipulation, since we are assuming that there are no chance fluctuations.

Example 1 — One Independent Variable. For the first example, assume that a two-group experiment is conducted to assess the effect of the volume at which music is played on the rating of the music. Each subject is asked to rate the same classical piece on a scale from 1 to 30. A score of 30 is the most favorable rating. Ten subjects rate the piece when it is played at a high volume setting, and ten others rate it at a low volume setting. This is a non-subject variable manipulation; it is possible to form equivalent groups prior to the introduction of the independent variable.

The results are clear. All subjects who hear the piece at low volume give it a rating of 20, and all who hear it at high volume give it 25. Thus, the volume manipulation had an effect of five units, since all subjects in the high volume condition rated the piece five units higher than all subjects in the low volume condition. The effect of the independent variable can be assessed by subtracting the average score of the subjects in one condition from the average score of subjects in the other. It should also be clear that there can be no interaction in this experiment, because there is only one independent variable; in order to obtain an interaction it is necessary to have two or more.

Example 2 — Interacting Independent Variables. Let us assume that a 2 by 2 factorial design is used. This means that there are two independent variables and two levels of each. The two independent variables are type of music and volume setting. The example is similar to the previous one in that a classical piece is played at low or high volume. In addition, rock music is played at low or high volume. Thus, there are four conditions. Once again each subject is asked to rate a piece on a scale from 1 to 30, and there are ten subjects in each condition. Both of the independent variables are non-subject variables, since it is possible to form equivalent groups prior to their introduction. The results of the experiment are presented in Table 3-1. The scores in each condition are the ratings of the ten subjects, one score per subject.

The effect of the manipulations can be assessed by comparing the mean scores for the subjects in each condition. A mean score for each group is obtained by adding all the scores for the group and dividing the sum by the number of scores. Since the subjects in each condition have the same score, the mean score is identical to that for each subject. A mean for the low volume conditions can be obtained by adding the mean scores for the two low volume conditions and dividing by two [i.e., $(10 + 20)/2 = 15$]. The mean for the high volume conditions can be obtained in a similar manner [i.e., $(25 + 25)/2 = 25$]. A comparison of the high and low volume conditions reveals that the effect of the volume manipulation was ten units (25 minus 15). The effect of the type of music manipulation can be determined by comparing the mean for the two rock music conditions [i.e., $(10 + 25)/2 = 17.5$] with the mean for the two classical music conditions [i.e., $(20 + 25)/2 = 22.5$]. Since the difference is five, it can be concluded that both the type of music manipulation and the volume manipulation influenced the rating obtained. Moreover, there was an interaction between the type of music and the volume setting.

TABLE 3–1

The Rating of Each of Forty Subjects as a Function of the Type of Music Presented and the Volume of the Music in Example 2 (fictitious data)

Type of music			
Rock		*Classical*	
Volume setting		*Volume Setting*	
Low	*High*	*Low*	*High*
10	25	20	25
10	25	20	25
10	25	20	25
10	25	20	25
10	25	20	25
10	25	20	25
10	25	20	25
10	25	20	25
10	25	20	25
10	25	20	25

Two independent variables interact if the effect of one is influenced by the level of the other. In the present example, the effect of the volume setting can be assessed separately for classical and rock music; for classical music it is five units (25 minus 20), and for rock music it is fifteen (25 minus 10). Since the effect is different for classical music than for rock, the two variables interact. Note that it is the independent variables themselves which interact and *not* the levels of the variables. That is, it is incorrect to say that low volume interacts with type of music or that rock music interacts with the volume setting. The two independent variables, type of music and volume setting, interact, not the levels of each.

Example 3 — Noninteracting Independent Variables. Assume now that the same experiment was conducted but that the results were different. These results are presented in Table 3-2. The volume manipulation had an effect of five units (i.e., 22.5 minus 17.5), and the type of music manipulation also had an effect of five (i.e., 22.5 minus 17.5). Note, however, that there was no interaction between type of music and volume setting. The effect of volume setting was the same for rock music (20 minus 15) as for classical music (25 minus 20). Thus, the effect of the volume setting did not depend on the type of music considered.

The use of concrete examples can be a very effective way for the student

TABLE 3–2

The Rating of Each of Forty Subjects as a Function of the Type of Music Presented and the Volume of Music in Example 3 (fictitious data)

Type of music			
Rock		*Classical*	
Volume setting		*Volume setting*	
Low	*High*	*Low*	*High*
15	20	20	25
15	20	20	25
15	20	20	25
15	20	20	25
15	20	20	25
15	20	20	25
15	20	20	25
15	20	20	25
15	20	20	25
15	20	20	25

to grasp the concept of interaction. This is particularly true if you generate your own examples. With a little effort, the reader should be able to think of variables that can be expected to interact. There is no good substitute for generating your own examples and considering all possible outcomes. If you do this, you should be able to demonstrate that it is possible for two variables to interact even when neither has an effect on overall performance.

The results presented in Tables 3-1 and 3-2 will appear very artificial to the reader since all subjects given the same treatment had the same score. For the present, however, there is no harm in assuming that all subjects are of identical ability, since this should make it easier to understand how the effects of independent variables and interactions are assessed. They are assessed in basically the same way when subjects are of differing ability, but then one has to be careful about concluding that an obtained difference between conditions is a result of the treatment manipulation. A difference may be due solely to the chance fluctuations that are always present. The problem of deciding when to attribute differences to the independent variable(s) plus chance, and when to attribute them solely to chance, will be considered in detail in subsequent chapters.

The topic of interaction will be returned to at various points in the text, so it is important that the reader understand what an interaction is. The discussion of interaction concludes the presentation of the three basic methods of research.

SUMMARY

The function of the observer is to record the behavior of interest. This is not an easy task because the observer may bias the observations, lack the proper skills or equipment to record the relevant behavior, or fail to agree with other observers.

The observational techniques fall into three classes: reactive measures, nonreactive measures without intervention, and nonreactive measures with intervention. A reactive measure is obtained whenever the observee is aware that his behavior is being recorded, or whenever he is placed in a new environment for the purposes of observation. His behavior may be influenced by his awareness of the investigator or the investigator's equipment. Nonreactive measures without intervention are obtained whenever the observee is unaware that his behavior is being recorded in some way and no changes are made in his situation. The behavior that occurs is natural. Nonreactive measures with intervention are obtained without the observee's knowledge, but with the investigator intervening in some way to assure that the appropriate circumstances exist.

Correlational techniques allow investigators to specify the degree of relationship between variables. Correlation can be used to predict. The accuracy of the prediction will depend on the magnitude of the correlation. Although it is not correct to infer a causal relationship from a correlation, the correlation may, in fact, be due to a cause-effect connection between the variables. If such a connection does exist, then the variables will be correlated. The reverse is not true however. Thus, correlational techniques can be used to "discover" causal relationships in that two highly correlated variables may prove to be causally related when submitted to experimentation.

The experimental method differs from the other approaches in that the experimenter manipulates one or more independent variables and assesses the effect of the manipulations on one or more dependent measures. The logic of the method is to treat equivalent groups identically in all respects except one. If the groups differ in performance following the introduction of the treatment, then the difference can be attributed to the effect of the treatment. The independent variable is what the investigator manipulates, i.e., the treatment. The dependent variable is what he measures to assess the effect of the independent variable.

A subject variable is a characteristic of the subject that can be measured. If a subject variable is used as an independent variable, it is essentially impossible to form equivalent groups prior to its introduction, since it is not possible to assure that any between-group differences are due solely to chance. The nature of the subject variable dictates the composition of the groups. Therefore, it is extremely difficult, if not impossible, to manipulate just one subject variable and thus to arrive at a cause-effect statement.

The use of the experimental method is not limited to situations in which only one independent variable is manipulated. Experiments can be conducted in which the independent variables are all nonsubject variable manipulations, in which some are subject variables and others are nonsubject variables, and in which all are subject variables. If two or more independent variables are manipulated in the same experiment, it is possible to assess whether they interact.

Independent variables interact, not dependent variables. Dependent variables are used to assess the effect of independent variables. If the effect of one independent variable is influenced by the level of another, they are said to interact.

QUESTIONS

1. What are the advantages and disadvantages of each of the three kinds of observational techniques? Give an example of how each of these techniques might be used.
2. Support or refute the view that it is impossible to demonstrate causality from correlational evidence.
3. What determines whether a positive or negative correlation is obtained? Are positive correlations better than negative ones?
4. What points should be considered before using a test to determine who should be admitted to medical school?
5. How can correlational techniques be used to "discover" causal relationships?
6. What are the advantages and disadvantages of the correlational and experimental methods?
7. Distinguish between independent and dependent variables, and give an example of each.
8. Distinguish between subject and nonsubject variables, and indicate the procedures used to manipulate each kind. That is, how do the procedures used for manipulating a subject variable differ from those for a nonsubject variable?
9. Why should an investigator who makes a subject variable manipulation avoid reaching cause-effect conclusions?
10. What does it mean to say that two variables interact? Give an example of two which can be expected to interact and indicate why this is a reasonable expectation.
11. What is the advantage of manipulating a subject variable and a nonsubject variable in the same experiment?
12. An investigation was conducted by Norris (1971) in which the crying and laughing behavior of ninety severely retarded children who were living at home was compared with that of fifteen such children who were living in a hospital. The children living at home attended a training center. Those in the hospital attended the hospital school. The investigator observed the children for ten consecutive school days. He concluded that those who lived at

home laughed more than those in the hospital, but that there was no difference in crying behavior between the two groups.

a. Describe the method used by the investigator. Be specific. For example, if the experimental method was used, indicate the independent and dependent variables.

b. Can the differences observed be attributed to where the children lived? Why or why not?

13. Cohen, Liebson, and Faillace (1972) performed a study in which alcoholics were tested under two different conditions. Each alcoholic was allowed to drink ten ounces of alcohol each day for the duration of the five week study. Each was tested under Condition A for the first, third, and fifth weeks, and Condition B for the second and fourth weeks. In Condition A the subject was given special privileges for drinking five or less ounces of alcohol each day. In Condition B no such special privileges were given. The major finding was that subjects drank less per day under Condition A than Condition B.

a. What method was used in this study? Be specific.

b. Can the differences in drinking be attributed to the special privileges manipulation? Why or why not?

14. Schusterman and Gentry (1971) studied four captive male sea lions, noting their annual weight fluctuation, food consumption, and territorial behaviors. They found that the annual weight fluctuation was related to the reproductive season. Seasonal fattening, which started at five years of age, was associated with increased signs of territoriality. What method(s) did the investigators use?

hypothesis testing

The purpose of this chapter is to provide an overall view of how ideas are tested experimentally. The major emphasis here and in most of the remaining chapters is on the various uses and problems of the experimental method. The chapter is divided into two major sections. The first is devoted to a brief overview of the major steps of hypothesis testing. These include formulating hypotheses, selecting an experimental design, performing the experiment, and analyzing the results. The second section examines the logic of the statistical analysis of experiments. Topics discussed include probability, frequency and sampling distributions, experimental error and rejecting the null hypothesis, and one-tailed versus two-tailed tests.

Some of the major steps in hypothesis testing have been considered in previous chapters, some will be considered here, and others will be mentioned briefly here and examined in detail later. The first step is to select a suitable problem and generate hypotheses which can be tested. This was discussed in Chapter 2. As we know, the nature of the problem selected and the quality of the hypothesis are of crucial importance. No methodological or statistical procedure can salvage a poor idea. It is impossible to separate the quality of the idea from the quality of the predictions which follow from it, since only testable ideas are of worth to the scientific community.

After a tentative solution has been generated, it is necessary to prepare a test of it. This means, of course, that the problem has to be stated in a way that allows predictions about observable events. The investigator can use the observational techniques, the correlational method, or the experimental method to test the proposed solution. Our central concern in this text is with the use of the experimental method. This method is emphasized because it is an extremely useful and powerful way to test explanations of phenomena. Observational and correlational techniques are also important, of course, but their use, at least at the level considered here, is relatively straightforward. Besides, an understanding of the experimental method should enable the student to use the observational techniques. The steps involved in computing correlations are considered in Section II of this book. The reader's main task is to gain an understanding of how the experimental method can be used to test hypotheses.

HYPOTHESIS TESTING AND THE EXPERIMENTAL METHOD

Research Hypothesis and Null Hypothesis

We test ideas by making predictions about observable events. Usually this means that the investigator asserts that a particular independent variable will have an effect on a dependent measure. Such an assertion is usually labeled the *research hypothesis*. The *null hypothesis* is the statement that the treatment manipulation will *not* have any effect, that there is zero effect due to the independent variable. If the null hypothesis is true then the obtained differences are due solely to chance fluctuations. If the research hypothesis is true then the differences are due to chance fluctuations *plus* the effect of the independent variable.

The major task is to obtain evidence to determine whether the research hypothesis or the null hypothesis is true. The only one that can be tested is the null hypothesis; the research hypothesis cannot be tested directly. Thus, the hypotheses must be formulated in such a way that they cannot both be correct. If the null hypothesis is false, then the research hypothesis must be correct, provided the experiment is methodologically sound. The experimenter must take care to avoid confounding the experiment. If it is confounded, there is usually no way to determine whether the manipulated independent variable or the confounding variable is the cause of the obtained difference. The next step is to select an experimental design.

Experimental Design

We will be discussing experimental design in the next two chapters. The main factor to consider here in the construction of an experimental design is the nature of the independent variable(s) selected for manipulation. The experimental design is the plan used to test whether a manipulation has an effect. Such designs can be divided into two categories, between-subject designs and within-subject designs. In a between-subject design each subject gets only one level of each independent variable. For example, if a between-subject design is being used to test the effect of alcohol on motor performance, each subject would either receive alcohol or not receive it. He would not be tested under both alcohol and nonalcohol conditions. In a within-subject design each subject would get more than one level of the independent variable. When each gets more than one treatment it is frequently possible to evaluate the effect of the treatment manipulation within each subject's data.

The various experimental designs can be viewed as different procedures for obtaining equivalent groups. There are two kinds of between-subject designs: random-groups designs and matched-groups designs. Random assignment is used to obtain equivalent groups in a random-groups design. In a matched-groups design, the groups are equated on the variables selected for matching. If a nonsubject variable is manipulated as an independent variable in a matched-groups design, then random assignment should be used along with matching so the investigator can be confident that the groups are equivalent. For a within-subject design, all subjects are tested at each level of the independent variable; this makes it possible to attribute differences in performance at the various levels solely to the effect of chance fluctuations or to chance fluctuations plus the independent variable, provided there are no confounding variables. Chance fluctuations are always present regardless of the design used, but their magnitude is influenced by the type of design.

The word *subject* in the name of the two designs may lead the reader to conclude that experimental designs are appropriate for experiments using animal and human subjects only. This is not the case. The subjects may be either inanimate or animate. *Subject* refers to the object or organism on which the manipulation is being made. The condition or performance of the subjects is compared to assess whether the difference in the way the subjects have been treated has had any effect. For example, an investigator interested in evaluating a new automobile paint could use automobiles as subjects and manipulate the kind of paint used for each as the independent variable. The dependent variable could be the amount of rust after a four year period. If only one kind of paint is used for each automobile, the investigator has used a between-subject design; if several kinds of paint are used for each, he has used a within-subject design. Between-subject designs are discussed further in Chapter 5, within-subject designs in Chapter 6.

Performing the Experiment

The execution of the experiment is discussed in detail in Chapter 7. Basically the task is to perform the experiment in a way that makes it possible to assess the effect of the independent variable(s). Some procedure must be used to obtain equivalent groups prior to the introduction of the independent variable. Then it will be reasonable to attribute any obtained difference to chance plus the effect of the treatment. The basic problem is to assure that the subjects in the various conditions are treated identically except for the intended manipulation. Following the data collection stage, the subjects' performance on the dependent variable can be analyzed to assess the influence of the manipulation.

Analysis of Experiments

Differences believed to be due to chance *and* the independent variable are attributed to the effect of the independent variable. That is, the distinguishing feature is whether the independent variable has an effect. Chance fluctuations are not distinguishing because they are always present. If the obtained differences are attributed to chance fluctuations, then, of course, the null hypothesis is not rejected. To determine whether or not such differences should be attributed to chance, one must consider the likelihood of particular outcomes if only chance is operating. Section II of this text is largely devoted to procedures for deciding such questions.

Relationship Between Design and Analysis

A word needs to be said about the relationship between design, considered in Chapters 5 and 6, and analysis, considered in Chapters 8 through 11. Design and analysis are interrelated, so considering how an experiment will be analyzed can be useful in detecting flaws in design. It is a very common mistake to design an experiment without considering how the results will be analyzed. If the experimenter makes no mistakes in design, then the subsequent analysis should not cause any particular difficulty. Unfortunately, in some instances experimenters expect to be able to salvage a poorly designed experiment by performing a sophisticated statistical analysis — an unreasonable expectation. The time to think about the analysis is before collecting the data. Considering the analysis and some possible outcomes of the experiment is one way to check the adequacy of the design.

THE LOGIC BEHIND THE STATISTICAL ANALYSIS OF EXPERIMENTS

It is important to understand the logic behind the statistical analysis of experiments. The basic task, as we know, is to determine whether the obtained differences are due to the effect of the independent variable or only to chance. In order to gain an appreciation of what is meant by chance fluctuations, we must consider the topic of probability.

Probability

Common Sense View of Probability. Most people have a good notion of what they mean by probability. The common sense notion usually consists of a subjective estimate of the likelihood that a particular event will occur (e.g., the probability of rain, the probability of winning a sporting event, the probability of getting married, the probability of passing a course). Since scientists have a penchant for quantification, they prefer a quantitative over a subjective approach to probability. Yet, it may be that the subjective view of probability that many people have also has a quantitative basis which is not articulated. For example, if you see dark clouds in the sky, you may predict that the chances of rain are about 90 percent. This prediction may be based on previous observations of similar weather conditions. Perhaps you have noticed that this particular weather condition occurred 100 times, and 90 times out of 100 rain followed within a three hour period. Given this information, it is reasonable to assert that the probability of rain is 90 percent. You expect that, given this same weather condition 100 more times, it will rain about 90 out of the 100 times.

Probability, Odds, and the Long Haul. The reader may be a little annoyed by the assertion that the probability of rain is 90 percent. After all, it either rains or it doesn't, so why assert that there is a 90 percent chance of rain? Many people would prefer simple rain-or-shine predictions. Why bother with probability statements? Does it really matter whether the probability of rain is 90 percent or 60 percent? In the long haul, it makes a great deal of difference; in making all-or-none predictions you can expect to be right 90 percent of the time in one set of circumstances and only 60 percent in the other. Or, the problem can be considered in terms of confidence in the prediction.

One way to assess confidence is to vary the odds in a betting situation. If the probability of rain is 90 percent and you predict rain, it is reasonable for you to give 9 to 1 odds (i.e., you pay 9 if you lose and receive 1 if you win) and still come out about even over the long haul. That is, if you make the same prediction 100 times under similar circumstances, you should expect to lose about 10 times and win about 90 times. The winnings (90 times 1 = 90) should be about equal to the losses (10 times 9 = 90). If the probability of rain is only 60 percent you would be very foolish to give 9 to 1 odds. In short, an exact probability statement makes sense if you consider the long haul or the odds in a betting situation.

Definition of Probability. The probability of an event can be defined as the ratio of the number of favorable events to the total number of possible events. The only effect which is assumed to operate is *chance*. Therefore, there is the same likelihood that each event will occur. A few simple examples should help to clarify the notion of probability. Consider the probability of drawing the ace of spades from a standard deck of well-shuffled playing cards. Since there is only one favorable event, the ace of spades, and 52 possible events, the probability is 1/52 or .019. If only chance is operating, then each card has the same probability of being drawn. Consider the probability of drawing any spade. In this case there are 13 favorable events (13 spades) and 52 cards in all, so the probability is 13/52 or .25.

The computation of the ratio of favorable events to total possible events to determine the probability of a particular event occurring is a simple procedure as long as one considers simple events, such as drawing a particular card, or rolling a seven with two dice. As the events become more complicated or the number of possible outcomes increases, it is no longer feasible to enumerate the number of favorable events and the total number of possible events. Examples of more complicated events and ways to compute the probability of their occurrence are presented in Appendix A-1. The student with even an elementary understanding of probability is better equipped to understand the risks involved in games of chance, such as roulette and lotteries, and games based partly on chance, such as poker.

Statistical Tests

All the statistical tests to be considered in the second section of this text deal with the probability of a particular event occurring by chance. The essential question is whether the results obtained are a common or rare occurrence when only chance is operating. A statistical test can answer this question. The end result of the test is a single number, which is then compared with a number found by referring to the appropriate statistical table. Whether the experimental outcome is a rare or common event *given that the null hypothesis is true* is determined by making this comparison. The statistical test is a procedure for evaluating the null hypothesis. If the experimental outcome is a rare event, the null hypothesis is rejected. If it is not rare, then the null hypothesis is not rejected.

Significant Differences. The obtained differences between groups are said to be *significant* if the results are unlikely to occur on the basis of chance. That is, if a particular experimental outcome is a rare event when only chance is operating, it is reasonable to assert that *more than* chance is operating and to reject the null hypothesis and accept the research hypothesis. In this case the investigator asserts that the differences between the treatments were not due solely to chance fluctuations, but to chance plus the effect of the independent variable. If the results are such that the null hypothesis can be rejected, the obtained differences are said to be *significant*. Statistical tests are often referred to as *significance tests* because they are designed to determine whether obtained differences are rare, and therefore a significant event, or common, an insignificant event.

Significance Level. The curious reader is probably wondering how rare an event has to be to be labeled as significant. That is, how rare does an experimental outcome have to be, assuming that only chance is operating, before the investigator will reject the null hypothesis and accept the research hypothesis? The actual level varies somewhat depending on the research area, but most investigators will accept an outcome that has a probability of .05 or less as a rare event. If the probability of an event occurring is .05, this means that it can be expected to occur five times in every 100 if only chance is operating. The level used to define a rare event is called the *significance level.* The name follows from the fact that the obtained differences are *significant,* i.e., attributable to the effect of chance *plus* the effect of the independent variable, if the probability of the experimental outcome is less than the significance level.

The significance level that is adopted defines what is meant by a rare event *and* what is meant by equivalent groups. Groups are said to be equivalent if the probability of the obtained outcome is greater than the significance level, assuming that only chance is operating. If an investigator selects the .001 significance level, then the probability of rejecting the null hypothesis when the null hypothesis is true is one in one thousand. In this case a rare event is defined as an event with a probability of .001 if only chance is operating. The probability of obtaining equivalent groups *prior* to the introduction of the independent variable is .999 if only chance determines the assignment of subjects to groups. If it is highly likely that the groups are equivalent *prior* to the introduction of the independent variable and the groups are *not* equivalent *after* the introduction of the independent variable, then it is reasonable to conclude that the independent variable influenced group performance.

The probability of a rare event and the probability of obtaining equivalent groups must sum to 1.00 since these are the only two possible events. Thus, if the .05 significance level is adopted and the null hypothesis is true, then the probability of a rare event is .05 and the probability of obtaining equivalent groups is .95. If the independent variable does not have any effect (i.e., the null hypothesis is true), the probability of obtaining equivalent groups *after* the introduction of the independent variable is the same as the probability of obtaining equivalent groups *prior* to the introduction of the independent variable. Thus, if only chance is operating then it is highly likely that "small" mean differences will be obtained on the dependent measure after the introduction of the independent variable, so the investigator will probably be unable to reject the null hypothesis. However, since it is possible to obtain "large" mean differences solely on the basis of chance, an investigator may occasionally reject the null hypothesis when the null hypothesis is true. Yet, most of the time when the null hypothesis is rejected it will, in fact, be false. That is, in most cases "large" mean differences between groups are due to the effect of chance fluctuations *plus* the effect of the independent variable.

To summarize, the important point is that the significance level defines what is meant by a rare event and what is meant by equivalent groups. If the obtained differences are so large that the probability that the outcome is due solely to chance is equal to or less than the significance level adopted, the null hypothesis is rejected. A rare event has occurred if only chance is operating, and the group differences are said to be significant. If the obtained differences are such that the probability that the outcome is due solely to chance is greater than the significance level adopted, the null hypothesis cannot be rejected. A common event has occurred, given that only chance is operating, and the groups are said to be equivalent.

It is important for the reader not to misinterpret the information presented in the preceding paragraphs. It does not necessarily follow that it is a good idea to adopt a stringent significance level to increase the probability of obtaining equivalent groups. The reason this may not be a good idea will be discussed later in the chapter. It should also be emphasized that the significance level is selected *prior* to comparing the performance of the groups. It should not be changed after the performance is known. The selection of a significance level is usually not an important consideration since the investigator has little latitude in making the choice. Most investigators adopt the .05 level. One who wants to convince others that his research hypothesis is correct is unlikely to do so if a very lenient significance level (say, .15) is adopted. The reason why most investigators select the .05 level is also considered later in the chapter.

In short, the crucial consideration in performing a statistical test is whether the outcome of an experiment is rare or common if the null hypothesis is true. The likelihood of a particular outcome is determined by comparing the obtained outcome with the distribution of possible outcomes. The distribution of possible outcomes is obtained from sampling distributions. In order to understand sampling distributions, it is first necessary to consider frequency distributions.

Frequency Distributions

Types of Frequency Distributions. A distribution is a set of values or scores for a particular attribute or variable. There are many different kinds of distributions. One could obtain a distribution of scores on a final examination, a distribution of annual salaries for all truck drivers in Texas, a distribution of the weights of all college professors in California, and so on. Let us consider a hypothetical distribution of scores on a final examination in a biology class of forty students. The scores are: 51, 56, 83, 42, 52, 54, 53, 58, 61, 42, 83, 53, 54, 53, 59, 48, 65, 72, 75, 59, 61, 68, 43, 38, 65, 56, 56, 57, 51, 53, 56, 57, 43, 58, 59, 56, 59, 64, 66, 42.

It is difficult to describe this set of scores as it presently stands. About all one can do is read the entire set. A frequency distribution can be obtained by simply arranging the scores in ascending or descending order and counting the number of times each occurs. That is, one determines the frequency of each score in the distribution. A frequency distribution for this set is presented in Table 4-1. A clearer description of the scores is arrived at when they are tabulated in frequency distribution form.

Usually an even clearer description is possible when the scores are grouped into categories as in Table 4-2. Although Table 4-2 is somewhat easier to read than Table 4-1, it is important to note that some information was lost in going from the frequency distribution to the grouped frequency distribution. It is not possible to determine how many students received each score by referring to the grouped frequency distribution.

TABLE 4-1

The Frequency Distribution for the Forty Scores on the Biology Final Examination

Score	*Frequency*	*Score*	*Frequency*
83	2	57	2
75	1	56	5
72	1	54	2
68	1	53	4
66	1	52	1
65	2	51	2
64	1	48	1
61	2	43	2
59	4	42	3
58	2	38	1

TABLE 4-2

The Grouped Frequency Distribution for the Forty Scores on the Biology Final Examination

Scores	*Frequency*
76–85	2
66–75	4
56–65	18
46–55	10
36–45	6

The grouped frequency distribution in Table 4-2 is presented in graphic form in Figure 4-1. When distributions are presented in graphic form, frequency is represented on the ordinate, or *y* axis (vertical axis), and the scores on the abscissa, or *x* axis (horizontal axis). For example, since there were 18 scores in the 56 to 65 interval (labeled 60.5, the middle point in the category), the height of the bar is 18 units on the ordinate for this interval. The graph in Figure 4-1A is called a bar graph or histogram. The same information is given in the graph in Figure 4-1B except that the form is different and one category at each extreme has been added so that the line,

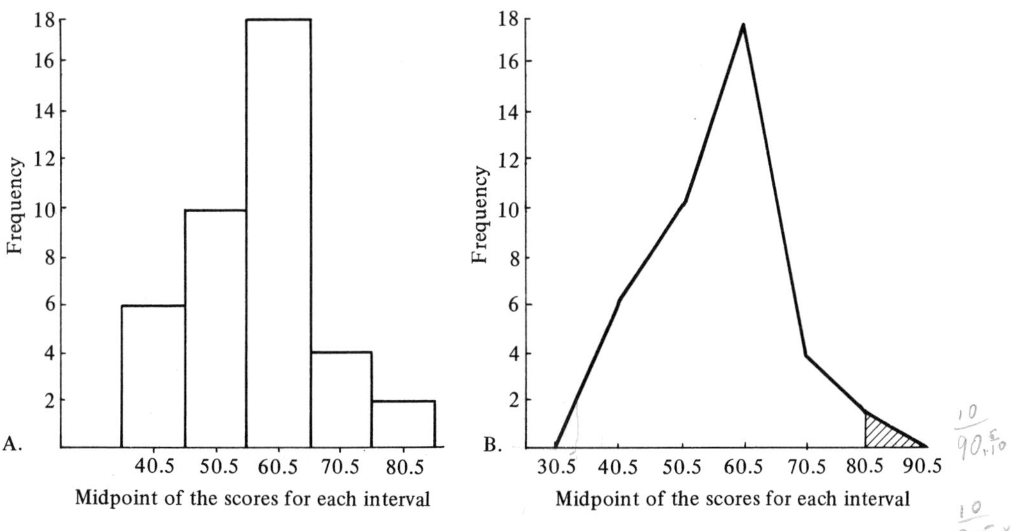

FIGURE 4-1

The grouped frequency distribution for the forty scores on the biology final examination. Figure A is a bar graph (histogram) and Figure B is a frequency polygon.

which connects the dots indicating the frequency of each category, touches the abscissa.

Probability and Frequency Distributions. A graph can be used to depict the probability of particular outcomes. For example, consider the probability of selecting a student from the biology class with a score of 76 or over if only chance is operating. Since there are two students in the 76 and over category, there are two favorable events. There are forty students in all, so the probability is 2/40 or .05. This means that if you made 100 selections and replaced your selection each time, you should expect to select a student with a score of 76 or more five times in the 100 attempts. Or, stated differently, the bar for the 76–85 category (labeled 80.5) in Figure 4-1A is 5 percent of the total of all the bars combined. This is, of course, simply another way of considering the number of favorable events relative to the total number of events.

The graph in Figure 4-1B can also be used to indicate the probability of a particular outcome. The area underneath the curve can be used to represent the total number of events. If this is done, then there is no need to worry about the absolute frequency levels for any score or block of scores. The relative height of the curve can be used to indicate the relative frequency of particular outcomes. The principal concern in hypothesis testing is whether a particular outcome is a rare event, so our concern will be with the end parts or extremes of each curve. For example, one can consider the probability of selecting a student with a score of 76 or more if only chancc is operating. To do this, one can divide the shaded area of the curve in Figure 4-1B by the total area under the curve.

Imagine that the area under the curve is a piece of pie, and consider what portion the shaded part is of the whole. Or, if you prefer, you can imagine that the piece of pie is a raisin pie and that there are 100 raisins equally distributed over the entire piece. If you select one raisin, what is the probability that it will come from the shaded portion given that only chance is operating? Selecting a particular raisin is analogous to conducting an experiment. The task is to assess whether the outcome of the experiment is a rare event (i.e., is in the shaded portion of the curve) if only chance is operating. We must next consider how one makes such an assessment.

Sampling Distributions

Empirical Sampling Distributions. Let us assume that a pseudo-experiment is conducted in which a random assignment procedure is used to form two groups of ten subjects each. The subjects in each group are a *sample* from a larger set of potential subjects. One group is labeled the Experimental Group and the other the Control Group. The experiment is a pseudo-experiment in that no independent variable is manipulated. The groups are treated identically. After the groups are formed, a score on the dependent variable is obtained for each subject. Then a mean score is computed for each group, and the Control Group is subtracted from the Experimental Group mean, resulting in a number that represents the difference between the two group means. If this procedure were repeated until the pseudo-experiment had been conducted 100,000 times, the result would be 100,000 numbers. Each number would represent the difference between an experimental and a control group mean.

A distribution using these 100,000 numbers could be made by plotting the frequency with which each mean difference was obtained. However, since this is a distribution of sample values, the difference between sample means, it is labeled a sampling distribution instead of a frequency distribution. It can be used to assess the probability of a particular result if only chance is operating, since no manipulation has been made. That is, this distribution is a null hypothesis sampling distribution.

Null hypothesis sampling distributions are used to evaluate experiments to determine if the obtained outcome is a rare or common event. The probability of the obtained outcome if only chance is operating is the basis for accepting or rejecting the null hypothesis. After determining the outcome of your experiment by, among other things, performing the appropriate statistical test, you refer to the appropriate table to determine if the outcome is rare or common if only chance is operating. These tables are based on null hypothesis sampling distributions. Each is based on a number of different sampling distributions because the magnitude of the mean difference between groups treated identically (i.e., with only chance differences) is influenced by the number of observations in each group. Chance fluctuations between group means tend to decrease as the number of subjects in each group increases. An example should clarify this point.

Suppose that you are interested in estimating the average (mean) I.Q. of the students at your college or university. To accomplish this you select two samples of five students each by drawing names out of a hat so that only chance determines which students are selected for each group. You determine the I.Q. for each student in the two groups and then compute the mean I.Q. for each group. Do you expect to obtain a large difference between the two mean I.Q.'s? Do you expect the difference to increase or decrease as the size of each group is increased, given that only chance determines what students are placed in each group? Hopefully, the reader appreciates the fact that the difference between the two means will tend to decrease as the group size increases. This is because each group mean is an estimate of the mean for the entire student body. The accuracy of each estimate, all things being equal, should increase as the number of students included in each estimate increases. Since both group means are estimates of the mean for the entire student body *and* these estimates become more accurate as the group size increases, it follows that the chance fluctuations between the group estimates should decrease as the number of students in each sample increases.

Mathematical Sampling Distributions. Sampling distributions obtained from a large number of samples are empirical in that samples are actually selected, observations made, the means computed, and so on. If an independent variable is not manipulated, then the sampling distribution obtained must be a null hypothesis sampling distribution. Fortunately, it is not necessary to determine the null hypothesis sampling distributions empirically. They can be derived by purely mathematical procedures. The sampling distribution obtained by using mathematics is essentially the same as the empirical sampling distribution.

Although the mathematical derivation of sampling distributions is beyond the scope of this text, you should remember that it is possible to use mathematics to obtain *null hypothesis sampling distributions.* It is not possible to use mathematics to obtain research hypothesis sampling distributions because the real effect of each independent variable is not known. Obviously, if the real effect were known, there would be little need for research. Since null hypothesis sampling distributions are the only ones available, there is no choice but to evaluate the research hypothesis by assessing its alternative, the null hypothesis. Rejecting the null hypothesis provides support for the research hypothesis.

Experimental Error and Rejecting the Null Hypothesis

Statistical tests are performed to assess whether obtained differences between conditions are significant. The investigator has some freedom to decide how "unlikely" the results have to be before they should be labeled significant. If he wants to be very careful and not claim that the manipulation has had an effect unless there is almost no question about it, he can accept a very stringent significance level such as .001. (This can be represented as $p < .001$; the p stands for probability.) If the obtained differences are so large that the results are significant at the .001 level, this means that there is less than one chance in one thousand that the results are due to chance. If the investigator attributes the obtained differences to the effect of the independent variable, there is some possibility that he is wrong. Perhaps only chance is operating. The point is that the possibility of being wrong when rejecting the null hypothesis cannot be eliminated, but the probability can be controlled. The probability of being wrong is equal to the significance level adopted. In the present case it is one in a thousand.

Rejecting the Null Hypothesis. Investigators attempt to reject the null hypothesis and, in general, are not interested in accepting it. If the null hypothesis is rejected then the research hypothesis can be accepted. However, if the null hypothesis is not rejected, then the research hypothesis should neither be accepted nor rejected. Investigators are free to accept the research hypothesis if they reject the null hypothesis because they know the probability of being wrong when they reject the latter. The probability of being wrong if the null hypothesis is accepted cannot be determined.

Type 1 and Type 2 Errors. Asserting that the independent variable has an effect (rejecting the null hypothesis and accepting the research hypothesis) when in fact it does not, is committing an error. This is called a Type 1 error, and the probability of committing it is equal to the significance level (also called the alpha level) adopted. However, it is possible to make another error. Asserting that the independent variable has no effect (failing to reject the null hypothesis) when in fact it *has* an effect is committing a Type 2 error. The reason investigators are reluctant to conclude, when they fail to reject the null hypothesis, that the independent variable does not have an effect, is that the probability of making a Type 2 error cannot be determined. The probability decreases as the real effect of the independent variable increases, but since the *real* effect of an independent variable is not known, there is no way to determine the probability of making a Type 2 error.

Sampling Distributions, Experimental Error, and Rejecting the Null Hypothesis

Another way to consider the question of experimental error and rejecting the null hypothesis is to imagine that we know the true state of affairs. That is, although we cannot determine mathematically what the sampling distribution would be when the research hypothesis is true, we can imagine several different situations that could arise.

Null Hypothesis Is True. Assume that a simple two-group experiment was conducted. For the first situation, assume that the null hypothesis is true. Figure 4-2A represents this state of affairs. The reader should note that the mean of the null hypothesis sampling distribution is zero since the null hypothesis predicts no difference between the groups. The curve represents the relative probability of particular outcomes. It is assumed that the Control Group mean is subtracted from the Experimental Group mean. The right portion of the curve represents the probability that the Experimental Group mean will be larger than the Control Group mean (i.e., a positive difference will be obtained). It can be seen that the probability of obtaining a large mean difference between the groups is less than the probability of obtaining a small mean difference. The left portion of the curve represents the probability that a negative difference will be obtained.

Only chance fluctuations should produce a difference between the two sample means since we have assumed that the null hypothesis is true. Thus, the probability of making a Type 1 error (concluding that the independent variable has an effect when in fact it does not) is equal to the significance level (say, .05). The probability of making a Type 2 error is zero since, in this case, we have assumed that the null hypothesis is true.

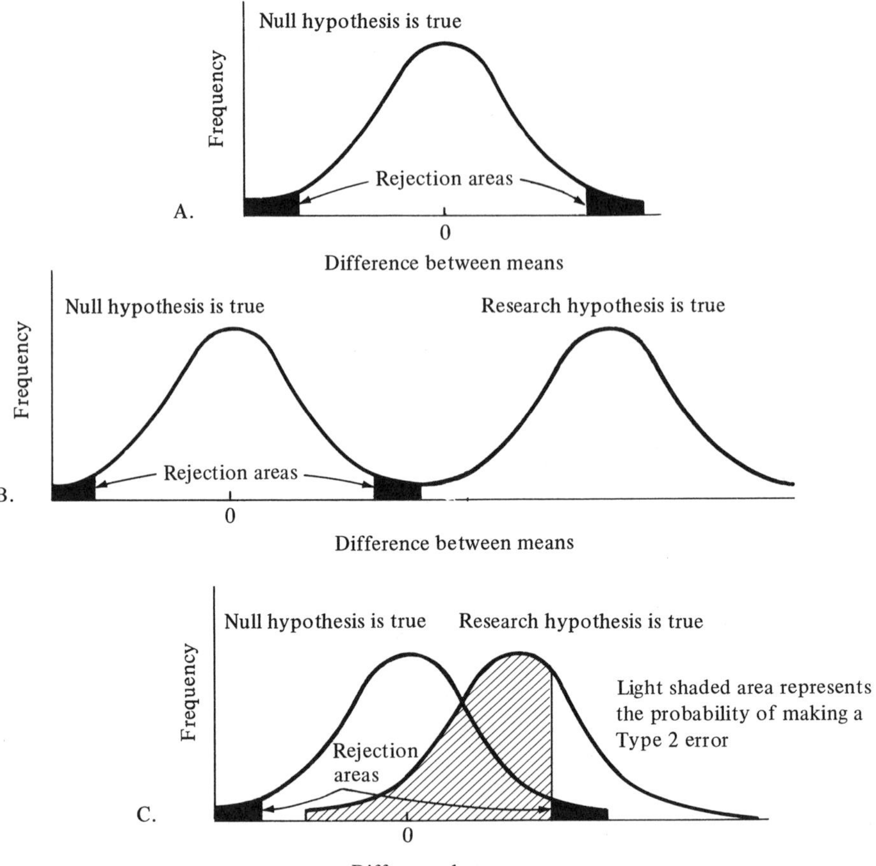

FIGURE 4–2

The null hypothesis sampling distribution and the "research hypothesis sampling distribution" for three possible situations. In A the independent variable has no effect. In B the independent variable has a large effect. In C the independent variable has a small effect.

Independent Variable Has a Large Effect. Assume that the independent variable has a large effect. Figure 4-2B represents this state of affairs. In this case the "research hypothesis sampling distribution" indicates the true state of affairs, but the null hypothesis sampling distribution is used to assess the effect of the manipulation since there is no way to obtain the "research hypothesis sampling distribution." The "research hypothesis sampling distribution" has almost no overlap with the null hypothesis sampling distribution. However, since the tails of each curve never touch the horizontal axis there is always some overlap.

The independent variable has a large effect, so a large mean difference between the samples is likely. That is, since the independent variable has a large influence on performance, it is likely that the mean difference between groups, which is based on the effect of the independent variable *plus* chance effects, will also be large. Since the obtained difference is evaluated according to the null hypothesis sampling distribution, it is almost certain that the null hypothesis will be rejected.

The probability of making a Type 1 error is zero since we have assumed that the independent variable has an effect. The probability of making a Type 2 error is very small since there is very little chance of obtaining a small difference between the two treatment means.

Independent Variable Has a Small Effect. Assume that the independent variable has a relatively small effect. Figure 4-2C represents this state of affairs. The probability of making a Type 1 error is still zero because the independent variable has an effect. The probability of making a Type 2 error is quite large however. The greater the overlap between the null hypothesis sampling distribution and the "research hypothesis sampling distribution" the greater is the probability of making a Type 2 error. Thus, the magnitude of the effect of the independent variable is one factor which influences the probability of making a Type 2 error. Since the real effect of the independent variable is unknown, it is not possible to calculate the probability of making a Type 2 error. Investigators are willing to reject the null hypothesis and accept the research hypothesis because they know the probability of making an error when they do this. They are reluctant to accept the null hypothesis (reject the research hypothesis) because they do not know the probability of making an error (Type 2 error) when they accept the null hypothesis.

Relationship Between Type 1 and Type 2 Errors. The probability of making a Type 1 error is equal to the significance level that is adopted, so adopting a more stringent significance level decreases the probability of making a Type 1 error. If this were the only consideration it would be a good idea to adopt a very stringent significance level. However, investigators are also concerned about making Type 2 errors, and the probability of making a Type 2 error is also related to the significance level. Adopting a more stringent significance level increases the probability of making a Type 2 error. This fact can be appreciated by examining Figure 4-2C. The shaded area in the "research hypothesis sampling distribution" represents the probability of making a Type 2 error. If the rejection area under the null hypothesis sampling distribution is increased (i.e., a more lenient significance level is adopted), the probability of making a Type 2 error decreases (i.e., the shaded portion under the "research hypothesis sampling distribution" decreases). The reverse is true if a more stringent significance level is adopted. Thus, the investigator who is more interested in avoiding Type 1 errors is likely to adopt a stringent significance level. The one who wants to avoid Type 2 errors is likely to adopt a lenient significance level. Most investigators are about equally interested in avoiding Type 1 and Type 2 errors so they take a middle position and select the .05 significance level.

One-Tailed versus Two-Tailed Tests

As we know, if the null hypothesis is true then the independent variable has no influence on the dependent measure, and if the research hypothesis is true then the independent variable does have an influence. Now, in some cases an investigator may want to be more specific about the effect of the independent variable on the dependent variable. Instead of simply asserting that the independent variable has an effect, he may want to specify the direction of the effect. For example, if a two-group experiment is conducted, the investigator may predict that the experimental subjects will be better than control subjects. The research hypothesis is supported only if the experimental subjects are better. The null hypothesis is accepted if control subjects are better than experimental subjects regardless of the magnitude of the difference between the two conditions. The investigator who predicts the direction of the results makes a one-tailed test. The investigator who does not predict the direction of the results makes a two-tailed test.

Advantages of a One-Tailed Test. The reason for the labels one-tailed and two-tailed can be appreciated by referring to the null hypothesis sampling distribution presented in Figure 4-2A. For demonstration purposes, assume that the Control Group mean is always subtracted from the Experimental Group mean. The investigator making a two-tailed test rejects the null hypothesis whenever there is a large difference between the two means regardless of whether the experimental mean is more or less than the control mean. He is interested in both tails or extremes of the sampling distribution curve. Thus, if the investigator selects the .05 significance level, 2.5 percent of the area under the curve at each tail is designated as the rejection area.

The "advantage" of making a one-tailed test is that 5 percent of the area under the curve at only one extreme is selected. If the 5 percent is selected at the right extreme only, then a smaller mean difference is needed to reject the null hypothesis, provided the results are in the predicted direction. Thus, if the results are in the predicted direction, the probability of rejecting the null hypothesis is greater with a one-tailed than a two-tailed test. Unfortunately, some investigators misuse one-tailed tests.

Misuse of One-Tailed Tests. Assume an investigator predicts that the experimental subjects will be better than control subjects. Since a directional prediction is made, the investigator plans to use a one-tailed test. Assume the investigator who adopts the .05 significance level can reject the null hypothesis if a mean difference of four or more is obtained, provided the results are in the predicted direction. Unfortunately, the results are in the opposite direction of what was predicted. The Control Group mean is six more than the Experimental Group mean. In this case the experimenter cannot reject the null hypothesis. The prediction was in the wrong direction so he cannot benefit from the fact that the obtained difference exceeded the difference needed for a one-tailed, or even a two-tailed, test of the prediction. If the experimenter switches to a two-tailed test after the results are obtained and reports the results as significant, then he has misused the one-tailed test. In this case the investigator actually used a two-tailed test and accepted the .075 level of significance (5 percent at one tail and 2.5 percent at the other).

Selecting a One- or Two-Tailed Test. In order to use a one-tailed test correctly it is necessary to make the prediction prior to collecting the data. If the results are in the opposite direction to that predicted, then the null hypothesis cannot be rejected even though large differences are obtained. An investigator who reports results as significant that are in the direction opposite to what he predicted is using a two-tailed test. Thus, before deciding to use a one-tailed test, you should ask yourself whether you are willing to accept the null hypothesis if the results are in the opposite direction and large differences are obtained. If you are not willing to do this, you should not use a one-tailed test. You would only be deceiving yourself about the significance level you have adopted.

One can argue that an investigator should be reluctant to make a one-tailed test because the results may go in the wrong direction. If a one-tailed test was planned, then the null hypothesis should be accepted. Since experiments supporting the null hypothesis are rarely published, the decision to make a one-tailed test may keep an interesting finding from the rest of the scientific community. Most investigators always use the more conservative, two-tailed test.

A one-tailed test should be made only if obtaining results opposite to the predicted results would have no practical or theoretical value. For example, if a new instructional technique is devised, the technique may be of value only if it is equal or superior to the present technique. A two-tailed test is not necessary because there is no practical or theoretical value in demonstrating that the new technique is inferior to the present technique. In this case, a one-tailed test is justified.

SUMMARY

The overall logic of hypothesis testing is actually rather simple. One starts with an idea that can be tested by making predictions about observable events. In many cases, this means that an experimenter predicts that an independent variable will have an influence on performance. Such an assertion is labeled the research hypothesis. The null hypothesis is the assertion that the independent variable will not have an effect. The testing procedure usually involves obtaining groups which are likely to be equivalent and then introducing the independent variable. The effect of the independent variable is assessed by comparing the performance of the subjects in the various conditions on the dependent variable.

After the results are obtained, the outcome is determined and compared with a distribution of possible outcomes based on the assumption that the null hypothesis is true. If the outcome is a rare event when compared with the appropriate null hypothesis sampling distribution, then the null hypothesis is rejected. The experimenter has reason to believe that the particular outcome is not a rare, chance event; instead, he attributes the obtained differences to the effect of the independent manipulation. Experimenters attempt to reject the null hypothesis and, in general, are not interested in accepting it. They know the probability of being wrong when they reject the null hypothesis, but they do not know the probability of being wrong if they accept it.

QUESTIONS

1. What are the steps involved in hypothesis testing?
2. What is the probability of a particular event occurring if only chance is operating?
3. Consider the following proposition. The task is to draw an ace from a standard deck of playing cards. You pay a dime if you fail to draw an ace and receive a dollar if you succeed. The cards are shuffled after every draw. Would you accept this proposition? Why or why not? Would you accept the proposition if each draw only cost a nickel?
4. Consider the following proposition. A roulette wheel is used which contains nine slots numbered 0 to 8. You can pick any number, or all the even numbers, or all the odd numbers. If you select even numbers or odd numbers and win, you win the same amount that you bet. On this type of bet you lose, of course, if the little ball ends up in the zero hole. If you select any single number from 0 to 8 and win, you receive seven times what you bet. Given that you have a strong urge to gamble, should you pick single numbers, odd numbers, or even numbers? Does it make any difference? Do you expect to win or lose?
5. Distinguish between research and null hypotheses.
6. What are sampling distributions and why are they important?
7. How are null hypothesis sampling distributions obtained?
8. Why is it important to state the research hypothesis in such a way that the null hypothesis and research hypothesis cannot both be correct, but one has to be correct, provided there is no confounding variable?
9. Distinguish between Type 1 and Type 2 errors. What factors influence the probability of making each kind of error?
10. What is meant by the term "equivalent groups"? How does the significance level adopted affect the meaning of equivalent groups?
11. Explain why investigators attempt to reject the null hypothesis and, in general, are not interested in accepting it.

12. Why does the probability of making a Type 2 error decrease as the magnitude of the effect of the independent variable increases?
13. What is the relationship between the significance level and the probability of making a Type 1 or Type 2 error?
14. What are the advantages and disadvantages of using a one-tailed test?

between-subject designs

The chapter is devoted to between-subject designs and related topics. Random sampling, random assignment, and the logic of analysis of variance are considered first in order to prepare the reader for the subsequent discussion of the two between-subject designs: random-groups designs and matched-groups designs. The properties, logic, and uses of random-groups designs are considered. Then matched-groups designs are discussed, first for subject variable and then for nonsubject variable manipulations. The topics considered include the prerequisite for matching, reasons for matching, and procedures for matching.

Three topics have to be considered in order to lay the groundwork for our discussion of random-groups and matched-groups designs. These topics are random sampling, random assignment, and the logic of analysis of variance.

RANDOM SAMPLING

The purpose of random sampling is to obtain a sample that is representative of the population being sampled. The sample is usually a small portion of the subjects who could have been selected; the larger group of potential subjects is called the population. For example, fifty students could be selected randomly from all the undergraduates at the University of Texas at Austin. The fifty students would be the sample; all the undergraduates would be the population. The population can be defined as the total number of potential units for observation. It can have relatively few units (e.g., all the redheads at the University of Oregon), a large number of units (e.g., all humans in North America), or an infinite number of units (e.g., the possible outcomes obtained by tossing a coin an infinite number of times).

In order for a sample to be completely random, each subject in the population being considered should have an equal chance of being selected, and the selection of one subject should not influence the selection or nonselection of another. That is, all conceivable samples should be equally likely.

The major reason for random sampling is to estimate the properties of the population. One can generalize from the properties of the sample to those of the population. The advantage to this procedure is that it is much simpler to obtain measures for a small sample. For example, it is much easier to assess the preferences of voters in the United States by interviewing a representative sample than by interviewing all the voters, which would be next to impossible.

Random Sampling Example

Let us assume you want to select a random sample of fifty students from a college having an enrollment of 1,000. One way you could accomplish this would be to print each student's name on a piece of paper, throw all the pieces into a large basket, mix them up, and then draw out fifty pieces of paper while you are blindfolded. You would obtain a completely random sample because each student, and any combination of fifty students, could be selected. However, this procedure would be very time consuming if a sample is being selected from a large population.

Instead of printing all the names on separate pieces of paper, you may decide to use the student directory, which provides an alphabetical listing of the 1,000 students. You write each number from 1 to 20 on a separate piece of paper, throw the pieces into a hat, mix them, and select one piece without looking. Let us assume you drew the number 14. You then go to the student directory and find the name in the 14th position. You select this student, and every 20th student thereafter in the alphabetical listing, until you have your sample of fifty students. Thus, the students in positions number 14, 34, 54, 74, and so on, are selected for the sample.

Every student had an equal chance of being selected, but every possible sample was not equally likely. That is, if only chance influences who is selected for the sample, it should be possible for the first fifty students in the alphabetical listing to constitute the sample. This is impossible with your procedure. Thus, the sample is not completely random. Although in the strictest sense every possible sample should be equally likely before one labels the sample as random, many investigators define a random sample simply as one in which every subject has an equal chance of being selected.

Random Sampling with Restriction

Sometimes it is necessary to place restrictions on random sampling in order to obtain a sample with certain characteristics. For example, if a random sample of 1,000 subjects is selected from the United States population, it may not contain any blacks. This is extremely unlikely, but it is possible. If it is important to include representatives of minority groups, then the sample can be randomly selected with the restriction that its minority group composition match that of the general population.

RANDOM ASSIGNMENT

It is important to distinguish between random sampling and random assignment. The purpose of random sampling is to obtain a sample that is representative of a larger population so that the properties of the population can be estimated. The purpose of random assignment is to obtain equivalent groups prior to the introduction of the independent variable so that the effect of the independent variable can be estimated.

Random Assignment with Restriction

It is not unusual for investigators to place restrictions on their random assignment procedures. When one is using a random-groups design there are advantages to randomly assigning the subjects to groups with the restriction that there be an equal number of subjects in each group. A simple way to assure this is to use the table of random permutations of the first eight digits, found in Appendix C-1. The table contains 500 random sequences of the eight numbers.

Random Assignment Example

An investigator wants to assign sixty subjects to three conditions such that there are twenty subjects in each condition. He can do this by using twenty of the sequences of eight numbers in Appendix C-1. The first step is to select the starting sequence by some random procedure. Say that he puts each of the numbers from 0 to 9 on a piece of paper and puts the papers in a hat. For the first draw, it is only necessary to use the numbers from 0 to 5 (since there are only 500 sequences in the table). For the second and third draws, all ten numbers should be used. After three draws the starting sequence would be selected. For example, if the numbers drawn were 2, 7, and 0, in that order, the starting sequence would be 270.

After the starting sequence is selected and located in the table, it is only necessary to note the ordering of the numbers 1, 2, and 3 in each sequence, since only three groups of subjects are needed; the other five numbers in each sequence are ignored. The order in the first sequence (i.e., sequence 270) is found to be 2, 3, 1, so the first subject is assigned to condition 2, the second to condition 3, and the third to condition 1. The same procedure is used to assign the other fifty-seven subjects to the three conditions. The next sequence (271) is used for the next set of three subjects, and so on. Thus, when twenty sequences have been used, there will be twenty subjects in each condition. The subjects will be randomly assigned to the three conditions with the restriction that there be an equal number in each.

Although it is permissible to place some restrictions on the random assignment of subjects to groups, it is crucial that only chance determine the condition to which a particular subject is assigned. The random assignment of subjects to conditions enables the experimenter to be reasonably confident that the groups are equivalent prior to the experimental manipulation.

THE LOGIC OF ANALYSIS OF VARIANCE

A knowledge of the logic of analysis of variance is important for a better understanding of experimental design. There is a close relationship between the design and analysis of experiments. Once the logic of analysis of variance is understood, the student will be able to evaluate experimental designs and procedures more effectively.

Obtaining Two Estimates of Population Variance

The crux of the analysis of variance with a random-groups design is to obtain two independent estimates of population variance. The subjects who are tested or observed comprise the sample or samples. It is possible, of course, to select more than one sample. The larger group of potential subjects is called the population. Variance is a measure indicating the extent to which scores differ. Scores differ because of differences among subjects in heredity, past experience, and so on.

Within-Group Variance. One estimate of population variance can be obtained by determining group variance. The variability in performance *within* each group provides an estimate of population variance, so there are as many estimates as there are groups. However, what is needed is a single estimate of population variance, based on the variance within each sample. Therefore, an average of the sample variances is the best within-group estimate of population variance.

This is not as complicated as it may seem. Within-group variance is merely a measure of the extent to which subjects in the same treatment condition perform alike. For example, if all the subjects in the Experimental Group obtain a score of eleven on the dependent measure and all the subjects in the Control Group obtain a score of eight, there is no within-group variance. Usually, subjects in the same condition do not obtain the same scores, so the within-group variance measure is greater than zero. The within-group variance measure increases as the fluctuations between subjects in the same group increase.

Between-Group Variance. The other estimate of population variance is based on group means. If the null hypothesis is true, the group means can be regarded as a distribution of sample means from the same population. This distribution of sample means can be used to obtain another estimate of population variance. Since this second estimate is based on group means, it is a between-group estimate of population variance. That is, the first estimate of population variance is influenced by fluctuations *within* each group, and the second, which is based on means, is influenced by fluctuations *between* groups (between means). A proof that two independent estimates of population variance can be obtained, one based on within-group variation and the other on between-group variation, is presented in Appendix A-2. However, the reader should delay examining the proof until the material in Chapter 10 has been considered.

Comparing the Two Variance Estimates

The two estimates of population variance can be compared to assess the effect of the independent variable. If only chance is operating, i.e., the null hypothesis is true, the two estimates of population variance should be about the same. Differences between them will be due solely to chance fluctuations. However, if the independent variable has an effect, then the two estimates should differ. The between-group estimate, based on group means, should be significantly larger than the within-group estimate.

The reason for this is simple enough. Let us reconsider the between-group estimate, based on group means. If the independent variable does not have an effect, then the group means can be considered sample means which are estimates of the same population mean. However, if the independent variable has an effect, the group means will not all be estimates of the same mean because the independent variable manipulation will result in an increase or decrease in the Experimental Group mean. In short, there should be greater fluctuations between the group means when the independent variable has an effect than when it does not. But there is no reason to expect within-group fluctuations to increase if the independent variable has an effect.

Therefore, the crux of the analysis of variance test is to compare the between-group and within-group estimates of population variance. If the two estimates are about the same, then there is no reason to reject the null hypothesis. If the between-group estimate is considerably larger than the within-group estimate, then the null hypothesis can be rejected. Thus, in order to conclude that the independent variable has an effect, the within-group fluctuations should be small relative to the between-group fluctuations.

Analysis of Variance and Experimental Design

An understanding of the logic of analysis of variance is important for methodological as well as statistical purposes because design and procedural decisions can have a marked influence on the within-group and between-group estimates of population variance. The reader should remember that investigators are interested in rejecting the null hypothesis. There is little satisfaction in failing to do so. In order to maximize the likelihood of rejecting the null hypothesis when the independent variable actually has an effect, it is necessary to keep within-group fluctuations as small as possible. That is, if an independent variable does have an effect on the dependent variable, the effect is more likely to be detected if the investigator is able to keep within-group fluctuations to a minimum. Thus, it is important to know what effect a particular design or procedure has on these fluctuations.

RANDOM-GROUPS DESIGN

Properties of the Random-Groups Design

In a between-subject design each subject receives only one level of each independent variable. For example, to assess the effects of reward on motor performance each subject would either receive the reward or not receive it. He would not be tested under both reward and nonreward conditions. The treatment is between subjects in that the performance of different subjects is compared to assess the effect of the independent variable. In random-groups designs, which are between-subject designs, each subject gets only one level of each independent variable. The second important characteristic is that random assignment is used so that the investigator can be relatively confident that the groups are equivalent prior to the introduction of the independent variable.

Logic of the Random-Groups Design

The random assignment procedure is meant to assure that between-group differences prior to the introduction of the independent variable will be due solely to chance fluctuations. If only chance determines the assignment of subjects to conditions, then the significance level that is adopted will determine the probability of obtaining equivalent groups prior to the introduction of the independent variable. An example should help clarify the logic of this design.

Assume that an investigator decides to use a random-groups design to assess the effects of a particular independent variable on heartbeat rate. Let us assume further that, unknown to the investigator, redheads have faster heartbeats than nonredheads. Will the random assignment procedure result in groups with approximately the same number of redheads so that group differences will not be attributable to having too many redheads in one group? If the .05 significance level is adopted, the investigator can be confident that random assignment will yield equivalent groups prior to the introduction of the independent variable approximately 95 percent of the time. Therefore, if significant differences between groups are found *after* the introduction of the independent variable, it is reasonable to assert that these differences are due to chance *plus* the effect of the independent variable, since the probability that they are due to chance alone is known to be small (i.e., .05). This probability is known to be small *because* the random assignment procedure was used to assure that only chance determined the assignment of subjects to conditions.

Uses of the Random-Groups Design

The random-groups design can be used whenever it is possible to randomly assign subjects to groups and then introduce the independent variable. It follows, therefore, that this design can be used to test essentially all independent variables except subject variables. A number of examples are given to demonstrate its usefulness.

Experiments with One Independent Variable. It is possible to assess, for instance, the effect of a new drug by using a random-groups design. The subjects are randomly assigned to either the experimental or control condition. Then the treatment is administered, and the effect of the treatment on some dependent variable is assessed. If the performance of the experimental subjects on the dependent variable differs significantly from that of the control subjects, then the difference can be attributed to the effect of the treatment. It is important to note that the control subjects should be treated the same as the experimental subjects except for the intended manipulation. To assure that the use of the drug is the only manipulation, the subjects must not be given any information about the treatment conditions. The control subjects are given a placebo; the experimental subjects are given the drug. Neither the subjects nor the person administering the treatments should know which treatment a subject receives. Experiments in which both the subjects and the person administering the treatments are kept unaware of the nature of the manipulation are frequently referred to as double-blind experiments.

Although a two-group experiment can be used to assess the effect of a particular manipulation, investigators frequently prefer to use more than two conditions. The use of additional conditions allows them to answer additional questions. For example, an investigator interested in the effect of a new drug may manipulate the amount of the drug administered. In this case a three-group random-groups design could be used. One group would receive a high dose; a second group, a low dose; and the third, a placebo. The investigator would be able to determine whether the drug has an effect *and* whether the dosage has an effect.

Experiments with Pretests. One disadvantage of the random-groups design is that random assignment will not *always* produce equivalent groups. Sometimes it is possible to check on the equivalence of the groups by having the subjects perform a pretest. The pretest must be identical to or highly correlated with the dependent measure. The procedure is to assign the subjects to conditions randomly, administer the pretest, introduce the independent variable, and measure performance on the dependent measure. This allows the investigator to determine whether the groups were equivalent prior to the introduction of the independent variable. In the rare case in which random assignment does not produce equivalent groups, it would be possible to make them equivalent prior to the introduction of the independent variable, or to correct for the differences in the pretest scores when analyzing the scores of subjects on the dependent measure.

There are some limitations to the use of a pretest. It may be prevented by practical or methodological considerations. In some cases there is not enough time; in other cases an appropriate pretest is not available. For example, pretests are not feasible in many memory experiments because subjects must memorize a particular set of items; if these items are used in the pretest, they cannot be used later. Another difficulty is that the pretest may influence the results. The independent variable may have an effect only if a pretest is used. This is the case when a pretest "prepares" the experimental subjects for their treatment. If the investigator has reason to believe that the effect of the independent variable depends on the influence of a pretest, he can use a factorial design to evaluate this influence.

Pretests and Factorial Designs. The investigator who wants to use a pretest but is concerned that the use of one may influence the results can use a factorial design. If there are two levels of the independent variable, then a four-group experiment is needed. Subjects are randomly assigned to the four groups. Two groups are given a pretest and two are not. Of the two groups given the pretest, one is an experimental group and the other a control. Also, of the two groups *not* given the pretest, one is an experimental group and the other a control. Thus, a 2 by 2 factorial design is used. The experimental versus control manipulation is one independent variable, and the presence or absence of the pretest is the other. The design is a 2 by 2 because there are two levels of each independent variable; it is a factorial because every level of one independent variable is combined with every level of the other.

The results can be analyzed to assess whether each independent variable has an effect. For example, if the performance of the two groups who are given a pretest differs significantly from the groups not given a pretest, it is fair to conclude that the pretest influenced performance. More importantly, if the effect of the experimental versus control manipulation is dependent on the presence or absence of a pretest, then the two variables interact. If they interact, it follows that the results obtained when the pretest is used are different from those obtained when it is not. The major point is that in some cases the conclusions that experimenters reach will depend on the type of design used. Fortunately, it is usually possible to determine to what extent, if any, a conclusion depends on the use of a particular design.

Subject and Nonsubject Variable Experiments. It is common for investigators to use a random-groups design to assess the effects of two or more independent variables in the same experiment, as in the one just considered. It is also possible to combine the investigation of a subject variable with a nonsubject variable in the same experiment. A random-groups design can be used for the nonsubject variable manipulation but not for the subject variable manipulation.

Let us consider a hypothetical experiment in which the two types of variables are manipulated. Imagine that you are interested in the effect of diet on intellectual development; you believe that adequate protein is extremely important, particularly during the early stages. For ethical, practical, and legal reasons you are not able to use human subjects in your experiment, so you use rhesus monkeys. Assume that a reliable and valid test of intellectual development is available and that the test can be administered to all subjects when they are mature at four years of age. This test is the dependent measure. The diet of each subject is controlled for a one year period. During the period in which diet is not controlled, the subjects are given their regular, normal protein diet. Since diet is a nonsubject variable it is possible to evaluate its effect by using a random-groups design.

The subject variable is the age of the subject when diet is manipulated. The manipulation is made during the first, second, or third year of life. Since age is a subject variable, you cannot randomly assign the monkeys to the age conditions. Rather, the subjects you have *selected* are equal numbers of newborns, one year olds, and two year olds; and you manipulate diet at each age level. The newborns, then the one year olds, and then the two year olds are randomly assigned to a low or high protein diet for a one year period. The only restriction placed on the random assignment is that there must be an equal number of subjects in each of the six conditions.

There are two different treatment conditions at each of the three age levels, so the six conditions cover all possible combinations of the variables. The design is a 2 by 3 factorial since there are two levels of one variable (diet) and three levels of the other variable (age of subjects). The number of different treatment conditions in a factorial design is equal to the number of levels of the first independent variable multiplied by the number of levels of the second independent variable, and so on. The design of this experiment is presented in Table 5-1.

You are not particularly interested in comparing the performance of newborns, one year olds, and two year olds. Since these subjects were not assigned randomly to the three age conditions, there is no way of knowing what nonmanipulated variables may be responsible for performance differences. However, since you were able to use a random assignment procedure for the diet manipulation, you can attribute significant differences between high protein and low protein subjects to the manipulation. That is — to review — the newborn subjects were randomly assigned to the low protein and high protein conditions; the one year olds were randomly assigned to the low and high protein conditions; and the two year olds were randomly assigned to low and high protein conditions. Thus, you can be reasonably confident that the low and high protein subjects at each age level were equivalent prior to the introduction of the independent variable.

The major reason for combining the manipulation of the nonsubject variable (diet) and subject variable (age at the start of the diet) is to assess whether the effect, if any, of the nonsubject variable depends on the type of subject. This knowledge can be valuable. If a variable such as protein level has an influence on intellectual development, it is important to determine the circumstances under which it has an effect. For example, if lack of protein

TABLE 5–1

Design of the Experiment in which Diet and Age of the Subjects at the Start of the Diet Are Manipulated

Age of the subjects at the start of the diet					
Newborn		*One year*		*Two years*	
Low protein diet	High protein diet	Low protein diet	High protein diet	Low protein diet	High protein diet

during the first year has a strong effect on development, but lack of protein thereafter has very little effect, then providing an adequate diet during the first year can be given top priority.

This experiment can be criticized because there is a confounding variable. The time between the manipulation of diet and the test of intellectual development is confounded with the age at which the diet was manipulated. Between the end of the manipulation and the test of intellectual development, one, two, or three years had elapsed for the two year olds, one year olds, and newborns, respectively. Thus, one can argue that differences in the test performance of newborns, one year olds, and two year olds may be due to the time lag rather than to their age. Fortunately, the presence of this confound is of no great concern because the time variable is confounded with the subject variable (age of the subjects at the start of the diet) and not with the nonsubject variable. The reader should recognize, however, that the effect of the diet manipulation may depend on the length of time between the manipulation and the test instead of on the age of the subjects at the start. The results of the experiment may allow the investigator to decide which of these two interpretations is more reasonable. For example, if the effect of the manipulation is greatest for newborns, then the age of the subject at the start of the diet is probably the important variable.

This experiment can also be criticized because it lacks a control group. One could argue that a normal diet group should have been used as well as the low and high protein conditions. If the control condition had been included, then there would have been three levels of diet (low protein, normal protein, and high protein) at each age level. Without the control condition it is not possible to determine, assuming a protein effect was obtained, whether low protein retards intellectual development or high protein facilitates it. You can indicate the difference between low and high protein, but you cannot make any assertions about low and high protein relative to the normal level. You must limit the conclusion to the levels of the independent variable used.

There are designs that allow one to make statements about levels of an independent variable other than the levels included in the experiment, but these designs will not be treated in this text. The designs in which it is necessary to limit conclusions to the levels of the independent variable manipulated use what is called a "fixed effects" model. Only fixed effects models are considered here.

MATCHED-GROUPS DESIGNS

A matched-groups design is a between-subject design in which the groups are equated on one or more matching variables (e.g., intelligence). Matching variables are subject variables. If a nonsubject variable is held constant for all conditions (i.e., the groups are equated on a nonsubject variable), it is said to be controlled. For example, if the experimental subjects and control subjects are given the same amount of time to complete their tasks, the time variable is controlled. Time is, of course, a nonsubject variable. In short, investigators *match* groups on subject variables and *control* nonsubject variables. The reasons for matching and the procedures used depend upon whether the independent variable is a subject or nonsubject variable.

Matched-Groups Designs and Subject Variables

The reason for using a matched-groups design for a subject variable manipulation is readily understood. In a subject variable manipulation, as we have seen before, it is not possible to equate the groups prior to the introduction of the independent variable because the nature of the independent variable determines the composition of the groups. For example, assume an investigator devises a test to identify people with high levels of anxiety and people with low levels, and then compares them on a learning task. If the two groups differ it is not reasonable to conclude that the differences in anxiety level were responsible for the learning differences because high and low anxiety people may differ in many other ways than anxiety.

Now let us assume that the investigator is aware of the fact that other subject variables may be responsible for the learning differences. To circumvent this problem, he decides to use a matched-groups design. He gives 3,000 subjects a number of tests and obtains biographical information on each subject. He then uses the results of the anxiety test to obtain a pool of 500 high anxiety subjects and 500 low anxiety subjects. Then the results of the other tests and the biographical information are used to select two groups of 50 high anxiety and 50 low anxiety subjects who are equal on a number of other characteristics, such as intelligence, achievement motivation, number of siblings, past achievement, and intelligence of parents. Then the investigator compares the learning scores of the two groups and obtains a significant difference. Is it reasonable to conclude that the differences in anxiety were responsible for the differences in learning?

Researchers are likely to disagree somewhat on the answer to this question. Most would probably argue that the evidence for a causal relationship is less than overwhelming. Many would reject the evidence because a particular variable (e.g., ability to create images) was not used as a matching variable. Yet, if given a choice between this procedure and the manipulation of a subject variable without matching, most would prefer the matching procedure, provided the variables that are known to influence learning are matched.

If the use of the matching procedure is the best method available to study the effects of a particular subject variable, there is little choice but to use it. Note that this use of the matched-groups design is essentially the same as computing a correlation between two variables while holding other variables constant. The reader will recall that the manipulation of a subject variable is similar to the use of a correlational technique in that cause-effect conclusions are, from a theoretical point of view, almost never warranted.

Matched-Groups Designs and Nonsubject Variables

The investigator who makes a nonsubject variable manipulation does not have to be overly concerned about obtaining equivalent groups prior to the introduction of the independent variable, since a random-groups design can be used for this purpose. The decision to use a matched-groups design instead is frequently difficult to make because there can be both advantages and disadvantages to the use of this design. The advantages are methodological or theoretical in nature; the disadvantages are all practical. In principle, matching can never be worse than relying solely on random assignment.

Prerequisite for Matching. The investigator who is contemplating whether or not to use a matched-groups design should first consider whether there is a suitable matching variable. There is no reason for matching unless the matching variable is related to the *dependent* measure. Matched-groups designs are used to exert some control over the subjects' performance on the dependent measure. If the matching variable is unrelated to the dependent variable, then matching will have no effect. Although this may strike the reader as being obvious, there are many studies in the literature in which the matching variable was unrelated to the dependent variable. For example, several decades ago, investigators tended to match on intelligence routinely. Apparently they believed that intelligence is related to just about every conceivable dependent variable. It isn't.

If there is a subject variable that is highly correlated with the dependent variable, you can then consider whether it is feasible to match on this variable — that is, whether the advantages to be gained are great enough to justify the time and effort necessary to do the matching. In many cases the advantages are too slight to justify the use of the matched-groups design. In many other cases there isn't a subject variable that is known to be highly correlated with the dependent measure.

Reasons for Matching. There are two major reasons for using a matched-groups design with a nonsubject variable manipulation. The first is to provide greater assurance that the groups are equivalent prior to the introduction of the independent variable. For example, let us assume that hair color is highly related to performance on the dependent measure. Redheads perform better than nonredheads. The investigator who is aware of this may elect to match the groups on hair color by having the same number of redheads and nonredheads in each group. Of course, he must randomly assign subjects to conditions except for the limitation that the matching restriction places on random assignment; he must not decide which redheads and nonredheads will be in each group. The procedure used in matching will determine whether the matched-groups design will influence anything besides the equivalence of groups prior to the introduction of the independent variable.

The second major reason for matching is to reduce within-group variance. The within-group variance, as we know, is a measure of the extent to which subjects in the same group perform alike. If the within-group fluctuations can be reduced by using a matching procedure, then there is a greater likelihood of detecting the actual effect of the independent variable. Remember that the effect of an independent variable is assessed by comparing a between-group estimate of population variance with a within-group estimate. If the within-group estimate is small relative to the between-group estimate, the null hypothesis can be rejected. The probability of detecting the real effect of an independent variable increases as the within-group fluctuations decrease. The influence of a matched-groups design on the detection of such an effect depends on the procedure used in matching.

Matching Procedures and Nonsubject Variables

Matching which Reduces Within-Group Variance. Let us assume that intelligence is highly correlated with the dependent measure. People with high I.Q.'s get high scores on the dependent measure, and people with low I.Q.'s get low scores. If the investigator uses a random-groups design and subjects who vary considerably in I.Q., then there will be considerable within-group fluctuation in the scores on the dependent measure. The subjects of high intelligence will get high scores, and those of low intelligence will get low scores.

If the independent variable does not have an effect, the two estimates of population variance will usually be about the same, and they will tend to be small, since they will be due solely to chance. For the purposes of illustration, assume that the between-group estimate of population variance is equal to 30 and the within-group estimate is also equal to 30. If the between-group estimate is divided by the within-group estimate, the quotient is 1. Since a quotient of 1 is likely to occur on the basis of chance, the null hypothesis cannot be rejected. The reader should remember that the two estimates will probably *not* be *exactly* the same if the null hypothesis is true. For the purpose of this example, however, there is no harm in assuming that they are the same.

Now assume that the independent variable has an effect. If so, the between-group estimate should increase, all else being equal, but the within-group estimate should not increase. Say that the effect of the independent variable is to increase the between-group estimate of population variance by 20. This means that the quotient obtained when the between-group estimate is divided by the within-group estimate is 1.67 (50 divided by 30 = 1.67).

A random-groups design was used in the above example. A matched-groups design could have been used. The investigator could match on intelligence in such a way as to reduce both variance estimates, by using only subjects who have, say, an I.Q. of 110. This would reduce within-group fluctuation since, in this case, I.Q. is highly correlated with the dependent measure. It would also reduce between-group fluctuation since the groups have been equated on I.Q.; therefore, the mean performance of each group is more likely to be the same if matching is used than if it is not used, provided the matching variable is highly correlated with the dependent measure. These two variance estimates from the matched-groups design, then, will be smaller than the corresponding pair from the random-groups design.

Now, if the independent variable does not have an effect, these two matched-groups estimates of population variance will be about the same, within the limits of chance fluctuation. Let us say that the between-group estimate is equal to 10 and the within-group estimate is also equal to 10. The quotient obtained by dividing the between-group estimate by the within-group estimate is equal to 1.

Now, if we assume, as we did earlier, that the effect of the independent variable is to increase the between-group estimate by 20, the advantage of using the matched-groups design becomes clear. The quotient obtained by dividing the between-group estimate by the within-group estimate is 3.0 (30 divided by 10 = 3.0). The larger the quotient, all things being equal, the greater is the likelihood that the null hypothesis can be rejected. In the present example, a quotient of 3.0 was obtained with the matched-groups design and a quotient of 1.67 with the random-groups design. Thus, there would be a greater likelihood of rejecting the null hypothesis with the matched-groups design if the independent variable actually had an effect.

Note that we have assumed that the effect of the independent variable is the same regardless of whether the subjects vary considerably in I.Q. or not. For the purpose of our example, there is no harm in making this assumption. However, selecting subjects on the basis of their performance on a matching variable can reduce the generality of the finding. For example, if all the subjects have an I.Q. of 110, some investigators would argue that there is little reason to believe that the same finding would be obtained with subjects with markedly higher or lower I.Q.'s. That is, if I.Q. and the independent variable are *both* manipulated as independent variables, the two may interact.

The numbers used in the above example were for illustrative purposes only. The use of a matched-groups design may not decrease the within-group estimate of population variance by so much. The important point is not the magnitude of the reduction but the fact that a reduction in within-group variance increases the likelihood of rejecting the null hypothesis if the independent variable has an effect.

The way the matching is carried out will determine its effect. In the previous example, the within-group and between-group estimates of population variance were decreased by the matching procedure, so the procedure had a desirable effect. The important point is that *within-group* variance was reduced. The reduction of between-group variance is not necessarily desirable. Unless the matching procedure reduces within-group variance, matching is a questionable practice.

Matching which Reduces Between-Group Variance. If the sole purpose of matching is to provide further assurance that the groups are equivalent prior to the introduction of the independent variable, then matching may not be justified. Recall the earlier example of the groups matched on hair color by assignment of the same number of redheads and nonredheads to each group. (Hair color was assumed to be related to performance on the dependent measure.) This matching procedure should have no effect on within-group fluctuations but should tend to reduce between-group fluctuations. Having the same number of redheaded subjects in each group increases the probability that the groups will be equal prior to the introduction of the independent variable. Perhaps another example will help to clarify this point.

Assume once again that intelligence is highly correlated with performance on the dependent measure. If a random-groups design is used, the between-group and within-group estimates of population variance will be about the same if the independent variable has no effect. If a matched-groups design is used to increase the likelihood that the groups are equivalent prior to the introduction of the independent variable, the matching procedure *could* result in the reduction of the between-group estimate of population variance without having much of an effect on the within-group estimate. Suppose that the investigator matches on intelligence by making sure each group has the same mean and variance on the intelligence variable. Unless he excludes subjects with extreme scores on the matching variable, the procedure will have little effect on the within-group estimate of population variance. Equating the means will reduce only the between-group variance. There is not much advantage to reducing between-group variance unless within-group variance is also reduced. The effect of reducing between-group variance depends on whether the null hypothesis is true or false.

The issue of interest is whether it is a good idea to use a matched-groups instead of a random-groups design if the matching only reduces the between-group estimate. If the null hypothesis is true, there is a slightly greater probability of committing a Type 1 error (concluding that the independent variable has an effect when in fact it does not) with the random-groups design than with the matched-groups design. The mean differences between groups on the dependent measure are likely to be smaller for a matched-groups than a random-groups design, because the former equates the group means on the matching variable. If the independent variable does not have an effect, these smaller group differences will result in fewer Type 1 errors. That is, the matching is functionally the same as setting a slightly lower significance level.

If the null hypothesis is false, the use of a matched-groups design will result in a greater probability of rejecting the null hypothesis about half the time and a smaller probability of rejecting it about half the time, depending on whether the chance fluctuations are in the same direction as the treatment effect or in the opposite direction. That is, one can expect greater mean fluctuations due to chance with a random-groups than with a matched-groups design, assuming the matching variable is highly correlated with the dependent measure. If random assignment results in the placement of "brighter" subjects in the experimental condition *and* if the experimental treatment facilitates performance, then the probability of rejecting the null hypothesis will be greater with the random-groups design. But if random assignment results in the placement of "brighter" subjects in the control condition, then the probability will be greater with the matched-groups design. Thus, the overall probability of correctly rejecting the null hypothesis is not influenced by which design is used if the matching only reduces the between-groups variance estimate.

In short, the net result of using a matching procedure that reduces differences between groups prior to the introduction of the independent variable but does not affect within-group fluctuations, is that the likelihood of making a Type 1 error is decreased. Yet, it is highly unlikely that the slight reduction in the probability of making such an error is worth the extra effort involved in matching. The goal of decreasing the probability of making a Type 1 error can be accomplished more easily by adopting a more stringent significance level, say .01 instead of .05.

Matching on a Subject by Subject Basis. Matching that is done by obtaining pairs or sets of subjects who are equal on the matching variable makes it possible to use a within-subject instead of a between-subject analysis. For example, assume that an investigator wants to match the groups on weight prior to investigating the effectiveness of three dieting programs. There are two treatment conditions and one control condition. He recruits three people who weigh the same and randomly assigns one subject to each condition. This is repeated for successive sets of three people. The use of this procedure will allow the investigator to analyze the results so that fluctuations due to initial starting weight will not be included when the size of the chance fluctuations is determined. If the matching is carried out in this way, the design is similar to the within-subject designs discussed in the next chapter.

SUMMARY

The purpose of random sampling is to obtain a sample that is representative of the larger population being sampled. In the strictest sense, a random sample is one in which all conceivable samples are equally likely, but many investigators define it as one in which every subject has an equal chance of being selected. The purpose of random assignment is to obtain equivalent groups prior to the introduction of the independent variable.

The crux of analysis of variance with a random-groups design is to obtain two independent estimates of population variance. One estimate can be obtained by determining within-group variance, which is a measure of the extent to which subjects in the same treatment condition perform alike on the dependent measure. The other estimate is the between-group variance, based on group means. The two estimates of population variance tend to be about the same if the null hypothesis is true. If the independent variable has an effect, the between-group estimate tends to be larger than the within-group estimate. In order to maximize the likelihood of rejecting the null hypothesis when the independent variable actually has an effect, it is necessary to keep within-group fluctuations as small as possible.

In a between-subject design each subject receives only one level of each independent variable. A random-groups design is a between-subject design in which random assignment is used in an effort to assure that the groups are equivalent prior to the introduction of the independent variable. Equivalence of groups permits subsequent differences in performance to be attributed to the effect of the independent variable. Random-groups designs can be used whenever it is possible to randomly assign subjects to groups before introducing the independent variable.

A matched-groups design is a between-subject design in which the groups are equated on one or more matching variables. Matching variables are subject variables. Investigators *match* groups on subject variables and *control* nonsubject variables. Matched-groups designs are used with subject variable manipulations in an attempt to equate the groups on the relevant subject variables that are not being investigated. When the investigator is able to match on these nonmanipulated subject variables, there is more reason to attribute any obtained differences between groups to the subject variable that was manipulated.

A number of considerations are involved in the question of whether to use a matched-groups design when a nonsubject variable manipulation is made. There is absolutely no reason to consider matching unless the variable to be matched is related to the dependent measure. One reason for matching is to provide greater assurance of equivalent groups. Another reason is to reduce within-group variance. If the matching procedure does not reduce within-group variance or does not allow the investigator to use a within-subject instead of between-subject statistical analysis, then the use of a matched-groups design is a questionable practice.

QUESTIONS

1. Indicate how you would select a random sample of 100 subjects from your college or university. How would you select a random sample of 100 subjects from your state or province?
2. Distinguish between random assignment and random sampling.

3. What procedure would you use to randomly assign the members of your class to four groups?
4. What is the logic of analysis of variance? That is, why is it important to obtain two independent estimates of population variance?
5. Let us assume that a biochemist claims to have developed a pill which will increase I.Q. by five points for every pill administered. To test this claim, you do an experiment in which you randomly assign subjects to a 0, 1, 2, or 4 pills condition. All subjects in one group get no pills; all subjects in another get one pill, and so on. What will be the effect of the independent variable on within-group and between-group fluctuations if the biochemist is correct?
6. What is the logic of the random-groups design? Does the random assignment of subjects to conditions guarantee that the groups are equivalent prior to the introduction of the independent variable? Why or why not?
7. What are the advantages and disadvantages of using a pretest to determine whether random assignment produced equivalent groups?
8. When can you use a random-groups design?
9. What is the advantage of manipulating a subject variable and a nonsubject variable in the same experiment?
10. Why are matched-groups designs used when a subject variable manipulation is made? How is this design useful for evaluating subject variables?
11. What are the advantages and disadvantages of using a matched-groups design when assessing the effect of a nonsubject variable?
12. Explain why reducing within-group variance increases the likelihood of rejecting the null hypothesis if the independent variable actually has an effect.
13. An investigator used a matched-groups design in which intelligence was the matching variable. The groups were matched on intelligence by equating the group means and variances. That is, each group had the same mean I.Q. score and the same variance for their I.Q. scores. What factors should be considered when evaluating this procedure?
14. What factors should an investigator consider when deciding whether to use a random-groups or matched-groups design?

within-subject designs

The first section treats the properties of within-subject designs, the second section their advantages and limitations. The third section examines methodological and interpretational problems in using these designs, and the last section their appropriate uses.

The fact that between-subject designs can be used for so many different research problems may lead the student to conclude that there is little need for additional designs. But, although the between-subject designs are very broad in scope, research problems frequently arise for which the use of these designs is difficult, impractical, or impossible. The relative importance of between- and within-subject designs varies greatly from problem area to problem area and from investigator to investigator. In some areas, the research methodology is based almost entirely on one of the two designs. Yet, in other areas, investigators switch back and forth between the two, depending on the hypothesis under investigation. This chapter should give you a better understanding of why investigators use the designs they do, and how to determine the relative usefulness of between- and within-subject designs for your area of personal interest.

PROPERTIES OF WITHIN-SUBJECT DESIGNS

Within-Subject Manipulations

The label *within-subject* is appropriate in that sometimes one can obtain a good estimate of the effectiveness of the independent variable from the data of a single subject. For example, to use a within-subject design to compare the effectiveness of two brands of car paint, you would paint your car with both paints by alternating strips of Paint A and Paint B. Then you could evaluate the paints at a later date. The appearance of the paint would be the dependent measure. The single subject in this case is, of course, your car. By comparing the appearance of Paint A strips with that of Paint B strips, you can assess the effectiveness of the two paints within a single subject. For a between-subject design it would be necessary to compare different subjects (i.e., different cars) to assess the effect of the independent variable (i.e., type of paint).

The major distinguishing feature of a within-subject design is that each subject gets more than one level of each independent variable. In all the examples of within-subject designs in this text, each subject receives all levels of each independent variable. Since each subject can provide information about the effect of the independent variable, you may be willing to conclude that, except for the problem of the generality of the finding, one subject is all that is needed to make the evaluation. Sometimes this is true, but in many instances it is necessary to obtain data from more than one subject.

The label *within-subject* should not be interpreted to mean that one subject is enough.

Nonsubject Variable Manipulations

Within-subject designs can be used to evaluate the effectiveness of nonsubject variables only. It is, of course, impossible to manipulate subject variable characteristics such as age, intelligence, or number of siblings, in a within-subject design. Yet, as is true with between-subject designs, it is possible to study a subject variable and nonsubject variable manipulation in the same experiment. A within-subject design can be used for the nonsubject variable manipulation; this procedure makes it possible to assess whether the effect of the manipulation depends on the type of subject tested.

Unfortunately, it is not possible to specify the exact conditions under which a particular design should be chosen. Within-subject designs can be used for many of the same purposes as between-subject designs. Although it is frequently *possible* to use either one, a thorough analysis of methodological, practical, and statistical considerations should lead the investigator to conclude that one design is better than another for the intended purpose. To make a thorough analysis one must be aware of the advantages and limitations of within-subject designs.

ADVANTAGES OF WITHIN-SUBJECT DESIGNS

Number of Subjects

Fewer subjects are needed to evaluate the effectiveness of an independent variable in a within-subject than in a between-subject design. In the former, each subject is tested at every level of the independent variable; thus, more information is obtained from each. The number of subjects needed depends on several factors. One is the number of times each subject is tested in each condition. For example, an investigator interested in the effect of three levels of illumination on visual acuity may test the same subject hundreds of times under each level of illumination. A considerable amount of information can be obtained from a single subject when such repeated observations are made. Yet, for many experiments, it is only possible to test each subject once in each condition. All things being equal, the number of subjects needed will decrease as the number of times a subject is tested in each condition increases.

Other factors in determining the number of subjects needed are the number of levels of the independent variable used, and the magnitude and consistency of the effect. Usually the number of subjects needed increases as the number of levels of the independent variable increases, because more subjects are required to balance out the effects of nonmanipulated variables. But the number of subjects needed tends to decrease as the magnitude and consistency of the effect of the independent variable increases. For example, if five subjects are tested and the same effect is obtained for each, most investigators would probably accept the finding as being reliable, particularly if a large effect were obtained. However, if five subjects are tested and the manipulation has one effect for four subjects and the opposite effect for one subject, then most investigators would probably prefer more information before deciding whether to accept or reject the finding.

Efficiency of Within-Subject Designs

A within-subject design is a very powerful way to assess whether an independent variable has an effect. The power or efficiency of a design is analogous to the power of a microscope or telescope. Increasing the power of a microscope enables the observer to see smaller objects. Similarly, the use of a within-subject design sometimes allows the investigator to detect effects which cannot be detected with a between-subject design. It allows him to determine whether the mean differences in treatments are greater than might be expected on the basis of chance fluctuations within individuals. Chance fluctuations within individuals tend to be smaller than those between individuals. That is, the performance of the same person at two different times tends to be more alike than the performance of two different people at the same time, provided some subject variable, known or unknown, is correlated with the performance measure.

The reader will remember that a matched-groups design can be used to reduce within-group variance if the matching subject variable is highly correlated with the dependent measure. Remember that it is possible, for example, to reduce within-group variance by using only subjects who have an I.Q. of 110 if intelligence is highly correlated with the dependent measure. When within-group variance is decreased, the probability of rejecting the null hypothesis is increased, provided the independent variable has an effect.

The use of a within-subject design carries the matching procedure to the extreme in that using this design is functionally the same as matching the groups on *all* subject variables. If the same subjects are used in all treatment conditions then, of course, the treatment conditions are matched on all subject variables. When a within-group design is used, the chance fluctuations in performance within *individuals* are used to assess the effect of the independent variable, not the fluctuations within *groups*. Chance fluctuations in the performance of one person at two points in time tend to be less than the fluctuations of two people at the same point in time because all the subject variables are matched in one case but not in the other.

To illustrate, let us assume that an investigator has developed two tasks, A and B, of *identical* difficulty. You are tested on Task A and then on Task B, with ample time for rest between the two sessions. Two other people are randomly selected and then tested on Task A only. The question is whether your two scores will be more alike than the two scores obtained by the other two subjects. That is, do within-subject chance fluctuations tend to be greater or smaller than between-subject chance fluctuations? The answer depends on whether any subject variables are correlated with performance on the tasks. For example, if intelligence is highly correlated with task performance, then your scores should be more alike than the two scores of the other subjects since you have, presumably, the same I.Q. when you perform Task A as when you perform Task B. It is unlikely that two people selected at random would be of equal intelligence, so their scores would be more likely to vary. The same argument can be made for any other subject variable. Thus, within-subject chance fluctuations will tend to be the smaller since there are usually some subject variables that are correlated with performance on the dependent measure.

Efficiency is defined in terms of the size of the chance fluctuations used to evaluate the effect of the independent variable (i.e., the variance of the null hypothesis sampling distribution). The smaller the chance fluctuations the greater the efficiency. Since the chance fluctuations within subjects tend to be smaller than those between subjects, it follows that within-subject designs are usually more efficient than between-subject designs. The likelihood of rejecting the null hypothesis tends to be greater, all things being equal, for a within-subject design, provided that the independent variable actually has an effect.

In some cases it is an understatement to say that there is a statistical advantage to using a within-subject design. The advantage of such a design is so marked under some conditions that there is little or no need for statistics. If it is possible to obtain a stable rate of responding, introduce the independent variable, and obtain a change in responding, there may be no need for statistical techniques. This is particularly true if it is possible to modify the level of responding at will by alternating the presence and absence of the treatment manipulation, as in many operant conditioning experiments.

LIMITATIONS OF WITHIN-SUBJECT DESIGNS

Inappropriateness of the Design for Some Problems

The use of a within-subject design is not appropriate for some experiments because it is not possible nor feasible to administer all the treatments to a single subject. For example, an investigator interested in the effect of a particular training technique should not test subjects in both the trained and nontrained condition because the use of one treatment precludes the use of the other. Once a subject is trained it is not possible to untrain him. Testing all the subjects in the untrained condition first is not an acceptable solution because any obtained differences may be due to either the ordering of the treatments or to their nature.

The within-subject design may be inappropriate because of practical considerations involved in obtaining the data. If it takes four hours to test each subject when using a within-subject design and thirty minutes when using a between-subject design, then practicality may dictate the use of the latter.

Demand Characteristics

Another limitation of within-subject designs is that demand characteristics are likely to be a bigger problem than in a between-subject design. Demand characteristics are those aspects of the experiment that allow a subject to make a good guess about what the experimenter "wants." The results of the experiment may be drastically influenced if a subject can determine what it is all about or how the experimenter would like him to respond. He may attempt to please the experimenter and provide what he believes to be the desired results. Human subjects are more likely to be able to figure out the experimenter's expectations when a within-subject design is used because they experience all the levels of the independent variable.

Controlling Nonmanipulated Variables

The problem of controlling nonmanipulated variables tends to be greater in within-subject designs because the subjects are always tested at two or more points in time. Therefore, the experimenter has to take steps to assure that time-related variables such as the ordering of the treatments, or practice and fatigue effects, are not responsible for any obtained differences between the treatment conditions. Time-related variables may limit the use of within-subject designs because it is sometimes difficult or impossible to control these effects. Our next task is to consider the methodological and interpretational problems in using a within-subject design.

METHODOLOGICAL AND INTERPRETATIONAL CONSIDERATIONS

Counterbalancing

Nature and Purpose of Counterbalancing. Counterbalancing refers to the use of procedures which distribute the effects of nonmanipulated variables over the treatment conditions so that obtained differences can be attributed to chance and the treatment manipulation and not to the nonmanipulated variables. (It is *not* used to eliminate chance fluctuations.) Counterbalancing is accomplished by varying the order of treatments within or between subjects. It is important to control the effects of ordering because a subject may become practiced or fatigued as the experiment progresses. If each subject gets each treatment a number of times then it is possible to balance out the effects of time-related variables by presenting the treatments in a random order. If each subject receives each treatment only once, then more than one subject is needed to balance out time-related variables. For example, when there are two treatments, A and B, and all subjects receive Treatment A followed by Treatment B, it is not possible to attribute any obtained differences to the effect of the treatment; perhaps the ordering of the two treatments was the important consideration. But if half the subjects receive Treatment B followed by Treatment A, the results obtained from all subjects can be combined to balance out the effect of the order of presentation (provided there is equal transfer from A to B and B to A, a point which will be considered in detail later).

The purpose of counterbalancing is to compensate for the effects of time-related variables. The procedures used depend on the number of subjects available and the number of treatment conditions. When complete counterbalancing is used, every treatment is presented in each position an equal number of times, and every treatment follows every other an equal number of times. Let us look at an example.

Complete Counterbalancing. An experiment is conducted to assess the effect of dress and grooming on judgments about personality and intelligence. The experimenter has four confederates wear four different disguises; each wears the same four. To avoid numerous costume changes a colored slide is made of each confederate in each disguise. A within-subject design is used so that each subject can rate all four disguises. Each subject is tested individually. Each sees only one slide of each confederate since the subjects may become suspicious if two slides of the same confederate are used. The order of presentation of the confederates (not the roles, however) is the same for all subjects. In order to be able to conclude that differences between the ratings that subjects give to the four disguises are due to chance effects plus the disguises and not to other factors, it is necessary to counterbalance the presentation order of the disguises.

To completely counterbalance the order of the four disguises (A, B, C, D) it would be necessary to have twenty-four subjects. One subject would get each presentation order, since there are twenty-four different orders of the four disguises. The twenty-four possible orders are presented in Table 6-1. Note that each disguise is presented in each position six times and that each disguise follows every other six times. Each subject is randomly assigned one sequence from 1 to 24; the sequences are not used in the same order in which they are presented in the table. Only chance determines which sequence each subject receives.

Let us assume that the twenty-four subjects are randomly assigned to the twenty-four possible sequences with the restriction that each sequence be used only once. The subjects are tested and the results analyzed. The analysis indicates that the evaluations subjects give the four confederates differ markedly as a function of the disguise. The subjects rated the confederates who

TABLE 6–1

The Twenty-four Possible Sequences of Disguises for the Experiment Investigating the Effect of Physical Appearance of Judgments About Nonphysical Characteristics

Sequence number	*Order of disguises*	*Sequence number*	*Order of disguises*
1	A B C D	13	C A B D
2	A B D C	14	C A D B
3	A C B D	15	C B A D
4	A C D B	16	C B D A
5	A D B C	17	C D A B
6	A D C B	18	C D B A
7	B A C D	19	D A B C
8	B A D C	20	D A C B
9	B C A D	21	D B A C
10	B C D A	22	D B C A
11	B D A C	23	D C A B
12	B D C A	24	D C B A

employed the current in-group styles more favorably than those who were not dressed and groomed according to the in-group styles. Since all subjects saw the four confederates in the same order, the results are not attributable to the particular confederate. That is, each confederate was shown in each disguise six times. Also, it is not reasonable to attribute the results to the particular order in which the roles were presented, since all possible orders were used.

When a large number of treatments are given, it is no longer feasible to use complete counterbalancing because there are so many different possible orderings of the conditions. For example, there are 120 different presentation orders of five conditions. With a large number of treatments or a limited number of subjects, it is necessary to use partial counterbalancing.

Partial Counterbalancing. Now let us assume that only twelve subjects are available, rather than twenty-four. The twelve subjects are randomly assigned to twelve of the twenty-four sequences such that each disguise is presented in each position three times. It is likely that most investigators would accept this counterbalancing procedure and not be concerned about any confounding effects due to confederates and presentation order even though each condition did not precede and follow every other condition an equal number of times.

Evaluation of the adequacy of a counterbalancing procedure comes down to a question of belief. Do other investigators believe the controls are adequate? It is unlikely that many investigators would accept the counterbalancing procedures if, say, only two sequences were randomly selected and six subjects were tested in one sequence and six in the other. But as the number of different sequences used is increased, the likelihood of adequately controlling for possible confounding effects is also increased.

There is no absolute point at which one can say the counterbalancing is adequate (e.g., seven or more sequences) since some investigators will be more concerned about the adequacy than others. You should do the best job that conditions allow. If you can obtain twenty-four subjects, there is little reason not to use complete counterbalancing. If you can only obtain twelve subjects, you have to settle for a less than complete procedure, but using each disguise in each position in the presentation sequence an equal number of times would still convince most investigators that you had counterbalanced adequately. Obviously, if conditions are too unfavorable (e.g., you only have a few subjects), you should not do an experiment which requires extensive counterbalancing between subjects in order to control the effects of time-related variables.

Similar procedures can be used if each subject receives each condition more than once. For example, if there are two conditions, A and B, and each subject is to receive each condition twice, then half the subjects could receive an ABBA, ABBA sequence, and the other half could receive a BAAB, BAAB sequence.

Differential Transfer

Counterbalancing the order in which treatments are presented is a very useful way to control for ordering effects — but it does not always work. It may not balance out presentation order effects if there are differential carry-over effects from one treatment condition to the next. If the results obtained with Condition B are different when C precedes B than when A precedes B, there is differential transfer. When there are such transfer effects, it may be impossible to counterbalance the order of treatments to control position effects.

To illustrate what is meant by differential transfer, let us assume that you are concerned with investigating the effects of alcohol on motor performance. You assess motor performance by using a pursuit rotor, an instrument which has a moving disk, much like a phonograph record, with a small target on the disk. The subject's task is to keep a stylus on the target while the disk is moving. The difficulty of the task can be varied by increasing or decreasing the speed of the disk. A clock can be hooked up with the pursuit rotor so that the time on target is recorded. The amount of time a subject is on target in ten test trials of one minute each is the dependent measure. The independent variable is whether subjects have two ounces of alcohol, four ounces of alcohol, or no alcohol (control) one half hour before being tested. You would, of course, administer the alcohol in such a way (e.g., in a very large glass of orange juice) that the subjects would not be fully aware of their treatment condition. A question of some importance is whether a within-subject design could be used.

The motor performance of subjects when given no alcohol is likely to be influenced greatly depending on whether the no alcohol treatment precedes or follows the other two alcohol conditions. Imagine a subject given the sequence of two ounces of alcohol, thirty minutes of rest, pursuit rotor test, four ounces of alcohol, thirty minutes of rest, pursuit rotor test, no alcohol, thirty minutes of rest, pursuit rotor test. It would be unreasonable to argue that the last test was actually under a no alcohol condition. The effect of the no alcohol manipulation in this sequence of treatments is apt to be vastly different than in the sequence in which no alcohol is given as the first treatment. Since carry-over effects from prior treatments are probable, it is only possible to assess the effect of the first treatment administered. In this case, it is more reasonable to use a between-subject design and randomly assign subjects to groups. Or, you could counterbalance the three treatment conditions, use a within-subject design, and administer one treatment each day for three consecutive days.

The above example is an obvious case of differential transfer. The carry-over effects between the alcohol and no alcohol treatments depend on the ordering of the treatment. In many instances, however, it is not clear whether differential transfer effects will be obtained. For example, if the independent variable is task difficulty, the effect of having an easy task may be quite different when preceded by a difficult task than when preceded by another easy task. If there is reason to suspect that carry-over effects will make it difficult to interpret the treatment manipulation, it is a good idea to opt for the random-groups design.

Generality of Research Findings

Interest in Establishing Generalities. It is possible to manipulate subject and nonsubject variables in the same experiment regardless of whether a between- or within-subject design is used to assess the effect of the nonsubject variable manipulation. Manipulating both kinds of variables enables the experimenter to determine if the effect of the nonsubject variable manipulation depends on the type of subject being used. If it does not, then the finding can be said to have greater generality.

Investigators differ considerably regarding their interest in demonstrating the generality of a finding. Some of them assume that it is unnecessary because they believe in the generality of behavioral laws. That is, they believe one should not worry about a separate set of laws for each type of subject. It follows from this view that a manipulation that is effective with one subject should be effective with others. Thus, some investigators will accept a finding that has been obtained by testing one subject in a within-subject design.

On the other hand, some investigators are unwilling to generalize such evidence much beyond the one or two subjects tested. If the effect of a nonsubject variable manipulation *does* depend on the characteristics of subjects, and if only one or two subjects are used, the experimenter may have happened to use only the type of subject who shows the desired effect. Some investigators place less weight on the evidence obtained in this way because generalizing such results to a larger population tends to deny the importance of subject variables.

There is something to be said for both points of view. Obviously, there is a need to assess when subject variables are important and when they are not. If subject variables are relatively unimportant for many nonsubject variable manipulations, then much time and effort can be wasted in the attempt to demonstrate the generality of particular findings. There can be little question that the generality of very important findings should be determined by such methods as using different types of subjects. However, it seems unreasonable to insist that each experiment contain a large sample of subjects so that the pervasiveness of an effect can be determined; it is simply more economical to determine, first, whether the effect actually exists.

Design and Generality. The reader may be curious about the relationship between design and generality. Specifically, which of the two basic designs yields findings of greater generality? There is no clear answer to this question because each design has an advantage and a disadvantage. The advantage of a between-subject design is that more subjects are tested. The greater the number of subjects tested, all things being equal, the greater the generality of the results. The disadvantage of this design is that the effect of the independent variable cannot be assessed for each subject but only for the group. However, if the effect is very large, e.g., if the worst subject in the experimental condition is better than the best subject in the control condition, it is probably fair to conclude that the independent variable influenced every experimental subject.

The situation is reversed in a within-subject design. Usually fewer subjects are used, but it is frequently possible to assess the effect of the independent variable for each. If all subjects tested demonstrate the same effect and many subjects are tested, then most investigators would be very willing to generalize the finding. Usually, however, the number of subjects tested is quite small when the effect of the independent variable can be assessed for each. In sum, the generality of a research finding tends to be independent of the type of design used. Findings of little and of considerable generality can be obtained with each type.

SELECTING A WITHIN-SUBJECT DESIGN

We have now reached the point where it is possible to discuss some general considerations relating to the selection of a within-subject design. The task for the investigator is to weigh the advantages and disadvantages of each type of design and then select the one which will provide the best test of the effectiveness of the independent variable.

The major factors to consider are the nature of the independent variable, the number of subjects available, the resources available, and the statistical advantages. The single most important consideration is the independent variable since its nature will frequently dictate what type of design can be used. In some cases within-subject designs are ruled out because testing each subject in more than one treatment condition would be impossible, or would result in differential transfer, destroy the intended manipulation, or alert subjects to the "real" purpose of the experiment. Yet, when a limited number of subjects are available, or when subjects can be tested in all treatment conditions, the investigator should give serious consideration to the within-subject design. Methodological and practical considerations may suggest the use of one type of design over the other; if not, the decision can be based on statistical considerations. Since the within-subject design is the more efficient, it is to be preferred, if possible.

In sum, there is no list of rules that an investigator can apply when selecting a design. In general, however, within-subject designs should be seriously considered whenever a small number of subjects are available, extensive training or testing is required, differential transfer does not loom as a confounding variable, or the magnitude of the effect of the independent variable is believed to be small, i.e., when an efficient design is needed.

USES OF WITHIN-SUBJECT DESIGNS

General Usefulness

Most investigators who study nonsubject variables use within-subject designs at one time or another. Investigators in some areas, e.g., perception and operant conditioning, rarely use anything else. Moreover, within-subject designs are being used to investigate an increasing number of problems in applied research. Although both between- and within-subject designs have been used in applied research for a number of years, the use of the latter with a small number of subjects is more recent.

Research with One Subject

The basic task in using the experimental method is the same regardless of the number of subjects tested; it is to determine whether the treatment manipulation influences behavior. When only one subject is used and it is impossible to repeat the manipulation numerous times, it is necessary to obtain relatively stable behavior in order to do research. An example should clarify this point.

Let us assume that an investigator wants to assess the effect of the withdrawal of attention on the temper tantrums of a four-year-old boy. First it is necessary to establish how many times a day the child has a temper tantrum under "normal" conditions. Say that he has had 7 to 10 tantrums per day during the two weeks before the treatment manipulation. The treatment is to ignore the boy every time he has a tantrum. In all other respects, the same relationship with him is maintained. If there is a sharp drop in the number of tantrums (i.e., to zero or one per day for the second week of treatment), it is reasonable to conclude that withdrawal of attention was responsible for the change in behavior (which is also to say that attention *reinforced* the tantrums).

Should the investigator want to be even more convinced that the manipulation was effective, he could reinstate the "normal" conditions (i.e., pay attention to the child during a tantrum) to see if the child will resume the tantrum behavior. Let us assume that over the period of one week the child gradually returns to having 7 to 10 temper tantrums per day. If the withdrawal of reinforcement treatment is reinstated and the tantrum behavior quickly drops to zero again, there can be little doubt that the manipulation was effective (see Wolf and Risley, 1971).

The reader should not imagine from this example that there are few, if any, problems in doing applied research with a small number of subjects. An interesting and informative account of some of the problems involved in research of this nature is available in a chapter by Wolf and Risley (1971). These authors emphasize the fact that it may be necessary to introduce the treatment manipulation more than once to make sure that the results are not due to a confounding variable. In the above experiment, for example, the investigator attributed the reduction in tantrum behavior to the manipulation. Yet, it is possible that the little boy stopped having tantrums for other reasons. Perhaps the little girl next door gave him a long, wet kiss as a means of providing consolation. The boy, a keen observer of behavioral contingencies, noted the tantrum-kissing contingency and decided to discontinue tantrums. This alternative explanation can be rejected if the investigator makes the withdrawal of reinforcement manipulation on a number of occasions and obtains a marked reduction in tantrums each time.

Research with Established Baselines

The use of within-subject designs with a small number of subjects is likely to be effective only if the experimenter has enough control over the situation to obtain a stable rate of responding. Or, in some cases, he can make use of the fact that a stable rate of responding exists even though he has little control. For example, a drug addict or alcoholic may have a stable rate of using drugs or drinking. It may, therefore, be possible to assess the effects of different treatments and still avoid the ethical problems involved in using a control group. In order to use a random-groups design to assess the effectiveness of a particular treatment for alcoholism or drug addiction, one must assign the subjects to treatment and no treatment conditions. Many investigators and practitioners are unwilling to do this because they believe it is unethical to deny treatment to anyone. This difficulty can be avoided with a within-subject design in that it is possible to treat everyone and compare the level of responding before and after treatment. Although this approach has advantages, it has a few disadvantages too. One particularly troublesome difficulty is demand characteristics. The fact that subjects and patients try, in general, to do what experimenters and therapists want them to do makes it difficult to isolate the effects attributable to the treatment.

SUMMARY

The major distinguishing feature of a within-subject design is that each subject gets more than one level of each independent variable. In a between-subject design each subject receives only one level of each independent variable. Within-subject designs can be used to evaluate nonsubject variables only. Since the two types of designs can be used for many of the same purposes, it is frequently possible to use either one to investigate a particular effect.

The advantages of the within-subject design are that fewer subjects are needed, and the design is usually more efficient than a between-subject design because the independent variable is assessed in terms of chance fluctuations within subjects. Chance fluctuations within subjects are smaller than those between subjects because all subject variables are matched in the one case but not in the other.

Within-subject designs are simply not appropriate for some experiments because it is not possible or feasible to administer all the treatments to a single subject. Demand characteristics are likely to be a bigger problem in these designs because the subject has a better chance of determining what the experimenter wants in the way of results if he is tested in all treatment conditions. Also, it is necessary to control time-related variables because subjects are tested at two or more points in time.

The major methodological problems involved in within-subject designs are counterbalancing the effects of time-related variables and determining whether there is differential transfer between the various treatment conditions. The problem of the generality of the research findings does not appear to be any greater than it is in between-subject designs.

The nature of the independent variable, the availability of subjects and resources, and statistical considerations are the principal factors to consider when selecting a design. The nature of the independent variable is the single most important consideration since the nature of the manipulation will frequently dictate the choice of the design. Within-subject designs are useful in a wide variety of areas. They are especially useful in applied research because the effectiveness of treatment manipulations can be assessed with one subject; this makes it possible to give the treatment to all subjects.

QUESTIONS

1. Distinguish between within- and between-subject designs and give an example of each.
2. What is the purpose of counterbalancing? Why is counterbalancing used extensively when within-subject designs are used?
3. How would you counterbalance if you had three treatments, a within-subject design, and twelve subjects?
4. What is differential transfer? Give an example of an independent variable that you believe would produce differential transfer effects. Give an example of one that you believe would not produce such effects. How would you determine whether you were correct in your judgments?
5. What are the advantages and limitations of within-subject designs?
6. Explain why a within-subject design is likely to be more efficient than a between-subject design. How is efficiency defined?
7. Assume that an investigator is interested in the effect of a physical disability on inducing compliance behavior. The independent variable is whether the experimenter's confederate wears an eye patch or does not. The dependent variable is the number of letters, if any, that the subject agrees to write to aid the confederate's "Help Save the Redwoods" campaign. Each subject is led to believe that the confederate is another subject serving in the same experiment. The experiment is actually conducted while both "subjects" are supposedly waiting for the experimenter. What type of research design should be used? Why?
8. Assume that you are given the responsibility for evaluating the effect of a new rehabilitation program in a state prison system on the rate of recidivism. You have the authority to decide whether a prisoner is assigned to the new or old program, or both. What type of design would you use? Why?
9. Assume that a new drug has been developed to reduce hypertension. The independent variable is whether the drug or a placebo is administered to the subjects. The dependent measure is blood pressure. What type of design would you use? Why?
10. Assume that you have been hired by the state to evaluate the claims made by the advocates of a speed reading course. You have the cooperation of the people who conduct the course. What design would you use to evaluate it? Why? What would you use as the dependent measure?
11. Let us assume that you want to test the view that the ability to discriminate among fine wines is developed as a result of experience, that people who have consumed a number of fine wines develop their powers of discrimination. Assume that large quantities of wine and time are available. What type of design would you use to test the view that there is a causal relationship between consumption and the ability to make fine discriminations among wines? Why? What treatment conditions would you use? Would you use a double-blind procedure for the testing stage?
12. How would you evaluate the effectiveness of heroin substitutes, e.g., methadone, for reducing drug addiction?
13. How would you evaluate the effectiveness of two different fabric softeners, hand lotions, soaps, lipsticks, coffeepots, paints, or fertilizers?

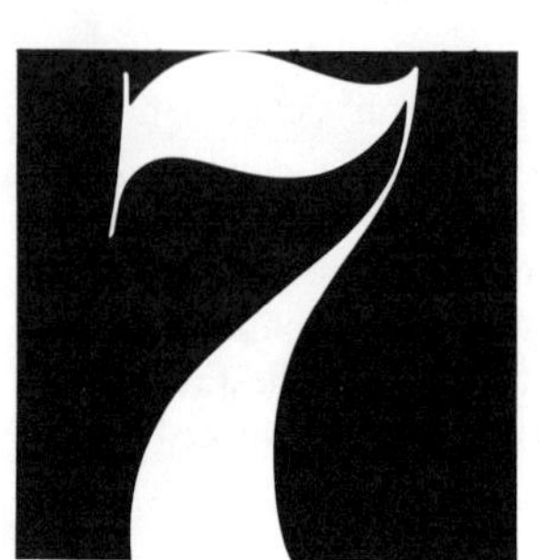

performing the experiment

The chapter begins with a brief review of the overall task of testing ideas. Then the decisions to be made and the problems to be solved in collecting data are considered. The first section deals generally with facilities, special skills, and equipment. The second section deals with subjects. The topics discussed include selecting subjects, the number of subjects per condition, and whether they should be tested individually or in groups. The third major section is about confounding. The topics considered include the number of experimenters, demand characteristics, confounding with between-subject designs, confounding with within-subject designs, and the testing of subjects. Some of the consequences of procedural decisions are discussed.

The purpose of this chapter is to consider difficulties that the experimenter may encounter while executing the experiment. The student who has accepted the invitation to be an active participant has already made many decisions. He has selected a problem area of interest and generated a testable idea. If the experimental method is appropriate then the task becomes an exercise in hypothesis testing. The experimenter is interested in whether the planned manipulation has an influence on performance. A testable idea must predict that an independent variable will have an effect on a performance variable. The research hypothesis is that the independent variable will have an effect; the null hypothesis is that it will not.

The factors to consider in selecting an experimental design have been discussed. After selecting the appropriate design, the experimenter needs to consider the problems involved in collecting the data. He has to obtain the necessary facilities and equipment, select and obtain subjects, decide what testing procedures are most appropriate, and eliminate any confounding variables. He has to be aware of the ways that an experiment can be confounded owing to inadequate testing procedures, so that these potential confounds can be avoided. These considerations are discussed in this chapter. After the data are collected, the only remaining task is to analyze and report the results. These topics will be considered in Section II of the text.

FACILITIES, SPECIAL SKILLS, AND EQUIPMENT

The facilities, special skills, and equipment that researchers use vary greatly depending on the problem to be investigated. For example, physiological psychologists usually have surgical skills, knowledge of instrumentation, and elaborate facilities and equipment. Investigators who use computers for the collection and analysis of data frequently have considerable understanding of computer technology. Yet, technical skills and elaborate equipment are not necessary or even useful in many areas of psychological research. For example, much of the research in testing, human learning, and communication and persuasion is accomplished with little more than typewriters, duplicating machines, paper, and pencils. Yet, it is clear that many problems could not be investigated without the use of complicated equipment. For example, multivariate analyses (more than one dependent measure) would be very difficult to do without computers. And physiological psychologists have been able to study the innermost portions of the brain only *after* the development of stereotaxic, stimulating, and recording instruments.

Role of Computers

The importance of computers in psychological research has increased markedly during the last decade. They are now commonplace tools for analyzing the results of experiments. They make possible the analysis of data that would otherwise be virtually impossible to analyze. Moreover, the tool function of computers has increased far beyond the data analysis stage. They are used extensively as a means of data collection. It would be impossible to perform some experiments if computers were not available. In many cases the computer has replaced the experimenter for the data collection stage because it can do the job more efficiently. It can also make possible the avoidance of procedural difficulties. For example, if the data are collected by having the subject interact solely with a computer, there is no chance that it will, inadvertently, give the subject clues regarding the purpose of the experiment.

Computers are also used in the "idea stage" of experimentation. For example, they may be used both as models of information processing and to assess such models. Many students of information processing develop their ideas by noting and testing similarities between computers and man. Thus, computers are useful at all three of the major stages of investigation: formulating ideas, collecting relevant data, and analyzing the data. There is little doubt that they will continue to play an important role in psychological research. However, there are also dangers in using complicated pieces of equipment.

Disadvantages of Complicated Equipment

One difficulty with complex equipment is that it is possible to spend as much time trying to make it work properly as is spent in other research activities such as designing, conducting, analyzing, and reporting experiments. If the equipment is essential for the research then, of course, there is no choice but to work with it until it is functioning properly. Unfortunately, in some cases working (playing) with the equipment becomes an end in itself and not a means to conduct research.

Another difficulty is that an investigator may believe that owing such a piece of equipment will make him a more effective researcher. But unless the nature of the problem dictates that the equipment be used, the investigator may be better off without it; otherwise, he may find himself attempting to design experiments to fit it. Equipment should serve the researcher. He should not place himself in the position of trying to generate ideas that can be tested by a particular machine.

Selecting a Laboratory

There are very few limits on where and how data can be collected. Experiments need not be conducted in the laboratory. Data can be collected in a classroom, at a football game, in a bar, in a laboratory, and elsewhere. The only limits on where and how the data should be collected are ethical, practical, and methodological. A laboratory is a good place to work because distractions can be kept to a minimum. With more control over the situation there is less chance that the dependent measure will be influenced by other variables.

To illustrate, let us assume that you want to conduct a three-group, random-groups design experiment. It is necessary to test the subjects individually, but the materials are such that the subject can perform the task in many different settings, such as a laboratory, home, bar, or classroom. The problem is to decide whether or not all subjects should be required to come to the laboratory.

The other option is to take the materials and look for subjects in blocks of three. If you find three people in a dormitory who are willing to participate, you can *randomly assign* them to the three conditions such that one subject serves in each condition and then test the subjects in the dormitory. Next, you find three classmates who are willing to stay after class to serve in the experiment. You *randomly assign* them to the three conditions such that one subject serves in each condition. You repeat this procedure with successive blocks of three subjects in various locations until you have collected the data. The issue is in what way, if any, the data that is gathered in the various "laboratories" will differ from the data that would have been obtained from the same subjects in one laboratory.

Number of Laboratories and Confounding. Your first reaction may be that the experiment which was conducted in various locations is confounded, whereas one conducted in the laboratory would not have been confounded. This is an erroneous belief. To argue, convincingly, that an experiment is confounded it is necessary to demonstrate that the level of the confounding variable was different for the various treatment conditions. For example, if all subjects in one condition were tested in a bar, all subjects in another condition tested in a classroom, and all subjects in the third condition tested in a dormitory, the experiment would be confounded. You would not know whether to attribute the results to the independent variable or the location variable. If the level of the confounding variable (i.e., the locations) differs for the treatment conditions, then it is reasonable to argue that the location variable may have been responsible for any obtained differences between conditions.

A confounding variable has the same characteristics as the independent variable. This is the problem. If, inadvertently, two variables are manipulated when the experiment was designed to assess the effect of only one, no clear interpretation of the results is possible. However, in the case considered above, one subject in each condition was tested in each of the locations. Since the levels of the location variable were the same for all conditions, it is unreasonable to argue that the different locations produced differences between the treatment conditions. The locations were *controlled* in that each location was used once for each condition. Assuming you are now convinced that the use of various locations did not confound the experiment, it is possible to consider the actual effect of using different locations.

Number of Laboratories and Within-Group Variance. Let us assume that some locations are more conducive to high performance than others. If the type of location influences performance and every subject in each condition is tested in a different location, then the within-group variance should be greater for the experiment conducted in several locations than for the experiment conducted in the laboratory. The between-group variance may also be somewhat greater for the experiment conducted in various locations, but it is extremely unlikely that the increase in the between-group estimate will be greater than the increase in the within-group estimate. The effect of the different locations should be about the same for each treatment condition since all treatments are tested at each location.

Any variable which increases the within-group and between-group estimates of population variance about the same amount will decrease the likelihood of rejecting the null hypothesis when the independent variable actually has an effect. The reader should remember, from the discussion in Chapter 5, that the results are analyzed by dividing the estimate of population variance which is based on between-group variance by the estimate based on within-group variance. If both variance estimates are increased then the effect of the independent variable on between-group variance has to be greater in order to reject the null hypothesis. For example, assume that both variance estimates are increased from 20 for the experiment conducted in one laboratory to 30 for the experiment conducted in various laboratories, and that the independent variable increases between-group variance by 40. The quotient obtained by dividing the between-group estimate by the within-group estimate would be 3.0 in the first instance and 2.33 in the second. Thus, the use of several locations will result in a more stringent test of the treatment manipulation and will decrease the chance of detecting a "real" effect of an independent variable when the effect is small. If a significant difference is obtained under these stringent conditions, one can be confident that the independent variable actually has an effect.

Deciding Where to Conduct the Experiment. There is no set of rules that can be applied to determine whether it is better to test subjects in the laboratory or in real life situations. In making this decision one should consider the ethical, practical, and methodological problems raised by the particular experiment. After doing so, one may decide that the decision as to whether a single laboratory or various locations should be used for testing is arbitrary. There are many such decisions to be made in conducting research. If one's interest is in obtaining significant differences between treatment means, the "arbitrary" decisions should be made in such a way that the likelihood of obtaining significant differences is maximized; in this case, the investigator would decide to test all subjects in the laboratory. However, an investigator who is only interested in manipulations that have a large effect and generality is likely to opt for the use of various locations. He may not consider the manipulation very interesting or important unless the effect can be obtained in "real life" situations.

Procedures Specific to Research Areas

If the problem area of interest has been studied by other researchers, it is likely that certain procedures have been used so often that they can be considered standard. For example, the paired-associate, serial learning, and free recall procedures are standard techniques for investigating verbal learning. Social psychologists who test dissonance theory also tend to use standard procedures. If an idea can be tested by using a standard procedure, then it is possible to compare the results with those of other investigations in which the same procedure was used. If different experiments share a common procedure then the facts can be organized on this basis. More importantly, new findings can be evaluated primarily in terms of the independent variable manipulations that the experimenter made and not in terms of arbitrary experimental procedures. Although there are good reasons for adopting standard procedures, there are several dangers in doing so.

One danger is that using a standard procedure will become so important that investigators will become less creative in the generating and testing of ideas. If an idea can be tested by using a standard procedure, there is little reason to adopt a new one. However, if the idea cannot be tested by standard procedures, then the procedures, not the idea, should be discarded. A standard set of procedures can be considered a tool. If the tool is useful, use it. If it is not useful, set it aside.

Another danger is that a standard procedure or method will become so pervasive that it becomes an end and not a means. Instead of being used to test ideas about important phenomena, procedures and methods may be investigated for their own sake (see Tulving and Madigan, 1970, p. 442). This is not to argue that research on methods and procedures should be discontinued, of course. It is just that such research can hardly be considered a satisfactory end result. Investigators should be willing to evaluate the standard procedures of their research area to determine whether these procedures are helping or hindering the development of the field.

SUBJECTS

Selection of Subjects

Psychologists have used many different kinds of subjects for psychological research, but rats, pigeons, rhesus monkeys, and humans are used most frequently. The concentration on only a few different kinds of lower animals has not gone without criticism. For example, Beach (1950) and Lockard (1968) have bemoaned the fact that psychologists have used the albino rat so extensively. One reason for the emphasis on rats, pigeons, rhesus monkeys, and humans is availability. A researcher interested in using lower animals can purchase rats, pigeons, or monkeys from private sources.

The decision about whether to use lower animals or humans will probably be dictated by the nature of the research problem. Many manipulations can be made with animals that would be impossible or unethical with humans. For example, genetic studies and physiological studies either must be done, or are better done, with lower animals as subjects.

Use of Human Subjects. The use of human subjects in psychological experiments poses a special set of problems. As is the case when lower animals are the subjects, availability will be an important determinant of which subjects are selected. The problem of obtaining people who are willing to serve in psychological experiments is difficult to solve in that, generally, an adequate supply of money is not available to pay people for their time. Thus, the experimenter is forced either to abandon the research or to seek other means of obtaining subjects. Usually the problem is solved by encouraging students to take part.

The most common way to obtain subjects for experiments is to ask students in introductory psychology classes to participate. The ethical problems involved in recruiting subjects from classes are considerable. The typical procedure is to provide a reasonable alternative to research participation, to provide as much information about the experiment as possible, and to obtain the subject's informed consent whenever possible. In addition, the experimenter should treat the participant with respect and dignity, assure him that he can discontinue the experiment at any time, and provide him with feedback on the results of the experiment. Most such research is evaluated by a committee or faculty member to determine whether it is ethical before the researcher is allowed to solicit subjects from classes.

Use of More than One Type of Subject. Some researchers may be fortunate enough to have several different subject populations available and may decide, therefore, to compare them. If the only point of interest is to compare two subject populations on some dependent variable, then it will only be possible to conclude that one population does better on the task than the other. It is not reasonable to attribute the difference to any specific variable because there is no way of knowing all the variables on which the two populations differ. Of course, there are many occasions when it is important to know which population will do better on a particular task. The investigator may want to compare the populations for practical reasons or to determine whether there is a phenomenon to investigate further. If he obtains differences between populations, then he can design additional studies in an attempt to discover the reasons for the differences.

Number of Subjects Per Condition

The number of subjects tested in each condition should depend on the effect of the independent variable, the type of design, and whether the investigator is interested in detecting small effects. If the independent variable manipulation is so powerful that all the subjects in the Experimental Group are better than the best subject in the Control Group, then there is no need to test more than the usual number of subjects. If the groups are shown to be equivalent prior to the introduction of the independent variable, then there is some justification for using fewer than the normal number of subjects.

For some problems a large amount of data can be obtained from a single subject. For example, in some perceptual studies in which within-subject designs are used, the same subject can be tested for long periods. The combination of a large number of observations on each subject and a within-subject design generally results in a need for fewer subjects. If you are interested in detecting *any effect,* no matter how small, due to the independent variable, and you are forced to use a between-subject design, then you should test a large number of subjects in each group.

The probability of detecting a real difference increases, all things being equal, as the number of subjects per condition increases. Yet, if one has to test a great many subjects in each condition to obtain a significant difference statistically, it is questionable whether the effect is of any psychological importance. If in doubt one can determine by checking the literature how many subjects investigators in a particular area believe it is proper to test. Usually, the researchers in each area tend to test approximately the same number of subjects. For example, human learning and memory experiments usually use from ten to twenty subjects in each condition. For any given experiment, there are computational advantages to having an equal number of subjects in each condition.

The issue of how many subjects to test boils down to a question of belief. The task is to convince the scientific community that the results of the experiment are attributable to the independent variable and not solely to chance, or worse, to a nonmanipulated but confounded variable. The purpose of conducting and analyzing experiments is to convince others and yourself of the effectiveness or ineffectiveness of a particular manipulation. Thus, the astute approach is to determine what would convince other investigators and then meet or better their criteria. Although you may be convinced that the manipulation has an effect after testing only five subjects in each condition, others may be harder to convince if most investigators agree that from twelve to sixteen subjects should be tested in each condition.

The nature of the finding can also be a factor determining how many subjects to test; if it is consistent with the earlier literature, then there is little reason to test more than the usual number. However, if the finding is so important that the dominant theoretical notions may have to be reformulated to accommodate it, then others may be reluctant to accept it. In this case, instead of increasing the number of subjects per condition, a complete replication of the experiment might be more convincing. Should the same result be obtained with the replication, then, provided the two experiments are methodologically sound, the burden of proof would be on the nonbelievers.

Individual or Group Testing

All Conditions Represented. The nature of the experiment may allow testing of subjects individually or in groups. The obvious reason for testing in groups is to collect the data more rapidly. Testing subjects in each of the conditions at the same time may make it possible to gather all the data with just one session. Besides the obvious practical advantage here, there may be a methodological advantage. There may be less within-group variance when subjects are all tested at the same time than when they are tested individually. The reason for the expected difference in within-group variance is that situational testing variables are likely to influence the group tested and individually tested subjects differentially. Let us look at an example.

Assume that a two-group, random-groups design is used and that subjects can be tested individually or in groups. The experimenter decides to test individually the sixteen subjects in each group. Let us further assume that it takes one hour to test a subject and that the experimenter has two free hours in the morning and two hours in the afternoon. One subject from each condition is tested in the morning and one from each condition in the afternoon. Thus, half the subjects in each group will be tested in the morning and half in the afternoon. If subjects perform differently at different times of the day, then the time-of-day effect should increase within-group variance but should affect all groups equally. A similar argument can be made for many other time-related variables. Thus, there is likely to be less within-group variance when subjects are tested at the same time if time-related variables have an effect on the dependent measure.

Even though all the situational variables should be the same for subjects tested at the same time, the size of the groups may have some effect on performance. For example, some subjects may cooperate more fully when they are tested individually. The failure of some subjects to follow instructions could have an effect on the difference between group means, since uncooperative subjects may not be assigned equally to all conditions. Such failure to follow instructions should cause within-group variance to increase. Thus, the advantages and disadvantages of group and individual testing depend on the problem.

One Condition Represented. If subjects cannot be tested in all conditions at the same time, then it is questionable whether anything other than individual testing should be used. For example, it may be possible to test many subjects at the same time but only subjects from one condition in any one session. If there are three treatments, one could test all the subjects in the first condition, then all the subjects in the second, and then all the subjects in the third. This is a poor procedure since there are several confounding variables (e.g., order of testing, experience of the experimenter) which may be responsible for any obtained mean differences. Testing subjects individually instead would permit an order of testing that would balance the effects of the confounding variables over the three conditions such that differences between treatments could be attributed to the effect of the independent variable.

Let us assume that you acknowledge that individual testing is methodologically sound and testing all the subjects in one treatment condition at the same time is unacceptable. If you can only test subjects from one condition in any one session, is it permissible to test more than one at a time? Assume that you decide to test three subjects from the same condition at the same time, If you test a total of fifteen subjects in each condition then you will have five different testing sessions for each condition. In order to balance the effects of time-related variables (e.g., time of day, experience of the experimenter), you determine the order of testing randomly with the restriction that the number of subjects tested in one condition does not exceed the number tested in the other conditions by more than three. The issue is whether testing the subjects in blocks of three is acceptable. It should be clear that this procedure is much better than testing *all* the subjects from one condition at the same time. Yet, the likelihood of balancing out time-related variables is greater if subjects are tested individually than if they are tested in groups of three.

It is not possible to conclude that testing in blocks of two or more is right or wrong. Some investigators will object to this procedure. They will argue that the data from each block of subjects should be treated as though it were obtained from one subject. That is, for statistical purposes the mean score for each block of subjects is treated as the score for one subject. If each block of subjects is treated as one subject, then there is little advantage to testing subjects in blocks. However, other investigators will accept this procedure as methodologically sound and analyze the data in the same way that they would if each subject were tested individually.

The decision as to whether testing subjects from the same condition in blocks is permissible is a question of judgment. Those who believe that this procedure balances out the effects of time-related variables are likely to use it and accept its use by others. Those who are skeptical will probably not use it and will be reluctant to accept the findings of experimenters who do. It is unlikely, however, that very many investigators will accept or reject the results of an experiment solely on the basis of whether or not subjects from the same condition were tested in blocks of two or more. They are more likely to evaluate the experimental procedure along with such factors as the magnitude of the effect, and the consistency of the results with earlier findings.

CONFOUNDING

Number of Experimenters

The nature of an experiment may be such that the data can be collected much more rapidly or efficiently if there are two or more experimenters. In such a case, each experimenter must, of course, test the same number of subjects in each condition so that significant group differences can be attributed to the effect of the independent variable and not to the use of different experimenters. If one experimenter tests all the subjects in one treatment condition and another tests all the subjects in the other condition, the experiment would be confounded (assuming the experimenter variable was not the intended independent variable).

The methodological considerations in using two or more experimenters are similar to those in using two or more different laboratories to collect the data. If the characteristics of the experimenters influence the performance of the subjects and both experimenters test subjects in all conditions, then the within-group variance will increase and the chances of obtaining significant mean differences will decrease. However, if the results are analyzed to assess whether there is an experimenter effect, then it is possible to subtract any such effect from the within-group variance. That is, one can treat experimenters as an independent variable, obtaining the within-group variance by considering the fluctuations of subjects who are tested in the same treatment by the same experimenter. If one experimenter tests half the subjects in one condition and a second experimenter tests the other half, then the within-group variance is calculated for each half separately. Thus, even if there is an experimenter effect, it will not increase the estimate of population variance which is based on within-group variance.

Demand Characteristics

Nature of Demand Characteristics. Assume that you are engaged in doing research on a problem in which you have great personal interest. In addition, you may have a considerable amount of bias. It would probably be gratifying to you to have any prediction you might make supported by experimental results. Yet, hopefully, you want the results to reflect the true state of affairs and not your bias. Thus, it is important to minimize the likelihood that your biases will affect the results. The work of Orne (1959, 1962) and Rosenthal (1963, 1966) has demonstrated that the experimenter's expectations or biases can influence the results of psychological experiments. Orne points out that a human subject will, generally, attempt to determine the purpose of the experiment and then do what is necessary to make it succeed.

Each experiment has *demand characteristics* from the point of view of the subject. Subjects are sometimes able to determine what the experimenter wants and respond accordingly. Moreover, the effect of finding out what the experimenter wants may be influenced markedly by the treatment condition the subject is in, since experimenters rarely want the same performance from subjects in different treatment conditions. If the subject detects that he is in the "special" group, his interest and performance level may increase. And, if he detects that he is in the "control" group, his interest and performance may decrease. Such an experiment is confounded in that there is no way to know whether the results are actually due to the independent variable or to the effect of demand characteristics.

It is also possible, of course, that the subjects will determine what the experimenter wants and then respond in just the opposite way. Yet, most subjects tend to be cooperative. You can assess whether a subject is cooperative by asking him to hold a large chunk of ice. If you return forty minutes later and the subject is sitting in a puddle of water clutching a small chunk of ice, you have a cooperative subject (Hanley, 1969).

Pervasiveness of Demand Characteristics. Although there is no question that experimenter bias and demand characteristics can influence the results of psychological studies, there is disagreement over the pervasiveness of the effect. Neisser (1967) attributed the findings of some dream, imagery, perceptual defense, perceptual fragmentation, sensory deprivation, shadowing, subliminal perception, visual search, visual word recognition, and word association experiments to the effects of demand characteristics. In many cases it is likely that the subject is able to pick up cues from the experimenter or from other characteristics of the experiment to determine what is expected. Then he has the option of "cooperating" with the experimenter. Yet, Barber and Silver (1968) argue that the experimenter bias effect is difficult to demonstrate and less pervasive than Rosenthal claims.

In any case, you should do whatever is necessary to eliminate, or at least to minimize, the effect of demand characteristics. When you provide cues that enable the subjects to discern what results you want, you have a confounded experiment. Any significant mean differences could be attributed to the effect of the independent variable or to the demand characteristics. Perhaps the subjects were only trying to please you by doing what you wanted them to do.

The extent to which demand characteristics loom as a confound will depend on the nature of the problem. For example, in studying the experimental control of dreaming, one should take precautions to eliminate or minimize the effects of demand characteristics. Direct instruction or hypnosis can be used to attempt to influence dream content, but it is difficult to determine the success of such an attempt. Perhaps the subjects will react to the demand characteristics of the experiment and report the type of dream that they think the investigator wants them to report, regardless of their actual dreams. Patients in psychoanalysis tend to report having the type of dreams that their analysts expect. Patients of Adlerians have Adlerian dreams, patients of Freudians have Freudian dreams, and so on. Is this because the analysts are controlling the dream content? Or, is the effect due to demand characteristics?

At the opposite extreme, in a study in which all conditions are tested at the same time, and the experimenter does not have any knowledge of what condition each subject is being tested in, and the subjects are not able to detect whether they are in an experimental or control condition, there is little reason to be concerned with the confounding effects of demand characteristics.

Experimenter Attitude and Demand Characteristics. You should evaluate your attitude and your experiment to assess whether demand characteristics are likely to be responsible for differences between the groups. If you are interested in obtaining the facts, then you will want to eliminate any possible confounding effect due to demand characteristics. But if you are intent on obtaining support for your theoretical notions regardless of the facts, then you should change your attitude or not do research. The task of determining the facts is difficult enough without adding personal biases.

It is necessary to distinguish between biases in connection with the selection of a problem area and generating of ideas, and the *testing* of ideas. Since experimenters should select problems and hypotheses in which they have a personal interest, a certain amount of bias is probably inevitable in planning an experiment. However, personal biases should not be allowed to influence the testing process.

To illustrate, suppose you have a great deal of personal interest in a football team, the Mudville Mites. You are extremely biased in their favor. You watch them practice, lead the fans in cheering, and extol their virtues while imbibing in the local gin mill. Moreover, you believe that winning is everything. Yet, when it comes time for the test, you want it to be unbiased. You would not think of bribing the opponents or an official. You want the Mudville Mites to win on their merit alone. Similarly, you should want your ideas to be tested on their merit alone, or you should get out of the business of testing ideas. If you carry your biases into the testing arena, then you risk not giving your ideas a fair test.

Controlling Demand Characteristics. If a problem is selected in which demand characteristics loom as a confound then the experiment should be designed so that the effects of these characteristics can be assessed. For example, if one group of subjects is more likely to detect the real purpose of the experiment than the other group, you may attempt to manipulate the cooperativeness of the subjects (by providing incentives or by adopting a gentle, considerate manner for only one group) as an additional independent variable. If you are able to manipulate cooperativeness and the other independent variable produces the predicted effect for both cooperative and uncooperative subjects, then it is reasonable to conclude that the results are not due to demand characteristics.

Even if there is little reason to think that subjects can discern the purpose of the experiment or can detect how you "want" them to perform, you should take precautions to avoid having the results influenced by demand characteristics. Subjects may be very subtle in detecting your expectations. Sometimes it is possible to test them without knowing the particular condition to which each is assigned. When subjects are tested individually, however, it is usually impossible for the experimenter not to know the condition of each. In such a case it may help to have them tested by another experimenter who is unaware of the purpose of the experiment. Care should be taken to assure that he is unbiased. In some cases, it is feasible to "bias" experimenters in opposite directions and analyze for the effect of biasing.

In short, you should be aware of the fact that subjects may determine what you are trying to do and may perform accordingly. The danger of confounding the experiment in this way is present in both between-subject and within-subject designs, but is usually a greater threat in within-subject designs. In fact, a consideration of demand characteristics may lead you to choose a between-subject design if testing each subject in all conditions would disclose the purpose of the experiment. Also, it may lead you to automate the experiment as much as possible. For example, the instructions could be tape recorded to minimize the possibility that the experimenter, while reading the instructions, would provide differential cues to subjects in the various conditions.

Confounding with a Between-Subject Design

Failure to Obtain Equivalent Groups. A confounding which is specific to between-subject designs is the failure to obtain equivalent groups, or the destruction of such groups. As you recall, each subject receives only one level of each independent variable for a between-subject design. It is important that there be a high probability of obtaining equivalent groups prior to the introduction of the independent variable. Therefore, except for the limits of the design and procedure, it is necessary to assign subjects to conditions on a random basis. If a matched-groups design is used, subjects should be assigned randomly with the restriction that the groups be equated on the matching variable. As long as the independent variable is something other than a subject variable manipulation, there should be little difficulty in obtaining equivalent groups *most of the time* through the use of the random assignment procedure.

Random assignment will not always produce equivalent groups, so you have to expect to be wrong a small portion of the time when you reject the null hypothesis. Investigators have to be able to live with a small probability of error; the task is to keep it small. If you want to manipulate a subject variable, there is virtually no procedure that allows you to be reasonably confident that the groups are equivalent except for the subject variable of interest. For example, if you want to manipulate political party, Republican versus Democratic, how are you going to obtain two groups that are equivalent except for their different political beliefs? You cannot use random assignment because political belief determines the subject's condition. Even if you were to randomly select from the entire population of Republicans and Democrats to obtain your sample, you could not be certain that any obtained differences in your dependent measure were attributable to political belief. Obviously, Republicans and Democrats differ on variables other than political belief, e.g., wealth and occupation.

Destruction of Equivalent Groups. Assuming that equivalent groups are obtained by the use of some random assignment procedure, it is possible that the nature of the independent variable may destroy their equivalence. For example, assume that you are interested in how performance on a task is influenced by the level of difficulty of the preceding task. The question of interest is whether a subject is more likely to perform at a higher level if the earlier laboratory experience were easy or if it were difficult. The subjects are randomly assigned to the two conditions. The experiment requires that each subject participate in two separate sessions on successive days. All subjects are given the same task on Day 2. On Day 1, one group of subjects is given a relatively easy task and the other group a relatively difficult task. After the subjects complete the Day 1 task, you thank them and ask them to return the next day for another session. Unfortunately, all the subjects do not return the second day. Of the twenty easy-task subjects, eighteen return for the second day. Of the twenty difficult-task subjects, only twelve return.

You are a little disturbed by the fact that some of the subjects did not return for the second session, but you analyze the data for those who did. You find that the difficult-task subjects have a higher mean performance on Day 2 than the easy-task subjects, even though all subjects were given the same task for Day 2. You conclude that, at least for this task, subjects tend to perform better if their previous laboratory experience was difficult than if it was easy. Is this conclusion justified?

It should be clear that the nature of the independent variable may have resulted in the destruction of equivalent groups. One could argue that the group differences are a result of nonequivalent groups. It is plausible that the eight difficult-task subjects who did not return for Day 2 were unlike the twelve who did return. More specifically, the eight who did not return may have been duller than the others. Thus, one could argue that the twelve difficult-task subjects were, on the average, brighter than the eighteen easy-task subjects. If more subjects are lost in one condition than in the other, the equivalence of the groups may be destroyed.

The destruction of equivalent groups is likely to be a serious methodological problem when a survey technique is used. Assume that the nature of the survey is the manipulation and that each form is mailed to a randomly selected sample of 100 subjects. Unless there is a high return of the surveys, it is difficult to know whether the subjects who respond are typical of the sample of 100 that received each form.

Failure to Control Nonmanipulated Variables. At the risk of laboring the obvious, let us point out again that investigators must control for the effects of nonmanipulated variables. The experimenter should make every effort to see that the groups differ only with respect to the intended manipulation. For example, if an investigator is studying the effect of a new drug with humans, it is important to treat the subjects in all groups alike except for the drug. This means that control subjects should be given seemingly identical injections or pills. The person giving the treatments should not know who gets the real drug and who gets the placebo. If subjects were told what treatment they were to receive, there would be no way to determine whether the effects were due to the drug or to the fact that subjects knew they were receiving a special treatment.

There are a number of ways that an experiment can be confounded by failure to control nonmanipulated variables. For example, if the independent variable is the type of strategy subjects are asked to employ, the experimenter should take care not to sound more encouraging in one condition than another. And, he should make sure that all subjects are given the same amount of time to perform the task that is used to assess the independent variable. In short, the investigator should examine the procedures carefully to make sure that only the intended manipulation is made. It is necessary to control for nonmanipulated variables regardless of whether a between-subject or within-subject design is used.

Confounding with a Within-Subject Design

The principal problem of confounding with a within-subject design is failure to counterbalance for practice and time-related effects. As you remember, each subject receives every level of the independent variable in a within-subject design. Since it is not possible to present all the levels of the independent variable at the same time, it is necessary to control for the effects of practice and time by making sure that each treatment is presented at each stage of practice an equal number of times. In addition, in some cases it is a good idea to have each treatment precede and follow every other treatment an equal number of times. This is particularly important if there is reason to believe that the effect of a treatment will be influenced by the immediately preceding treatment.

TESTING THE SUBJECTS

The difficulties involved in obtaining the data will vary with the particular problem investigated. In some cases you may have to do an extensive amount of work to get ready to conduct the experiment. Such tasks as recruiting subjects, finding a place to conduct the experiment, writing instructions for the subjects, preparing materials, and obtaining equipment can involve a lot of time and energy. Yet, this stage of the research is extremely important. Therefore, it is a good idea to double-check all preparations to make sure that you do not manipulate more than the independent variable, and thus confound the experiment.

If you make a mistake while conducting the experiment (e.g., give a subject the wrong instructions or the wrong amount of time), then you should replace the subject with another. Replacing subjects is no particular problem as long as it is not differential for conditions. If it is differential (i.e., if many subjects are lost in one condition and few subjects in the other conditions), the groups may not be equivalent. And you should not, of course, make mistakes in an effort to eliminate the subjects who are not performing as you would like. Moreover, it is important that the experimenter have the same attitude toward all subjects. You should not be friendly toward some and unfriendly toward others, even if you do prefer to test members of the opposite sex.

Finally, you should test a few subjects to make sure that the procedures, materials, and equipment are satisfactory before obtaining data that you will analyze. That is, you may want to conduct a short pilot study first. The results obtained by testing a few subjects in each condition should enable you to evaluate the arbitrary decisions (e.g., the amount of time, the nature of the materials), allow you to assess the clarity of the instructions, and give you an opportunity to eliminate errors in your behavior as experimenter. After you are confident that you can perform the experiment properly, you can begin collecting the data.

SUMMARY

The facilities, special skills, and equipment that researchers use vary greatly depending on the problem investigated. Computers are used extensively in psychological research to analyze data, to collect data, and as models of information processing. The major disadvantage to the use of complicated equipment is that it sometimes becomes an end in itself rather than a means for evaluating ideas.

Experiments need not be conducted in laboratories or in a single setting. The only limits on where and how data can be collected are ethical, practical, and methodological. The use of different settings does not necessarily confound the results of an experiment, but it is likely to increase the within-group variance if the various locations have any influence on performance. There are no rules to determine whether experiments should be conducted in laboratories or real life situations. Statistical considerations tend to favor the use of laboratories, but generality considerations favor real life situations.

The use of standard procedures for collecting data enables investigators to compare the findings of many different experiments and to evaluate new experiments according to their results, not their procedures. One disadvantage is that investigators may be less creative in generating and testing ideas if they restrict themselves to standard procedures. The other danger is that the study of procedures may become an end instead of a means.

Psychologists use many different kinds of subjects, both human and nonhuman. The major factor influencing subject selection is availability. The number of subjects that should be tested in each condition depends on the nature of the independent variable, the type of design, and the researcher's interest in detecting small effects. If it is possible to test subjects in each of the conditions at the same time, there is usually a statistical advantage to testing in groups rather than individually. If it is not possible to test subjects in more than one condition at the same time, then it is questionable whether anything other than individual testing should be used.

Each experiment has demand characteristics from the point of view of the subject. The effect of finding out what the experimenter "wants" may be influenced greatly by the subject's treatment condition, since experimenters rarely expect the same performance from subjects in different treatment conditions. The results of the experiment may be determined more by the subject's detection of the experimenter's expectations than by the effect of the independent variable. Thus, demand characteristics loom as a potential confound in many experiments. Although there is disagreement regarding the pervasiveness of the effect, there is little reason not to take steps to minimize, control, or assess the effects of demand characteristics.

The principal confounding problem with between-subject designs is the failure to obtain equivalent groups and the destruction of equivalent groups. In within-subject designs, the principal confounding problem is the failure to counterbalance for practice and time-related effects.

QUESTIONS

1. What are the advantages and disadvantages of collecting the data in one setting rather than in a number of different settings?
2. What are the advantages and disadvantages of using standard procedures when testing subjects?
3. What factors determine how many subjects should be tested in each condition?
4. What are the advantages and disadvantages of testing subjects individually or in groups? Why is the number of conditions represented during group testing an important consideration?
5. What are demand characteristics and why are they an important methodological consideration?
6. What are some general ways in which confounding may occur in a between-subject design? In a within-subject design?
7. An investigator was interested in the effect of experiences at a university on the stands students take on controversial issues. He obtained a random sample of 100 freshmen, 100 sophomores, 100 juniors, and 100 seniors at a large state university. All 400 students agreed to take a test. The investigator found a direct relationship between the number of years at the institution and the score on the test. Freshmen tended to be conservative, and seniors tended to be liberal. Assume that the test was reliable and valid. The investigator concluded that the experiences at the university caused the students to become more liberal. Do you agree with the investigator's conclusions? Why or why not?
8. An investigator was interested in the effect of violence in movies on the amount of violence reported in dreams. He randomly assigned a group of 100 subjects to two groups with the restriction that there were an equal number of subjects in each group. Each subject agreed to attend the movie of the investigator's choice if the investigator provided the ticket. One group viewed a very violent movie while the other group viewed a nonviolent movie. The subjects also agreed to record any dreams that they remembered having during the night immediately following the movie. The investigator analyzed the dreams for violent content and found there was a significantly higher incidence of violence for the subjects who saw the violent movie. He concluded that viewing a violent movie has a tendency to cause one to have violent dreams. Do you agree with the investigator? Why or why not?
9. An investigator was concerned with the effect of fear arousal on learning. He was keenly aware of the ethical problems involved in performing an experiment of this type. The subjects were told that there was a possibility that they would receive some "pretty stiff" shocks if their performance on a learning task was low. Each subject was promised five dollars for participating. After hearing about the general nature of the experiment, forty subjects agreed to participate. These subjects were randomly assigned to the two conditions such that there were twenty subjects in each. The investigator then told the subjects whether they were in the shock or no shock condition. Six subjects in the shock condition then decided not to participate, so the experimenter recruited six more as replacements. The shock and no shock subjects were tested on a

learning task. None of them received any shock, of course. The independent variable was whether they *expected* to receive shock for low performance. The results revealed that the shock subjects were better than the no shock subjects. The investigator concluded that the expectation of a shock resulted in higher performance on the learning task. Do you agree with him? Why or why not?

section

DESCRIBING ANALYZING AND REPORTING RESULTS

methods and procedures for describing results

The chapter begins with a brief overview of the contents of Section II. The first major section is devoted to the four scales of measurement. The descriptive measures discussed in the second section are the mode, median, mean, range, variance, and standard deviation. A number of examples are presented in the third section to demonstrate how to describe the results of various kinds of experiments. The steps in computing rank-order and product-moment correlations are given in the last major section.

The purpose of Section II is to discuss how experimental results are described, analyzed, and reported. Chapter 8 is devoted to the description of results obtained with observational techniques, correlational techniques, and the experimental method. Statistical tests for analyzing the results of experiments are discussed in Chapters 9 through 11. The task of reporting the results of psychological research is discussed in Chapter 12. As in Section I, the major emphasis in Section II is on problems one encounters when using the experimental method. This method is emphasized because of its importance and because more needs to be said about it.

In Chapter 8 we will consider the task of describing results. Since investigators manipulate independent variables to determine whether the manipulation has an effect on dependent variables, the description of results is often synonymous with the description of the scores subjects obtain on the dependent measure(s). It is not necessary to use the experimental method to obtain such scores, but the label *dependent measure* is generally restricted to cases in which this method is used.

The words *performance measure* or *behavioral measure* are usually used as labels for results obtained with a method other than the experimental. Yet, for the purpose of describing results, it makes little difference whether the scores are called performance measures or dependent measures. An investigator who observes the performance of an organism without manipulating an independent variable still has the task of describing the behavior observed. Or, if two measures are obtained on each subject, the investigator can describe the degree of the relationship between them by computing a correlation. Thus, investigators must describe their results regardless of whether they use observational techniques, the correlational approach, or the experimental method. The procedures and methods that can be used to describe results depend on the level of measurement obtained. Therefore, the first task is to consider the different levels of measurement.

LEVEL OF MEASUREMENT AND PERFORMANCE VARIABLES

There are numerous ways to describe behavior. One way is to list everything "important" that the subject does. For example, an investigator describing the mating behavior of the stickleback (see Tinbergen, 1952) is likely to use nonquantitative terms. He will describe in words the stages in the mating cycle of the stickleback. The goal of objectivity can often be attained by having a number of observers independently describe the behavior. The descriptions are then compared for interobserver reliability. Although descriptions should sometimes be given in nonquantitative terms, the advantages of quantification outweigh the disadvantages for most research purposes.

The advantages of quantitative descriptions are objectivity, comparability, and ease of communication. There is usually neither a problem of interjudge agreement nor a problem of communication when performance is described in terms of a score on some task or test. For example, if intelligence is defined in terms of performance on the Stanford-Binet Intelligence Test, there is no misunderstanding about what the investigator means by intelligence. Also, the use of a quantitative definition makes it easy to compare individuals on intelligence. It is particularly useful to have a quantitative measure of performance to assess the effect of different treatments.

Before assessing the effects of various treatment conditions one must understand the different levels of measurement, since the level of measurement obtained will determine what procedures can be used for describing and analyzing the results of experimentation. For example, it is necessary to classify the dependent measure according to the level of measurement obtained in order to select the appropriate statistical test. The four levels of measurement categories are nominal, ordinal, interval, and ratio. We will examine the characteristics of each.

Nominal or Categorical Measurement

A nominal classification system is one in which the different classes (categories) are qualitatively related. Different brands of soap or beer are examples of such a system. A particular brand of beer can be considered a point on the beer "variable." There is no single, quantitative variable that can be used to distinguish different brands. The differences between categories of a nominal system are of a kind and not of degree. They are qualitative, not quantitative.

It is relatively easy to construct nominal classification systems since the primary task is to select categories that are qualitatively related. Social scientists and laymen have not been reluctant to create such systems. You probably have at least some tendency to place people in categories. For example, you may classify them as right-handed or left-handed, male or female, workers or politicians. If you have served in the army, you may know that enlisted men have two categories for the manner of performing a task: the right way and the army way. If the categories are qualitatively different, then they belong to a nominal system. For many research problems it is important to be able to determine the number of individuals in each category so that the factors influencing the assignment to categories and the relationship between classification systems can be determined.

Ordinal Measurement

For nominal data it is assumed that differences between categories are of kind, not degree. However, frequently a single continuum will underlie a particular classification system. For example, it can be argued that a continuum of degree of maladjustment underlies the classification categories of psychotic, neurotic, and normal. If there is good reason to believe that a single dimension underlies a classification system, then it may be useful to rank the categories and treat the results as ordinal rather than nominal data. People in the normal, neurotic, and psychotic categories can be given the scores of 0, 1, and 2, respectively. The numbers indicate the *relative* amount of maladjustment. The difference in maladjustment between individuals in the 0 and 1 categories is not necessarily the same as the difference between those in the 1 and 2 categories. Of course, assignment to these categories must be reliable if the system is to have any potential usefulness.

Since it is usually possible to argue that subjects in different categories differ on one or more quantitative variables, the reader may conclude that it is good strategy to "convert" nominal measurement to ordinal by "detecting" an underlying quantitative dimension. This is not necessarily a good idea, however, because often there is no sound basis for selecting a quantitative dimension.

Consider, for example, the classification of individuals according to political party. It can be argued that a number of different dimensions underlie this classification, such as income, status, values, and occupation. However, such an approach would not be satisfactory because the use of these dimensions will not always result in correct classifications. For instance, Republicans tend to be wealthier than Democrats, but there are also very wealthy Democrats and very poor Republicans. Thus, the use of the income variable is not justified. There appears to be no single quantitative variable that can be used to classify people accurately according to their political preferences. If individuals in different categories differ in a number of ways, it is more reasonable to maintain a nominal classification than to attempt to rank order the categories on the basis of a single variable.

The point is that an ordinal scale represents a quantitative difference and a nominal classification system does not. Ordinal data can be obtained whenever it is possible to rank subjects or events along a single dimension. For example, ranking individuals according to physical strength is an instance of an ordinal scale. Ranking students according to performance on a midterm is another. An ordinal scale is one in which the scale values are quantitatively related, but the differences between successive values are not necessarily equal.

When numbers are used to indicate the amount of a particular characteristic, but the differences between successive units of measurement are not necessarily equal, then ordinal data are obtained. For example, if the members of a class are rank ordered according to leadership ability, the difference in ability between the persons holding ranks 4 and 8 is not necessarily the same as the difference between those holding ranks 16 and 20. But if a dependent measure does have equal intervals between successive units on the scale, then *interval* data are obtained.

Interval and Ratio Measurement

For interval data the scale values are related by a single, underlying, quantitative dimension, and there are equal intervals between successive values. Fahrenheit temperature is a good example of an interval scale. The units reflect a quantitative difference, and the intervals between successive units are equal. For example, the difference between 80 to 100 degrees is the same as the difference between 40 and 60 degrees. These are *equal volumetric changes* in the thermometer. Yet, the Fahrenheit scale is not a ratio scale because the ratio obtained by dividing one temperature by another is not meaningful. It is meaningless to say that 50 degrees is twice as warm as 25 degrees.

A ratio scale has equal intervals between successive units *and* an absolute zero. If a scale has these two features, then it is meaningful to consider the ratio of two numbers on the scale. Weight is a good example of a ratio scale; it has an absolute zero and equal intervals between successive units. It is meaningful to say that a 200-pound person weighs twice as much as a 100-pound person.

Determining the Level of Measurement

It is usually easy to ascertain if the level of measurement is nominal because one can readily determine whether values on a scale are quantitatively or qualitatively related. And, for our purposes, it makes no difference whether the level of measurement is interval or ratio. Thus, the major task is to decide whether the performance measure is an instance of an interval or ordinal scale.

Unfortunately, it is not always a simple matter to determine whether a particular measure should be classified as ordinal or interval. For example, scores on questionnaires, intelligence tests, and achievement tests are frequently viewed as interval data, but this view can be disputed. If the items are not homogeneous, then one can argue that the differences between successive units are not equal. Often it is unclear whether they are equal; then the investigator has to decide whether to regard the measurement as ordinal or interval. There are advantages to having interval data, so when in doubt most investigators treat their data as interval. Those who prefer a more conservative approach, however, will treat their data as ordinal.

DESCRIPTIVE MEASURES

The level of measurement determines the descriptive measures that can be computed. Description is straightforward with nominal data in that it is only necessary to indicate the number of cases in each category. Each subject provides the same amount of data, namely, one case in a particular category. However, if ordinal or interval data are obtained the subjects will almost certainly attain different scores. Therefore, it is more difficult to describe performance on the dependent measure. It is necessary to obtain average scores, and the way they are obtained will usually differ for ordinal and interval data because interval scores are additive and ordinal scores are not. It makes sense to add scores to obtain averages only if the differences between successive units on the scale are equal, i.e., mean the same thing.

The major goal of this section is to consider how interval data can be described. Since some of the measures to be discussed do not involve the addition or subtraction of individual scores, they are applicable to ordinal data as well. The steps in obtaining the various descriptive measures can be studied in the context of an example.

Let us assume that the performance measure is the number of strokes needed to complete a round of golf. The first step is to decide the level of measurement of the performance measure. The nominal option can be eliminated because it is clear that the scores have a quantitative rather than a qualitative relationship. A slight case could be made for regarding the scores as ordinal data in that one could argue that the difference between successive units is not necessarily equal. For example, the difference between a 2 and a 5, on a par 4 hole, may appear to you, if you are a golfer, to be much greater than the difference between a 7 and a 10 on the same hole. However, since most investigators and golfers would probably conclude that a stroke counts as a stroke regardless of quality, the scores can be viewed as interval measures. (That is, we will treat data as interval if there is some doubt about whether the scores are instances of ordinal or interval measurement.) Given that the level of measurement of the performance variable is interval, the next task is to describe the scores. There are two basic sets of descriptive measures for interval data: measures of central tendency and measures of variability.

Measures of Central Tendency

We fluctuate. Our performance varies as a function of many different factors such as time of day, amount of sleep, and level of interest. Thus, if the task is to decide who is better at a particular activity, such as golf, one should be reluctant to base the decision on limited information. To illustrate, assume that you decide to determine whether you are a better golfer than

Dana, one of your friends. You both agree to play 18 holes of golf per day for ten consecutive days.

After playing the tenth round you adjourn to a local pub to analyze the data. The question boils down, you both believe, to assessing who has the better *average* performance. Measures of central tendency must be computed in order to describe your average performance. Since you both want to appear fair, you agree to compute three different measures of central tendency: the mode, median, and mean.

Mode. The mode is the most frequently occurring score. To obtain this measure you count the number of 2's, 3's, 4's, 5's, 6's, 7's, and so on, that each player made on the 180 golf holes. If both players had more 4's than any other score, each would have a modal score of 4. It is not possible to obtain a modal score for the 18-hole total scores because neither player had a given total more than once. In a case in which the number of different scores is quite limited, such as the number of strokes per hole measure in the present example, the mode can be useful. Given a large sample of behavior (the 180 holes), the fact that one golfer has a mode of 4 and another a mode of 6 reveals a great deal about their respective golfing abilities.

However, if there are many possible scores, the mode can be very misleading, especially with a small sample of behavior. For example, if total scores of the ten rounds are considered instead of the 180 scores on individual holes, a golfer may have rounds of 73, 73, 74, 75, 76, 79, 82, 88, 88, and 88. In this case the modal score of 88 is not a good measure of average performance. In determining the modal score of 88 all of the data are ignored except for the most frequently occurring score. Therefore, this measure does not provide any information about the other scores. The median and the mean make greater use of the evidence available.

Median. The median is the value which divides the distribution in half after the scores are placed in ascending or descending rank order. In this case the total score for each 18-hole round is accepted as the best indicator of daily performance. Dana has rounds of 82, 84, 85, 86, 88, 89, 90, 91, 92, and 93. You have rounds of 79, 80, 82, 84, 85, 86, 87, 92, 99, and 116. Since there are ten scores, the middle score is halfway between the fifth and sixth. Thus, you have a median of 85.5 and Dana has a median of 88.5. You are pleased with the median scores as they indicate that, on the average, you are three strokes better than Dana. Dana argues that the median is not a satisfactory measure because it does not utilize all the available information. For example, even if your four lowest scores were reduced by 20, the median would be unaffected. The median is simply not sensitive to changes in extreme scores. In this case, Dana argues, the mean is a better measure. Note that the median score is useful with ordinal as well as interval data because it is not necessary to add or subtract scores to compute this measure.

Mean. The mean is computed by adding all the scores and dividing by the number of scores. To compute the mean total score for the ten rounds of golf, the individual round totals are added, and then divided by the number of scores used to obtain the total (i.e., 10). Your total number of strokes for the ten rounds was 890. You divide this by 10 to obtain a mean score of 89. The symbol $\overline{X}$ (called *x*-bar) is used as a label for the mean. Dana has a mean of 88 (880 divided by 10). Thus, Dana can argue that, on the average, you are one stroke poorer. You reply that you are three strokes better if median performance is considered.

Dana insists that the mean is much better than the median because all the scores are used in making the computation. You answer that this is not necessarily a favorable characteristic. You believe that extreme scores should be discounted instead of being emphasized. The days you scored 79, 99, and 116 were very unusual days for you emotionally. You scored 99 on the day you heard your mother-in-law was coming for a visit, 116 on the day of her arrival, and 79 on the day she left. Obviously, you argue, such extreme scores should not be used to compute typical performance. The mean is influenced unduly by extremes.

A less debatable example can be used to demonstrate the influence of extreme scores on the mean. Let us assume a woman is seeking employment with a small company, and the president of the company informs her that the average annual salary for executive personnel is $30,000. She is very impressed but skeptical. Upon further inquiry she finds that the figure represents the mean salary. The president makes $110,000 a year, and the other four executives each make $10,000 a year. The mean for the five executives is $30,000. In this case, however, the median salary of $10,000 is, from the prospective employee's point of view, a much more useful measure of central tendency, and the choice of the median measure over the mean is clear-cut.

The effort to determine the better golfer, however, is at an impasse. The two major measures of central tendency yield conflicting results, and there is no ultimate authority that you can appeal to for truth. The argument that extreme scores should not be used to determine performance can be countered by asserting that good golfers are consistent. Their scores rarely deviate much from their typical performance. A good golfer should not have a bad day just because his mother-in-law is coming to visit.

Hopefully, the reader is ready to concede that the question is not soluble. The measures used to assess central tendency may not be in agreement regarding which set of scores is higher if there are extreme scores and the scores are of about the same magnitude. The important issue, of course, is what the measures of central tendency reveal about the obtained scores, not which of the three is best. The suitability of the measures depends on the distribution of the scores. Although we tend to enjoy making value judgments, there is little to be gained by doing so for measures of central tendency. It is more important to understand the strengths and weaknesses of each.

The mode is simply the most frequently occurring score so it usually has limited usefulness. The mean utilizes more of the available information than the median, but it is not appropriate for describing ordinal data. If there are extreme scores you may prefer the median because the mean is greatly influenced by extremes.

Measures of Variability

Range. The problem is to obtain some measure of the extent to which scores vary. A very simple, but usually inadequate, measure is the range. The range is the difference score obtained by subtracting the smallest score from the largest. Although the computation is very easy, the measure is usually inadequate because it is based entirely on two scores. For the golf match example, you have a range of 37 (116 minus 79) and Dana has a range of 11 (93 minus 82). If there are only a few extreme scores, the range may give an unsatisfactory description of the variability of the scores. The variance is a far more precise measure in that all the scores are used in its computation.

Variance. The concept of variance is not as difficult as it may at first seem. The task is to measure the extent to which scores vary, and to do this it is convenient to have a reference point. The mean is the reference point. It is then possible to find the difference between each score and the mean, and add up the difference scores. That is, one can determine how much, if any, each score *deviates* from the mean by subtracting the score from the mean or the mean from the score. If this is done for each score and these deviations from the mean are added, the sum will be equal to zero.

The sum of the deviations from the mean is not a suitable measure of variability, since it will always be zero; the sum of the positive deviations is always equal to the sum of the negative deviations. The problem could be solved by ignoring the minus sign and adding all the deviations regardless of sign. Although this procedure would yield a measure of variability, there are statistical and practical reasons for using, instead, a measure obtained by squaring each deviation from the mean.

The variance of a population, then, is the sum of the squared deviations from the mean divided by the number of scores. In computing the variance for a sample of less than thirty scores from a population, the sum of the squared deviations is divided by the number of scores minus one. The reason for this is to obtain a more accurate estimate of population variance. Over the long haul, the sum of the squared deviations divided by the number of scores minus one provides a better estimate than the sum of the squared deviations divided by the total number of scores. If there are more than thirty scores, however, the variance is not influenced very much by which divisor is used.

Some investigators divide by the number of scores if their sole concern is *describing* the scores, and they divide by the number of scores minus one if their concern is *estimating* population variance. Since variance is usually computed for small samples (i.e., less than thirty scores per group or sample) and not for the entire population, many investigators always divide by the number of scores minus one. That is, they do not bother to distinguish between a variance for description and one for estimation; the variance for estimation fulfills both functions. In this text, variance will always be computed by dividing by the number of scores minus one, regardless of the size of the sample. The symbol s^2 is usually used for sample variance.

The scores from the golf match example are used to demonstrate the computation of variance. The scores for your ten rounds of golf and the variance computation are presented in Table 8-1. If you are unclear about how to use the deviation method, you should study this table further. Then, take Dana's golf scores (i.e., 82, 84, 85, 86, 88, 89, 90, 91, 92, and 93) and compute the variance using the deviation method. If you do this correctly, you will obtain a variance of 13.33. Note that your scores are considerably more variable than Dana's.

Using the deviation method should give you a good understanding of variance. It should be clear from the computation that the variance is nothing more than a measure of the extent to which scores differ from the mean score.

TABLE 8–1

The Total Scores for Each of Ten Rounds of Golf and the Computation of the Variance of These Scores. (The deviation scores are obtained by subtracting the mean from each score)

Golf score (X)	*Deviation score* $(X - \bar{X})$	*Squared Deviation Score* $(X - \bar{X})^2$
79	− 10	100
80	− 9	81
82	− 7	49
84	− 5	25
85	− 4	16
86	− 3	9
87	− 2	4
92	+ 3	9
99	+ 10	100
116	+ 27	729
Sum = 890	Total = 0	Total = 1122

$\bar{X} = 89$ $$\text{Variance} = \frac{\text{Sum of the squared deviation scores}}{\text{Number of scores minus 1}}$$

$$\text{Variance} = \frac{1122}{9} = 124.67$$

However, this method of computation tends to be cumbersome as the number of scores increase, particularly if the mean is not a whole number.

An example is presented in Table 8-2 to demonstrate both the deviation method and a computational method for computing the variance. The X refers to any score. The symbol $\overline{X}$ is used for the mean. The first term in the numerator for the computational formula is obtained by squaring each score and then summing the squared scores. The sigma sign is used to indicate the summing operation. The T in the formula refers to the total of all the scores, and the n refers to the number of scores. The second term in the numerator is obtained by squaring the total and dividing by the number of scores. The denominator is simply the number of scores minus one. A comparison of the two formulae reveals that the denominators are the same and the numerators are mathematically equal. The numerator of the computational formula is simply another way to calculate the sum of the squared deviation scores. It should be clear that the calculation of variance is easier with the computational formula, particularly if a calculator is available.

Standard Deviation. The computation of the standard deviation is easy if the variance has already been computed because the standard deviation is equal to the square root of the variance. It is a more useful descriptive measure than the variance because it is in the same units as the mean, whereas the variance is in different units than the mean. That is, the deviations from the mean are *squared* to obtain the variance. The fact that the variance is essentially an average *squared* deviation from the mean makes it somewhat unsatisfactory as a descriptive measure. In considering the difference between two means, it is useful to have a variability measure that is in the same units as the means. This measure can be obtained by taking the square root of the variance. The resulting standard deviation is used extensively as a measure of variability and can also be used as a unit of measurement. (The symbol s is used to denote the standard deviation of a sample.)

Standard Deviations as Units of Measurement

Comparing Scores from Different Distributions. The standard deviation of a set of scores can be used to compare scores from different distributions. The purpose of such a comparison might be to give individuals an indication of their relative performance in different situations. An example should help clarify this point. Assume that you are enrolled in a large psychology class and a large history class. You obtain a score of 84 on the history midterm. The mean score for the class was 74 and the standard deviation was 10. Your score on the psychology midterm was 69. The mean score was 60 and the standard deviation was 3. The question is whether your performance, relative to the other members of each class, was higher on the psychology or history exam.

The standard deviation can be used as a unit of measurement in that an

TABLE 8–2

An Example of the Calculation of the Variance by the Deviational and Computational Formulae

Deviational method			***Computational method***
Scores	$(X - \bar{X})$	$(X - \bar{X})^2$	*Scores*
38	– 5.25	27.56	38
55	11.75	138.06	55
62	18.75	351.56	62
25	–18.25	333.06	25
31	–12.25	150.06	31
46	2.75	7.56	46
45	1.75	3.06	45
50	6.75	45.56	50
42	– 1.25	1.56	42
39	– 4.25	18.06	39
41	– 2.25	5.06	41
45	1.75	3.06	45
	Sum = 0	Sum = 1084.22	$T = 519$
$\bar{X} = 43.25$			$\Sigma X^2 = 23{,}531$
$\text{Variance} = \dfrac{\Sigma(X - \bar{X})^2}{n - 1} = \dfrac{1084.22}{11} = 98.57$			$\text{Variance} = \dfrac{\Sigma X^2 - \dfrac{(T)^2}{n}}{n - 1} = \dfrac{23{,}531 - \dfrac{269{,}361}{12}}{11} = \dfrac{1084.25}{11} = 98.57$

individual can determine how many standard deviation units he is above or below the mean. The task is to determine the difference between the mean and the obtained score and then divide the difference by the standard deviation for the total set of scores. If you subtract the mean score for the history exam from your score, you obtain a difference of 10. You then divide this difference by the standard deviation of 10 and obtain a quotient of 1. Thus, you were one standard deviation unit above the mean on the history exam. If you perform the same operations for the psychology score, you will find that you are three standard deviation units above the mean on the psychology exam. Thus, even though you were 10 points above the mean on the history exam and only 9 points above on the psychology, your performance relative to other members of each class was far better in psychology than in history.

Standard Deviations and Normal Distributions. The use of the standard deviation as a unit can be clarified by considering the normal frequency distribution in Figure 8-1. The normal distribution is important because a number of variables are distributed normally. That is, scores tend to cluster around the mean, and the probability of obtaining a particular score decreases as the difference between the score and the mean increases, as is indicated in Figure 8-1. The standard deviation unit can be used to indicate the relative position of a score, particularly if the properties of the distribution of scores are known. Let us assume that the scores on the history and psychology midterms were normally distributed.

Figure 8-1 can be used to show why a score of three standard deviations above the mean is considerably better than a score of one standard deviation above. The height of the curve indicates the relative frequency of each score. The area under the curve can be used to determine the probability of obtaining a score greater or less than a particular score. It can be readily seen that the probability of obtaining a score of three standard deviations above the mean is considerably less than the probability of obtaining a score of one standard deviation above. The first probability is represented by the dark shaded area in Figure 8-1, the second by the entire shaded area, both dark and light. A score of 69 on the psychology exam was one of the best scores obtained, whereas a score of 84 on the history exam was more common.

If the distribution is normal then approximately 68 percent of the scores will be within one standard deviation above and below the mean, approximately 95 percent will be within two standard deviations of the mean, and approximately 99 percent will be within three standard deviations. Thus, a score which is three or more standard deviations above the mean is an unusually high score. A score which has been converted into plus or minus standard deviation units from the mean is call a *Z score.* That is, you have a *Z* score of +1 on the history test and +3 on the psychology.

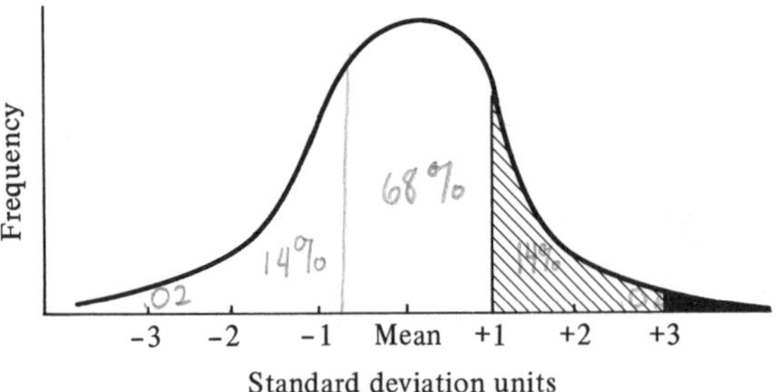

FIGURE 8-1

The normal curve is a graph of the normal distribution.

Standard Deviations and Nonnormal Distributions. The reader should *not* conclude that all scores are normally distributed. There are many possible distributions. Four different types are presented in Figure 8-2. If the scores are distributed as in A, the distribution is said to be skewed positive. If they are distributed as in B, it is said to be skewed negative. Distributions are skewed if there are more scores on one end than the other. They are symmetrical if there are the same number of high and low scores. The direction of the skew of a nonsymmetrical distribution can be determined by examining the extreme scores or "tail" of the distribution. If the extreme scores are below the mean the distribution is said to be skewed negative; if they are above the mean it is skewed positive.

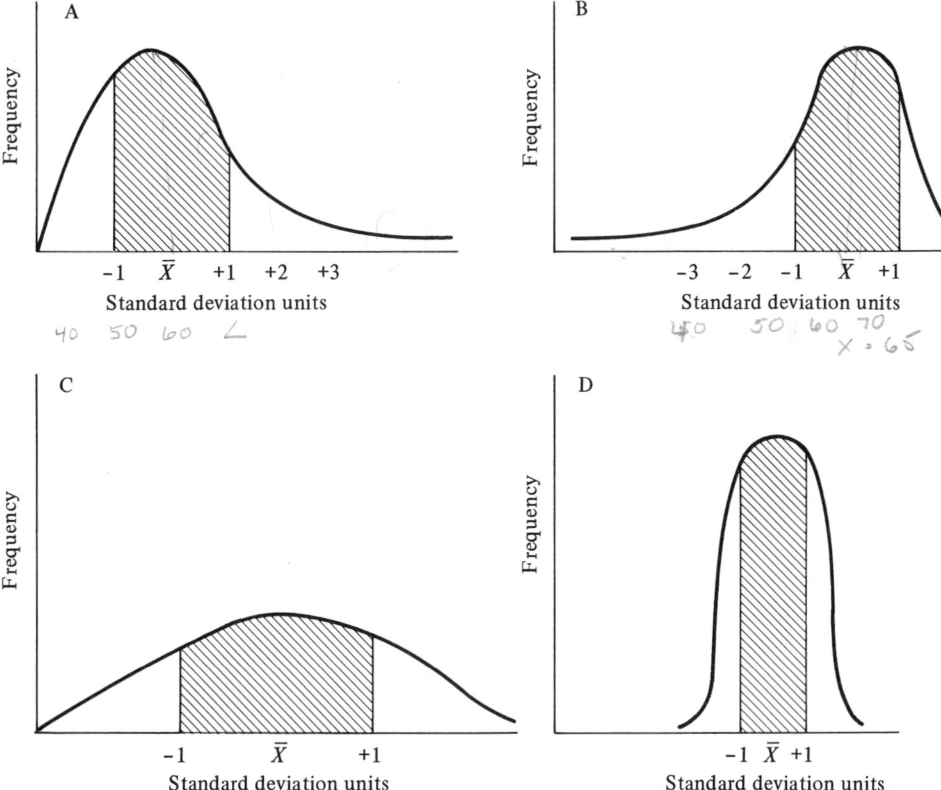

FIGURE 8-2

The above four distributions differ markedly from the normal distribution in Figure 8-1. Distribution A is skewed positive, and Distribution B is skewed negative. Distribution C is platykurtic, and Distribution D is leptokurtic. The shaded area of each curve indicates the portion of the curve within one standard deviation above or below the mean.

The interpretation of a score expressed in standard deviation units depends on the distribution. For example, the probability of obtaining a score which is at least two standard deviations above the mean is equal to the probability of obtaining a score which is at least two standard deviations below the mean if the distribution is symmetrical as in distributions C and D. This is not true if the distribution is skewed. There is a greater probability of obtaining a score which is at least two standard deviations above than a score which is at least two standard deviations below the mean if the scores are distributed as in A. The reverse is true if they are distributed as in B. Thus, one has to be careful when comparing scores from two distributions (e.g., the history and the psychology tests) if the distributions are not very similar.

Distributions may vary considerably in their flatness or peakedness. The flatness or peakedness of a distribution or curve is labeled kurtosis. A distribution or curve that is flat is platykurtic. One that is steep is leptokurtic. And one that falls between these two extremes is mesokurtic. The normal curve is mesokurtic. The curve in Figure 8-2C is platykurtic, and that in Figure 8-2D is leptokurtic.

An examination of the curves presented in Figure 8-2 should enable the reader to see that the size of the standard deviation is related to the shape of the distribution. In Figure 8-2D the scores tend to be clustered close to the mean so the size of the standard deviation is relatively small. In Figure 8-2C the scores do not cluster tightly around the mean so the standard deviation is larger. This should not be any surprise, of course, because the standard deviation is a measure of the extent to which scores cluster around the mean. It is a particularly useful unit of measurement because it increases as the variability of the scores increases. As a result, when the score is expressed in standard deviation units one can get a firm notion of its relative position in a distribution and, therefore, of the probability of obtaining it if only chance is operating. For most distributions the probability of obtaining a score which is within one standard deviation of the mean is between .6 and .7.

DESCRIBING THE RESULTS OF EXPERIMENTS

Now that you have been introduced to measures of central tendency and variability, you have the basic tools necessary to describe the results of most experiments. Even though you have the tools it is likely that you are not quite sure how to use them; you may not know when to compute a particular measure or how to present it once it has been computed. One particularly suitable way to present the results of experiments is to use tables and figures. Once again, we will use examples to demonstrate how results can be described for different kinds of experiments, including those in which nominal, ordinal, and interval data are collected.

Nominal Data

Political party can be used as an example of a nominal classification system because party preference is a qualitative distinction. Assume that an investigator wanted to assess the effect of a campaign to persuade voters to become Democrats. He took a random sample of 200 registered voters in a small town and learned the political party preference of each. Then he initiated a campaign to persuade voters to register as Democrats. After the campaign was concluded, he took another sample of 200 registered voters from the same town. The sample was random with the restriction that anyone selected in the first sample was not used in the second. Once again, the political preference of everyone selected was determined. How should the investigator describe the results?

There is no need to compute measures of central tendency or variability because each person selected contributes the same score. That is, each must indicate a preference for only one category — Democrat, Republican, or Independent. Therefore, it is easy to describe the results. All that is needed is the number of voters who selected each category. Of course, the results are calculated separately for the two samples so that the effect of the political campaign can be assessed. These results are presented in Table 8-3.

Note that it is not necessary to present the results in the form of a table. It would have been sufficient simply to state the number of voters who selected the Democratic, Republican, and Independent parties before the political campaign (i.e., 70, 70, and 60, respectively) and the number who selected each party after the campaign (i.e., 90, 60, and 50). If there are only a few numbers, then there is no compelling reason to present them in a table. However, as the amount of data to report increases, it frequently becomes necessary to use a table or figure to present the results. The reader will be prepared to analyze the results presented in Table 8-3 after reading Chapter 9.

TABLE 8–3

The Number of Voters in Each Sample of 200 Who Selected Each Political Party Before and After the Political Campaign to Encourage Voters to Become Democrats (fictitious data)

	Political party preference		
Nature of the sample	*Democrat*	*Republican*	*Independent*
Selected before the campaign	70	70	60
Selected after the campaign	90	60	50

Ordinal Data

Let us assume that the problem is to assess the effects of a plan to build self-esteem. The independent variable is whether or not the subject has participated in the plan. The dependent measure is the rank ordering of the experimental and control subjects according to successfulness. The proponents of the plan claim that people who complete the self-esteem course have a greater probability of being successful than those who do not. A random-groups design is used. Thirty subjects are randomly assigned to the experimental and control conditions such that there are fifteen subjects in each. The experimental subjects receive the "Learn How to Be Courageous" course and control subjects do not. Five years after completion of the course an evaluation team which is unaware of the purpose of the experiment obtains enough information to rank order the thirty subjects according to degree of success. The most successful person is given the rank of 30 and the least successful the rank of 1. How should the experimenter describe the results of this experiment?

The rank order and the treatment condition for each subject are given in Table 8-4. All the facts are presented in this way so that the reader can consider how best to describe the results. It is not correct to conclude that the results should be described as they are in Table 8-4. In most cases it is not

TABLE 8-4

The Rank of Each Subject in the Experimental (E) and Control (C) Conditions for the "Learn to Be Courageous" Experiment (The rank of 1 indicates the least successful subject; the rank of 30 indicates the most successful subject–fictitious data)

Subject	*Condition*	*Rank*	*Subject*	*Condition*	*Rank*
F. T.	C	1	K. S.	C	16
D. J.	C	2	D. A.	E	17
W. L.	C	3	W. H.	E	18
T. J.	C	4	A. M.	C	19
D. B.	C	5	R. M.	E	20
R. T.	C	6	R. W.	C	21
T. A.	C	7	G. V.	E	22
D. A.	E	8	M. K.	C	23
C. N.	C	9	L. W.	E	24
S. S.	E	10	J. S.	E	25
C. W.	C	11	T. S.	E	26
S. J.	C	12	C. G.	E	27
R. C.	E	13	T. B.	E	28
F. H.	C	14	H. B.	E	29
M. F.	E	15	B. C.	E	30

necessary to present the rank ordering for each subject. Usually, the principal concern is with whether the independent variable has an effect.

The effect of the independent variable is assessed by comparing the rankings of the experimental and control subjects. Since the level of measurement is ordinal, it is not permissible to add the ranks of the subjects in each group to obtain average scores. Adding the ranks for descriptive purposes is not defensible unless there is reason to believe that the differences between successive ranks are equal. In this case, there is no reason to believe that the data are any more than ordinal. The reader should not conclude, however, that ranks are never added. Some statistical tests with ordinal data require adding of rank scores.

Probably the best way to describe the data in Table 8-4 is to indicate the number of subjects in each condition who are above the median rank. If the results are attributable to chance then the number of experimental and control subjects above the median rank of 15.5 should be approximately equal. The fact that eleven of the fifteen subjects above the median are experimental subjects suggests that the independent variable had an effect. A statement of the number of experimental and control subjects above the median rank in combination with the results of the appropriate statistical test should provide an accurate description of the results of the experiment, i.e., should demonstrate the effect of the independent variable. The student will be prepared to analyze the results in Table 8-4 after reading Chapter 9.

Interval Data

The task of describing the results of experiments in which interval data are obtained is more involved than with a lower level of measurement because of the need to compute measures of central tendency and variability. This should not pose any real difficulty, however, because these are relatively easy to compute. Often the problem is deciding what measures to compute and how to present them. Once more, we will use examples to indicate some of the difficulties investigators may encounter.

Driver Education Example. An investigator uses a two-group, random-groups design to assess the effect of a driver education program on subsequent driving performance. The facilities at the school are limited, so only one-half of the students who want to take the driver education course can be accepted. In order to be fair, the students are randomly selected. This set of circumstances, though unfortunate from the point of view of those not selected for the program, provides an excellent opportunity to evaluate its effectiveness.

The independent variable is whether or not the student has received the driver education program. There are fifty students in each condition. Those not selected for the program learn to drive by other methods such as self-instruction, or instruction by a parent or sibling. The dependent measure is the number of arrests for driving violations in the ten year period after learning to drive. Assume that the investigator has no difficulty learning the number of arrests for each subject. How should the results be described?

The score for each subject is, of course, the number of arrests in the ten year period. The effect of the independent variable is assessed by comparing the average performance of the two groups. In most experiments in which interval data are obtained, the mean will be selected as the best measure of central tendency. However, if the distribution is markedly skewed, the median is likely to be a better indicator because the mean is influenced greatly by extreme scores. In this case, let us assume that the distribution of scores in each group is relatively symmetrical. Thus, the first task is to obtain the mean number of arrests for the two groups. Assume that the mean was 2.13 arrests for the Driver Education Group and 3.07 for the Control Group. Is this all the information needed to describe the results of the experiment?

It is necessary to know the mean performance of the two groups, but this information is not sufficient to assess whether the independent variable had an effect. It is not clear whether the obtained result is a common or rare outcome if only chance is operating. Therefore, an appropriate statistical test must be performed to determine whether the null hypothesis can be rejected. The important point is that the results of many experiments in which interval data are obtained can be adequately described by presenting the mean for each treatment condition and the results of the appropriate statistical test.

Factorial Design Example. Assume that a 2 by 2 factorial design is used to assess the effects of two independent variables. There are two levels of each independent variable so there are four different treatment conditions. The dependent measure is the score of each subject on a thirty-item test. Once again, the mean performance of each group is the most useful measure of central tendency. Reporting the four means plus the results of the appropriate statistical test will adequately describe the results. The task is to decide the best way to report the four means.

In this case there are a number of possible ways. The means could be presented in the text, in a table, or in a figure. The investigator has considerable choice because there are only four means. When there are a large number of means to present, there is little choice but to use either a figure or a table, depending on the experiment. If the investigator is in doubt, he should prepare the results both ways and then ask a few colleagues which presentation is clearer. For the present example, it is only necessary to list the four treatment conditions and the corresponding means if the results are presented in the text or in a table. However, if they are presented in a figure, the nature of the independent variable should determine the type of figure used.

The basic consideration is whether the independent variable is a quantitative or qualitative manipulation. If it is qualitative, one should use a bar graph, if quantitative, a line graph. Assume that the two independent variables for the present example are sex of the subject and type of task, verbal or nonverbal. Then the levels of each independent variable differ in a qualita-

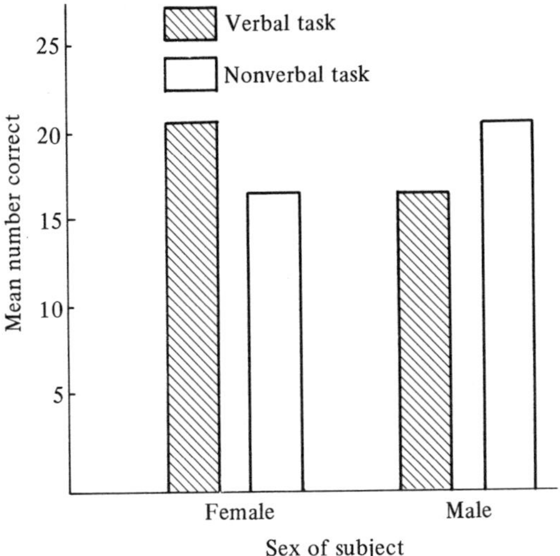

FIGURE 8-3

The mean number of correct responses on a thirty-item verbal task and a thirty-item nonverbal task as a function of sex (fictitious data).

tive sense and a bar graph is appropriate. The results of this hypothetical experiment are presented in Figure 8-3. As usual, the magnitude of the dependent measure is indicated on the ordinate or vertical axis. The independent variable is presented on the abscissa (horizontal axis) or in the body of the figure by using different kinds of lines, by labeling the lines differently, or, in a bar graph, by shading the bars differently. An examination of Figure 8-3 should lead the reader to conclude that there is probably a significant interaction between the type of task variable and the sex variable. Males do better on the nonverbal task, females on the verbal.

If the independent variable is a quantitative manipulation then a line graph should be used. Assume that the two independent variables are motivational level and task difficulty. In this case, the results of the hypothetical experiment could be presented as in Figure 8-4.

Instructional Method Example. Assume that an investigator is interested in the effect of instructional method (A, B, or C) on course performance. The course is divided into six segments, and a forty-item test is given at the conclusion of each segment. A random-groups design is used, and there are twenty subjects in each condition. How should the results of this experiment be described?

There should be little doubt that the mean performance for each of the six tests for each of the three conditions should be presented. The fact that many numbers have to be reported dictates the use of a table or figure. A

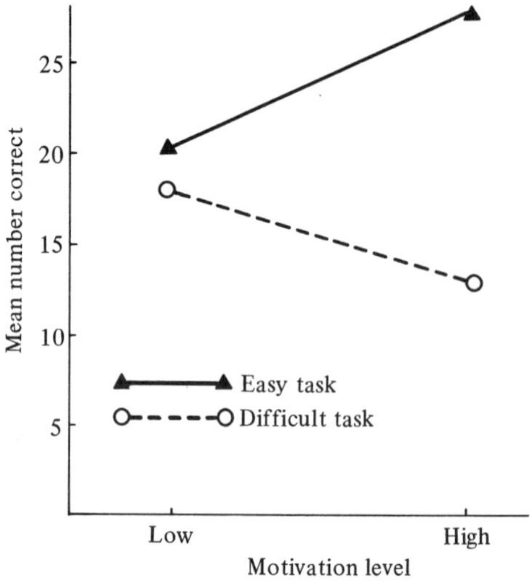

FIGURE 8-4

The mean number of correct responses on a thirty-item easy task and a thirty-item difficult task as a function of the motivational level of the subject (fictitious data).

figure is usually a clearer way to present the several mean scores when a task involves a number of stages or trials, and performance at each stage is of some interest. The results of this hypothetical experiment are presented in Figure 8-5.

Note that the six segments of the course are plotted on the abscissa. If, as in this case, each subject obtains more than one score on the dependent variable, the variable on which the repeated measures are obtained is plotted on the abscissa. Incidentally, the reader should note that the trend over the six segments for each condition is of considerable interest. This result would not have been described if the investigator had decided to present an overall measure of average performance for each of the three conditions.

Autistic Boy Example. For the last example, assume that you are an undetected observer in a school for the mentally retarded. The experiment that takes place will be "natural" in the sense that only the alert, undetected observer will realize that an experiment is being conducted. The data are collected by observing the behavior of a young autistic boy and of the ward attendant from 2:00 to 3:00 P.M. on Monday through Friday for a nine week period. The independent variable is the attention the ward attendant gives the boy whenever the boy engages in self-destructive acts. The dependent measure is the number of self-destructive acts committed by the boy in each

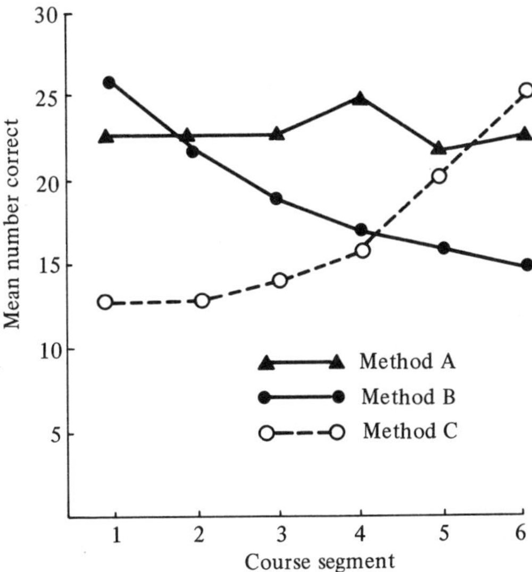

FIGURE 8–5

The mean performance on the test items for the six segments of the course for each of the three methods of instruction (fictitious data).

one hour observation period. The question of interest is whether the behavior of the ward attendant is at least partially responsible for the child's self-destructive acts.

During the first three week observation period, the ward attendant responds only after the boy commits some self-destructive act. The reason for this is easily understood. The ward is overcrowded and understaffed, so the attendant has to move from one crisis to another. Since there are many children seeking his attention, only those who are most in need receive it. In short, the situation is such that one effective way for the boy to receive attention is to do something unusual. In this case the unusual behavior is a self-destructive act.

For the second three week period the ward attendant changes strategy. He has noted that the level of self-destructive acts is high on the ward and believes his own responses may be partially to blame. Therefore, he decides to attend only to those children who are *not* engaging in self-destructive acts. The others are to be ignored.

This procedure is followed for three weeks until an administrator happens to pass the ward when a few children are engaging in self-destructive acts. The administrator is amazed that the ward attendant is ignoring these children and, instead, is playing with the other seemingly contented children. He makes it clear that the attendant had better change his behavior, so during the last three weeks the attendant responds to unusual behavior on the part of the children. How should the results of this "natural experiment" be described?

In this case there is no need to compute measures of central tendency or variability or to perform statistical tests. The only task is to report the number of self-destructive acts over the nine week period. It is crucial to have a session by session reporting as this is the only way that the effect of the manipulation can be assessed. That is, the "natural experiment" is an instance of a within-subject design in which only one subject is tested. To evaluate the effectiveness of the independent variable, one must compare the level of responding for the different treatment conditions.

If the level of responding is relatively stable from session to session within a treatment period and changes when a new treatment is introduced, then there is reason to believe that the treatment is responsible for the behavioral change. An examination of the results for the forty-five sessions should enable us to determine whether the treatment manipulation had any effect. These results are presented in Figure 8-6. Note that the sessions are plotted on the abscissa, the number of destructive acts per session on the ordinate. The results suggest that the manipulation had an effect.

EVALUATING RESULTS

The task of evaluating results cannot be clearly separated from the task of describing them. One can argue that the evaluation of a particular result is one step in the description process. That is, determining whether a particular outcome is a rare or common event if only chance is operating can be con-

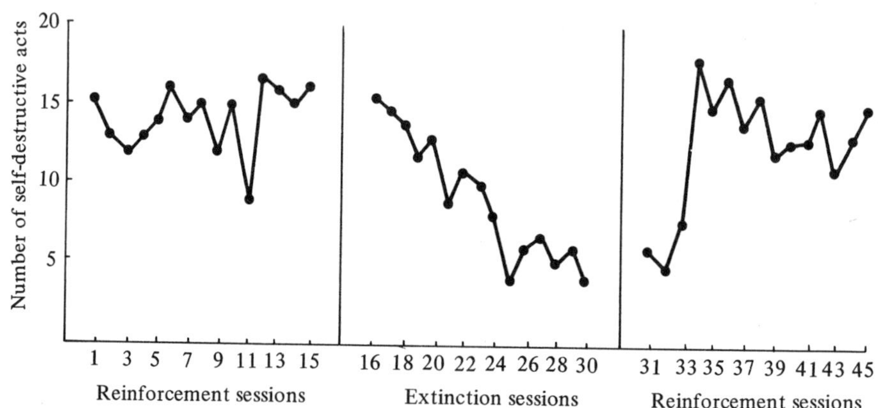

FIGURE 8–6

The number of self-destructive acts as a function of the reaction to these acts by the ward attendant (fictitious data).

sidered a descriptive task. Thus, the statistical tests considered in Chapters 9 through 11 can be viewed as procedures for describing the results of experiments. However, some readers will prefer to distinguish between the procedures involved in obtaining descriptive measures, which are discussed in this chapter, and the statistical tests involved in accepting or rejecting the null hypothesis. Bear in mind, however, that it may not be necessary to use statistical tests to evaluate a particular outcome. Thus, the distinction between describing and evaluating results is not always clear. The remaining topic to be discussed here is the description of results obtained with the correlational approach. For our purposes, this means computing correlations.

DESCRIBING THE RESULTS OF CORRELATIONAL RESEARCH

One way to describe the results of correlational research is to plot them in a figure. The values for the first variable are listed on the abscissa, the values for the second variable on the ordinate. Since each subject has a score for each measure, each subject's performance can be represented as a dot. The location of the dot for each person is determined by his score on the two measures being considered. Graphs of this nature are called scatter-plots. Four scatter-plots are presented in Figure 8-7. Figure 8-7A shows the name of the person represented by each dot to emphasize the point (no pun intended) that each dot indicates that person's score on two different measures. For example, Alice has a score of 40 on the mathematics test and 90 on the psychology test. Pete has a score of 18 on the mathematics test and 23 on the psychology test. Elsewhere the dots are not labeled because it is understood that each dot stands for the scores of one individual on the two variables.

The first three scatter-plots in Figure 8-7 represent a positive, negative, and zero correlation between the two variables. The fourth plot represents a more complex relationship, which will be discussed later. The reader can determine the plot which corresponds to each of these three relationships. Remember that a high positive correlation is obtained when high scores go with high scores, low with low, and middle with middle. When high scores go with low scores and middle scores with middle, a high negative correlation is obtained. In a zero correlation, individuals with a high score on one measure may have a high, medium, or low score on the second measure. The scatter-plot is a convenient way to represent pictorially the relationship between two variables.

Rank-Order Correlation

Correlations are extremely useful descriptive measures because they allow a precise indication of the extent to which two variables are related. We will

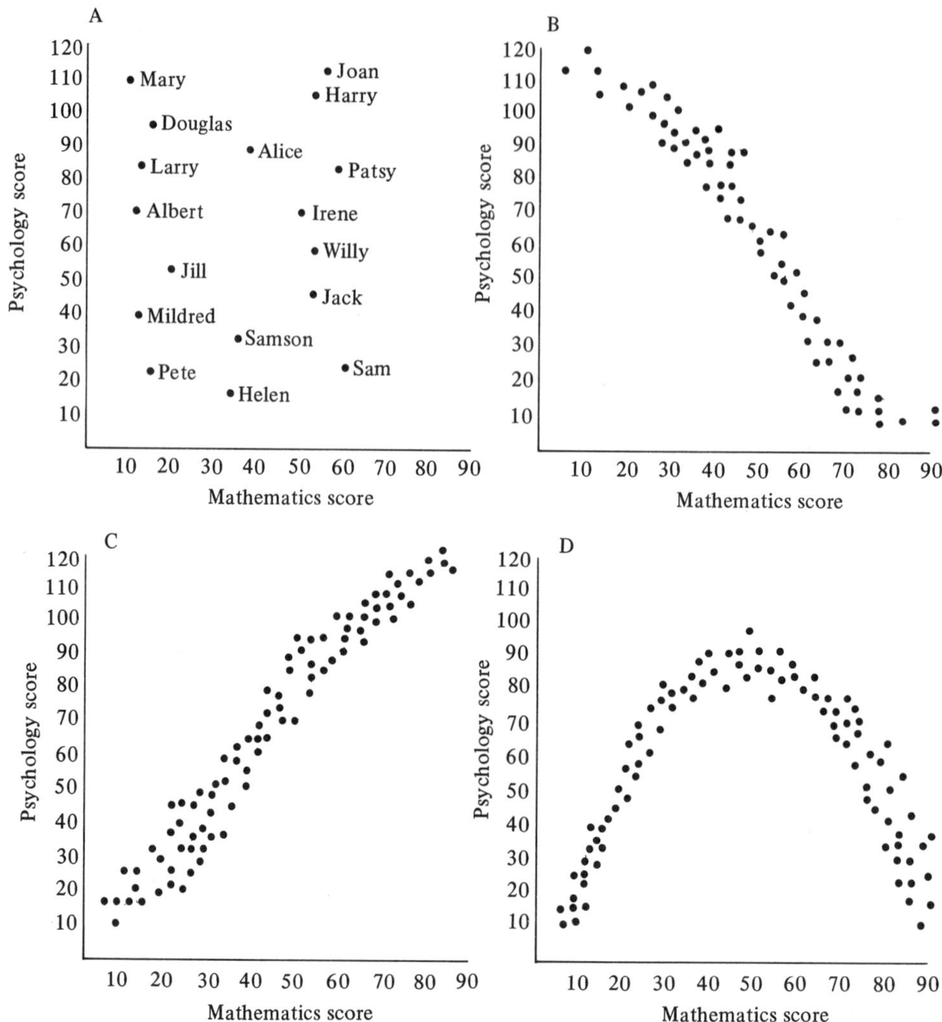

FIGURE 8–7

The scatter-plots for four different relationships between psychology and mathematics performance (fictitious data).

consider two widely used ways to compute a correlation, namely, the Spearman rank-order correlation and the Pearson product-moment correlation. The Pearson product-moment correlation is used for interval data, the Spearman rank-order correlation only for ordinal data. If both correlations are performed on the same rank-ordered data, however, the results will be identical. That is, the Pearson product-moment can be used with ordinal data; however, it is good practice to use it only with interval data in order to avoid interpretational mistakes. The interpretation of a product-moment correlation with interval data is not the same as the interpretation of a rank-order correlation with ordinal data.

Computation of the Rank-Order Correlation. Assume that you and another judge, named Harry, rate twelve male adult seals on aggressiveness. The rank of 1 is assigned to the most aggressive seal and 12 to the least aggressive. Then a correlation is computed between the two sets of rankings to determine the extent of agreement. Since rank data are obtained, a rank-order correlation can be computed. The two sets of rankings are presented in Table 8-5. There are no tied scores in this table. If two subjects had been ranked the same, then the two ranks in question would have been summed

TABLE 8–5

The Two Sets of Rankings for the Twelve Adult Male Seals and the Computation of the Rank-Order Correlation (The symbol d *is used to indicate the difference between the rankings for each seal)*

Seals	*Your ranking*	*Harry's ranking*	d	d^2
Killer	1	2	-1	1
Clyde	2	3	-1	1
Harry	3	1	2	4
Pete	4	4	0	0
Popeye	5	5	0	0
Fred	6	7	-1	1
George	7	6	1	1
Jack	8	9	-1	1
Adam	9	8	1	1
Sleepy	10	10	0	0
Milktoast	11	11	0	0
Fearful	12	12	0	0

Sum of $d^2 = 10$

$N = 12$

$$r_s = 1 - \frac{6(\Sigma d^2)}{N(N^2 - 1)}$$

$$r_s = 1 - \frac{6(10)}{12(144 - 1)}$$

$$r_s = 1 - \frac{60}{1716}$$

$$r_s = 1 - .035$$

$$r_s = .965$$

(e.g., $3 + 4 = 7$) and both subjects given the mean of the tied ranks (e.g., 3.5). (If there were a large number of tied scores on a particular measure, the formula given below would not be appropriate.) The formula for computing the rank-order correlation is:

$$r_s = 1 - \frac{6(\Sigma d^2)}{N(N^2 - 1)}.$$

In this formula r_s is used to designate the rank-order correlation. The sigma (Σ) is a symbol for the summing operation. The symbol d refers to the difference between the ranks for each subject. In this case d^2 follows the summation sign so the squared difference scores are added. The N refers to the number of pairs of scores which in this case is equal to 12. The 1 and 6 are always used in this formula so they are referred to as constants. Investigators use the symbol r_s for the rank-order correlation when it is computed for a sample and the Greek letter rho (ρ) when it is computed for the population.

Magnitude of the Rank-Order Correlation. The magnitude of the rank-order correlation indicates the degree of relationship between two variables. It is free to fluctuate between -1.00 and $+1.00$. Notice that if the two sets of rankings were identical, all the difference scores would be zero and, of course, the sum of the squared differences would also be zero. Since six multiplied by zero is zero, the numerator would be zero. And since zero divided by any number is zero, the second term of the equation would be zero. Thus the value of r_s when the two sets of ranks are identical is equal to $+1.00$.

Assume that *your* rankings are as presented in Table 8-5, but that Harry gives Killer a rank of 12, Clyde a rank of 11, and so on down the list. In this case the sum of the squared difference scores is as large as it can possibly be. If you do not believe this, arrange the rankings in any way you choose to produce a larger squared difference score. Given a set of rankings as in the present example, only the sum of the squared difference scores is free to vary. You should experiment with different sets of rankings, computing the sum of the squared difference scores, until you are convinced that r_s tends to be close to $+1.00$ when subjects with a high rank on one measure have a high rank on the other, middle ranks go with middle ranks, and low ranks with low; and that r_s tends to be close to -1.00 when subjects with a high rank on one measure have a low rank on the other, and middle ranks go with middle. The rank-order correlation tends to be about zero when individuals with a high rank on one measure may have a high, middle, or low rank on the other measure. In short, r_s varies from -1.00 to $+1.00$ depending on the degree and type of relationship between the two variables.

Product-Moment Correlation

In general, the comments made about the rank-order correlation are appropriate for the product-moment correlation, except that the rank-order is used for ordinal data and the product-moment for interval data. To demonstrate the steps involved in computing the correlation, we will use as our example the correlation between the intelligence of children adopted within the first three months of life and the intelligence of their genetic parents. The I.Q.'s of the adopted children were determined after they had attained adulthood. The I.Q. scores and the computation of the Pearson product-moment correlation are presented in Table 8-6. Computation of the correlation is relatively easy provided a calculator is available.

Computation of the Product-Moment Correlation. The formula and computations in Table 8-6 require some explanation. The large X refers to the mean intelligence score of each pair of genetic parents, the large Y to the I.Q. score of each adopted child, and the large N to the number of families considered (pairs of scores). The sigma indicates that the summing operation is performed. Thus, for ΣX you would sum the X scores. For ΣX^2 you would sum

TABLE 8-6

Average I.Q.'s of the Two Genetic Parents and the Adopted Child's I.Q. and the Product-Moment Correlation for These Measures (fictitious data)

Family	*Parents (X)*	*Child (Y)*	XY
A	102	105	10,710
B	112	109	12,208
C	89	110	9,790
D	102	120	12,240
E	75	80	6,000
F	130	132	17,160
G	83	100	8,300
H	112	120	13,440
I	87	86	7,482
J	99	135	13,365
K	102	110	11,220
L	120	94	11,280
M	74	91	6,734
N	115	116	13,340
	$\Sigma X = 1402$	$\Sigma Y = 1508$	$\Sigma XY = 153{,}269$
	$\Sigma X^2 = 144{,}106$	$\Sigma Y^2 = 165{,}924$	

$$r = \frac{N\Sigma XY - (\Sigma X)(\Sigma Y)}{\sqrt{[N\Sigma X^2 - (\Sigma X)^2]\,[N\Sigma Y^2 - (\Sigma Y)^2]}}$$

$$r = \frac{14\,(153{,}269) - (1402)\,(1508)}{\sqrt{[14\,(144{,}106) - (1402)^2]\,[14\,(165{,}924) - (1508)^2]}}$$

$r = .63$

the squared X scores. The same procedure is used for the Y scores. For ΣXY you would multiply each XY pair and sum the products. This is all done for you in Table 8-6. After completing these computations, it is a relatively simple matter to insert the values into the formula and compute the correlation.

Magnitude of the Product-Moment Correlation. Once again, the magnitude of the correlation depends on the particular pairings of the two scores. That is, some index is needed of the extent to which high X scores go with high Y scores. The product-moment correlation is an excellent index of this relationship.The magnitude of the correlation indicates whether the I.Q.'s of genetic parents and children are related when the children do not live with their genetic parents.

The magnitude of the correlation is unrelated to the absolute magnitudes of the intelligence scores; the correlation would be unaffected if 25 I.Q. points were added to the score of each child. The important factor is whether the high scores for one measure (parents with high scores) are paired with the high scores of the other measure (children with high scores). If you keep the same set of scores for the parents and the same set for the children and manipulate the pairings, you will, of course, produce marked changes in the obtained product-moment correlation. These changes will, however, influence only one term in the product-moment correlation formula, namely, $N\Sigma XY$. The values for the other terms will remain the same. Thus, to demonstrate that the product-moment correlation assesses the extent to which high scores go with high scores, all you have to do is manipulate the pairings and note the result. The sum of the X times Y cross-products is the largest when high scores of X are paired with high scores of Y. In short, both the rank-order correlation and the product-moment correlation can be convenient tools to describe the extent to which two variables are related.

Correlation, Sampling, and Monotonic Relationships

Correlation and Sampling. It is somewhat misleading to imply that the particular pairing of scores is the sole determiner of the magnitude of the correlation. This is true only when a specific set of scores for each measure is assumed. When one is collecting correlational data, the specific set of scores for each measure will not be "determined." In determining the correlation between intelligence test scores and productivity, for example, the investigator has some latitude with respect to the sample he selects. Both the kind and size of the sample are likely to influence the magnitude of the correlation. If a random sample is selected from a larger population for the purpose of estimating the magnitude of the population correlation, the accuracy of the sample estimate should increase, all things being equal, as the size of the sample increases. If a relatively homogeneous sample is selected, the range of intelligence test scores will not be very large. Such a limited range of scores will probably result in a smaller correlation, given that intelligence and productivity are related.

Selecting the subjects from a limited range of one variable is comparable to making a small manipulation of an independent variable. When a small manipulation is made, the chances of obtaining a significant effect are less than if a large manipulation is made, given that the variable actually has an effect. Obviously, if intelligence is related to productivity, one is more likely to detect this relationship through the use of subjects who differ markedly on intelligence than of subjects who differ only slightly.

Sample Correlation and Population Correlation. The correlation obtained with a sample can be used to estimate the extent to which two variables are correlated provided the sample is randomly selected from the larger population. The accuracy of the estimate should increase, all things being equal, as the size of the sample increases. If the sample is not randomly selected, then using the sample correlation to estimate the correlation in the population is not warranted. Even when the sample is random, a correlation of considerable magnitude may be due to chance; that is, it may be obtained even though the two variables are unrelated in the population.

If the two variables are unrelated then subjects with a high score on one variable may have a high, medium, or low score on the other. If, by chance, the investigator selects more individuals who have similar scores on the two variables than dissimilar scores, he may conclude, erroneously, that the two variables are actually related. A table to assess the statistical significance of rank-order correlations is presented in Appendix C-6, and a table to assess the statistical significance of product-moment correlations in Appendix C-7. These tables make it possible to determine whether an obtained correlation can reasonably be attributed to chance. If the correlation exceeds the table value, then it is possible to reject the null hypothesis that the population correlation is zero.

Correlation and Monotonic Relations. Figure 8-8 shows examples of linear, nonlinear, monotonic, and nonmonotonic relationships. The Pearson product-moment correlation is useful for assessing the degree to which two variables are linearly related. If they are linearly related, then an increase in one is accompanied by a constant increase (or, a decrease if the variables have a negative relationship) in the other for the entire range of both variables. The effect of an increase in one variable on the other does not depend on the value considered. For example, if $Y = 2X$, the variables Y and X are linearly related. Increasing the value of X by one unit is accompanied by a two-unit increase in Y regardless of the particular value of X that is considered. Although the Pearson product-moment correlation is an excellent technique for assessing linear relationships, it does not allow us to assess nonlinear relationships.

The Spearman rank-order correlation allows us to assess the extent to which two variables are monotonically related. If they have a positive monotonic relationship, then an increase in one is accompanied by an increase in the other, but the increase is not necessarily the same for the entire range of both variables. For example, if $Y = X^3$, the two variables X and Y are monotoni-

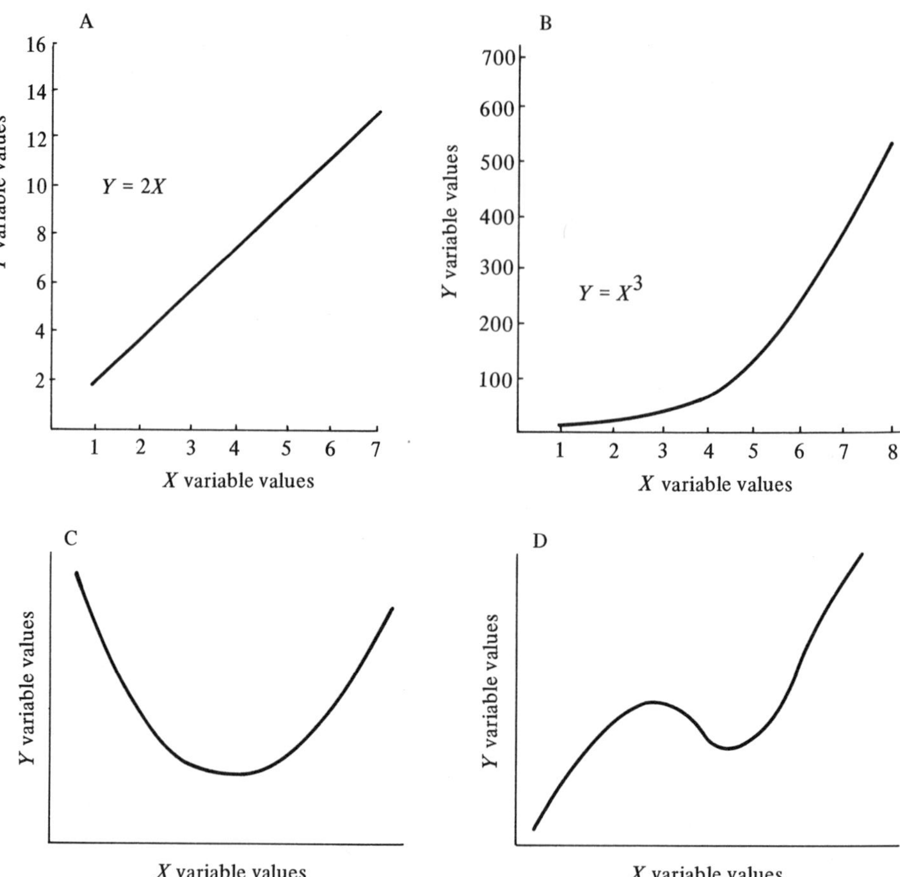

FIGURE 8–8

The relationship between variables X *and* Y *is linear in A and nonlinear in B, C, and D. (The curves in A and B both represent monotonic relationships between variables* X *and* Y. *The curves in C and D are nonmonotonic.)*

cally but not linearly related. An increase in X is accompanied by an increase in Y, but increasing the value of X by one unit is not accompanied by the same increase in the Y variable over the entire range of X values. Thus, a high rank-order correlation can be obtained if the two variables are monotonically related, even though they are not linearly related. It follows that investigators should not claim that two variables are *linearly* related just because a significant rank-order correlation is obtained. They *may* be linearly related, but many monotonic relationships are nonlinear. Neither of the correlational techniques discussed allows us to assess nonmonotonic relationships. A consideration of these is beyond the scope of this text. However, the use of scatter-plots will enable the investigator to gain a rough idea of these complex relationships between variables. For example, the scatter-plot in Figure 8-7D indicates that the variables are nonmonotonically related.

SUMMARY

There are four levels of measurement: nominal, ordinal, interval, and ratio. A nominal classification system is one in which the different categories are qualitatively related. An ordinal scale is one in which the scale values are quantitatively related, but the differences between successive values are not necessarily equal. An interval scale has the properties of an ordinal scale *and* the differences between successive scale values are equal. A ratio scale has all the properties of an interval scale plus an absolute zero. It is important to determine the level of measurement used, because the level of measurement determines how data can be described and evaluated.

There are two major sets of descriptive measures: measures of central tendency and measures of variability. The mode, median, and mean are measures of central tendency. The mode is the most frequently occurring score. The median is the value which divides the distribution in half after the scores are placed in ascending or descending rank order. The mean is the arithmetic average. The range, variance, and standard deviation are measures of variability. The range is the difference between the smallest and largest score. The variance is the average squared deviation from the mean. The standard deviation is the square root of the variance. Standard deviations are useful as units of measurement.

The type of descriptive measure that is computed and the way the data are reported depend on the level of measurement. If nominal data are obtained, the results can be described by indicating the number of individuals assigned to each category. If ordinal data are obtained, the results can frequently be described by indicating the number of experimental subjects above the median rank plus the results of an appropriate statistical test. If interval data are obtained, it is usually necessary to compute mean scores for each treatment. The mean scores can be reported in the text, in tables, or in figures. The use of tables and figures is warranted if there are a large number of means to report or if a table or figure would provide a clearer picture of the results. If a figure is used, the nature of the independent variable is an important consideration. Bar graphs are used for qualitative manipulations and line graphs for quantitative manipulations.

Correlations are extremely useful descriptive measures because they allow a precise indication of the extent to which two variables are related. The rank-order correlation and the product-moment correlation can be used to quantify the degree of relationship between two variables. The rank-order correlation is appropriate for ordinal data, the product-moment for interval data. The rank-order correlation indicates the degree to which two variables are monotonically related, the product-moment correlation the degree to which they are linearly related. Scatter-plots are a useful way to describe pictorially the relationship between two variables regardless of whether the relationship is monotonic or nonmonotonic.

QUESTIONS

1. What level of measurement is obtained in each of these examples? Why?
   a. Three hundred subjects are asked to give their political party preference: Republican, Democratic, or Independent.
   b. The thirty members of a class are rank ordered according to height. The shortest person is assigned the number 1; the second shortest, the number 2, and so on.
   c. A thirty-item questionnaire designed to measure altruism is administered to 100 people. A score from 1 to 30 is obtained for each person.
   d. The independent variable is whether subjects use the new "hair grower" scalp treatment. The dependent measure is the number of hairs in a square-inch patch on the top of each subject's head.
   e. A free association test is administered, and the amount of time each person takes to respond to each word is the performance measure. An average responding time is computed for each subject.
   f. Three judges rate twenty subjects on cooperation. Each judge rates each subject on a nine point scale from 1 (very uncooperative) to 9 (very cooperative). The median of the three judgments is used as the score for each subject.
2. Each of ten subjects was given a twenty-item current events test. The number of correct responses for each subject is given below. What are the mode, median, and mean scores? The scores are: 8, 13, 16, 14, 12, 13, 19, 6, 10, and 9.
3. What are the mode, median, and mean if the following scores are obtained: 14, 16, 16, 14, 16, 14, 14, 16, 14, 16?
4. What are the mode, median, and mean if the following scores are obtained: 18, 19, 3, 4, 8, 15, 2, 3, 3, 5? Is one measure of central tendency to be preferred over the others?
5. In Figure 8-2A would you expect the mean to be less than, equal to, or greater than the median? What would be the relationship between the mean and median for Figure 8-2B? Figure 8-2C?
6. Assume that you have the money and the inclination to sponsor a young golfer on the professional tour. Golfer A has a mean score of 72 and a standard deviation of four for 100 rounds. Golfer B has a mean score of 71.5 and a standard deviation of two for the same 100 rounds. Which golfer would you sponsor and why? There is no right or wrong answer to this question.
7. Compute the range, variance, and standard deviation for each set of scores given in Questions 2, 3, and 4.

8. What is the advantage of using the standard deviation as a unit of measurement?
9. Jane has taken two tests of self-esteem. On the first test she had a score of 25. The mean for the first test was 20 and the standard deviation was four. On the second test she scored 78. The mean for the second test was 70 and the standard deviation was nine. Which test indicates that Jane has higher self-esteem? Assume that the scores on both tests are normally distributed.
10. The results tabulated below were obtained in a learning experiment. Each subject was presented a list of fifteen common nouns and was asked to recall as many as possible. Five subjects were given a mnemonic system and five were left to their own devices. Describe the results. Compute the mean performance of each group for each trial and plot the results in a figure.

Mnemonic group

Subject number	*Trial 1*	*2*	*3*
1	10	12	15
2	12	15	15
3	9	9	13
4	15	15	15
5	13	14	15

Control group

Subject number	*Trial 1*	*2*	*3*
1	6	8	10
2	9	10	13
3	4	9	13
4	7	10	15
5	8	10	12

11. Each subject was rated on aggressiveness and on skill in playing bridge. The subjects were randomly selected from 300 members of a bridge club. Do a rank-order and a product-moment correlation. What do you have to do to the scores before computing a rank-order correlation? What size correlation would you expect if all 300 club members were used as subjects?

Subject number	*Bridge*	*Aggressiveness*
1	15	12
2	19	18
3	14	16
4	10	13
5	6	14
6	25	22
7	21	18
8	4	10
9	19	23
10	11	16

12. What size correlation would you obtain with the results on the following page? Does the variance of the aggression scores relative to the bridge scores influence the size of the correlation? Is it necessary to compute this correlation?

Subject number	*Bridge*	*Aggressiveness*
1	1	10
2	2	20
3	3	30
4	4	40
5	5	50
6	6	60
7	7	70
8	8	80
9	9	90
10	10	100

13. What size correlation would you obtain with the following results? Is it necessary to compute this correlation?

Subject number	*Bridge*	*Aggressiveness*
1	74	23
2	70	25
3	68	29
4	66	31
5	64	34
6	60	37
7	54	42
8	53	46
9	52	53
10	31	59

14. Assume that you test each of fifteen subjects, randomly selected from a larger population, on two different tests and then compute the correlation between the tests. Will the correlation you obtain be the same as if you had tested the whole population instead of a sample of fifteen? What would be your best guess of the relationship between the two variables, given that you only tested fifteen subjects? What should happen to the accuracy of the estimate of the population correlation as the sample size increases?
15. Assume that the two variables you are interested in (e.g., beauty and intelligence) are unrelated. That is, the real correlation is zero; the null hypothesis of no relationship between the variables is true. If you were to randomly select a sample of forty subjects, administer the tests, and compute the correlation, would you expect to obtain a correlation of zero? How would you describe your results if you were to repeat this procedure 100,000 times with a new sample each time? What would you call the distribution of results you obtain? How should the results be influenced by the size of the sample?
16. What factors are likely to influence the magnitude of a correlation?

statistical analysis of between-subject designs: nominal and ordinal data

The major purpose of the chapter is to consider the analysis of experiments in which between-subject designs are used and nominal or ordinal data are obtained. A between-subject analysis is used with random-groups designs and with subject variable manipulations. Matched-groups designs can be analyzed as between-subject or within-subject designs, depending on the procedure used in matching. The chapter begins with a consideration of the overall problem of selecting an appropriate statistical test. Then examples are given to demonstrate the use of the Chi Square, Median, and Wilcoxon-Mann-Whitney statistical tests. These tests are appropriate for between-subject designs in which nominal or ordinal data are obtained.

The purpose of Chapters 9 through 11 is to consider certain statistical tests for analyzing the results of experiments. Statistical tests allow investigators to determine whether a particular experimental outcome is a common or rare event if only chance is operating. The result of the statistical analysis can then be used to determine whether the null hypothesis should be rejected. Although some investigators may obtain only experimental results that are obviously common or obviously rare, thus rendering statistical tests unnecessary, most investigators in the social sciences have frequent use for statistical tests. Given that an investigator needs to perform a statistical test on a particular experimental result, the first task is to select an appropriate test.

SELECTING A STATISTICAL TEST

Selecting an appropriate test is crucial because only then will the results of the statistical analysis be meaningful. Note that the task is to select *an* appropriate test and not *the* appropriate test. It is often possible to use more than one test. Our goal, however, is not to discuss the relative merits of different statistical tests, but, instead, to provide a scheme for selecting an appropriate one. Then we will consider the steps involved in performing each of the selected tests.

The type of test that is appropriate depends on the type of design used and the level of measurement obtained. Since there are two main designs and three levels of measurement that are of interest to social scientists, there are six possible combinations of measurement level and design type. Given these six situations, the task is to select an appropriate statistical test for each. Such a selection is offered in Table 9-1. In order to use the table, the student should determine what kind of design was used and what level of measurement was obtained. For example, if a within-subject design was used and ordinal data were obtained, the Friedman Test would be suitable.

The structure of Table 9-1 should help the student to recall what he knows about the two major types of experimental design. A between-subject analysis is used with random-groups designs and with subject variable manipulations. In both of these cases it is necessary to compare the performance of different subjects in order to assess the effect of a manipulation. Thus, the comparison is between subjects. A matched-groups design can be analyzed as either a between-subject or within-subject design. If the matching is accomplished by equating the means and standard deviations of each group on the match-

TABLE 9–1

Statistical Tests for the Two Major Types of Experimental Design and Three Levels of Measurement Combinations

	Level of measurement		
Type of design	*Nominal*	*Ordinal*	*Interval*
Between-subject a. Random-groups b. Subject variables c. Matched-groups	Chi Square Test	Median Test or Wilcoxon-Mann-Whitney Test	Analysis of variance for between-subject designs
Within-subject a. Within-subject b. Matched-groups	Cochran Q Test	Friedman Test	Analysis of variance for within-subject designs

ing variable, then a between-subject analysis is used. If the matching is accomplished on a subject by subject basis, then a within-subject analysis is usually used.

The purpose of Chapter 9 is to consider the analysis of experiments in which between-subject designs are used and nominal or ordinal data are obtained. The analysis of between-subject designs with interval data is considered in Chapter 10, and the analysis of within-subject designs in Chapter 11. A study of these three chapters will provide the reader with an understanding of the statistical tests listed in Table 9-1. Chi Square is the first test discussed.

THE CHI SQUARE TEST

Obtained and Expected Frequencies

The Chi Square Test allows the investigator to assess whether the obtained frequencies in a set of categories differ significantly from the expected frequencies. The test is appropriate when each subject is placed in one and only one category. The obtained frequencies are the number of subjects placed in each category. The expected frequency in each category is generally determined by assuming that the variable of interest has no effect. That is, the expected frequencies are usually computed by accepting the null hypothesis. If the obtained frequencies are sufficiently different from the expected frequencies, then it is reasonable to conclude that the manipulation is in some way responsible for the difference.

Computation of Chi Square

The formula for computing the Chi Square is:

$$\chi^2 = \Sigma \frac{(O - E)^2}{E}$$

where O is the obtained frequency of a given category and E is the expected frequency. The actual computation is simple. The expected frequency is subtracted from the obtained frequency for each category; the difference is squared and divided by the expected frequency. This is done for each category. The Chi Square value is the sum of the values obtained with each category.

Evaluation of Chi Square

The next step is to determine whether the Chi Square value is large enough to permit rejection of the view that the observed results are attributable to chance. Note that as the discrepancy between the obtained and expected values increases, the value of χ^2 will increase. If the Chi Square value is significant, then the null hypothesis can be rejected. To assess the significance of the Chi Square, one must refer to a table of Chi Square values. However, since it is necessary to understand *degrees of freedom* to use the table of Chi Square values properly, we will first consider this question.

Degrees of Freedom. The degrees of freedom are calculated by determining the number of obtained category frequencies that are "free to vary" given that the total number of subjects is determined. For example, if the subjects are assigned to two categories there is one degree of freedom. Once the obtained frequency is determined for one category, it is determined for the other. Thus, only one category is free to vary and there is one degree of freedom. For current purposes, degrees of freedom can be defined as the number of categories in which the obtained frequencies are free to vary given that the size of the total sample is determined. Thus, if 100 people are assigned to three different categories there would be two degrees of freedom. Once the number of people in the first two categories is determined, the number in the third is determined. Only the frequencies in two of the categories are free to vary given that the total number of subjects is 100.

Chi Square Table. A table of Chi Square values is presented in Appendix C-2. The table values are based on Chi Square sampling distributions that would occur if only chance were operating. Given the Chi Square distribution, it is possible to determine the probability of obtaining a Chi Square of a particular magnitude. If only chance is operating, the probability of obtaining a large value for the Chi Square Test is less likely than obtaining a small value. For example, if there is one degree of freedom there is only one chance in 100 that a Chi Square value of 6.635 or greater will be obtained if only chance is operating. Since this result is unlikely, purely on the basis of chance, it is reasonable to conclude that the manipulation plus chance effects, and not just chance, are responsible for the obtained effect.

In general, the table value that is appropriate for evaluating a statistical test is determined by the significance level, degrees of freedom, and whether a one-tailed or two-tailed test is desired. The reader will probably remember from the discussion in Chapter 4 that in most cases two-tailed tests should be preferred over one-tailed tests. If a two-tailed test is used then the results can be evaluated regardless of their direction. For example, the investigator does not have to predict whether the experimental subjects will be better or worse than the control subjects, just that the independent variable will influence behavior. Table values are a little higher for two-tailed than one-tailed tests for any given significance level and degrees of freedom value.

All the values in the Chi Square table in Appendix C-2, however, are for two-tailed tests. This is because it is not meaningful to use a one-tailed test for a Chi Square value if there is more than one degree of freedom. Directional predictions are meaningless when there are more than two categories since the results can be in more than two directions. The use of the table is very simple. One selects a significance level (usually .05) and determines the appropriate degrees of freedom. Let us assume that there is one degree of freedom and the .05 significance level has been adopted. By referring to the table one can see that a value of 3.841 is needed to reject the null hypothesis at the .05 level of significance. If the obtained Chi Square value is greater than the table value, the null hypothesis is rejected; if it is less than the table value, the null hypothesis cannot be rejected. The use of examples should help to clarify the steps involved in using the Chi Square Test.

CHI SQUARE AND SUBJECT VARIABLES

The Chi Square Test can be used to evaluate subject variables and non-subject variables. The use of Chi Square to evaluate subject variables is very similar to the use of correctional techniques in that cause-effect conclusions are not warranted in either case.

Sex Education Example

Assume that an investigator is interested in the effectiveness of sex education courses in the schools. He believes that such courses should be an integral part of the curriculum. However, since he realizes that many parents object to having the school take this responsibility, he is attempting to obtain evidence for the importance of formal courses in sex education. Specifically, he sets out to determine whether unwed parents received adequate sex education relative to the general population of high school students. For the purposes of exposition, assume that a recent, properly conducted survey has revealed that only 50 percent of the high school students had accurate and reasonably complete information regarding sex.

The investigator obtains a random sample of 120 unwed parents (either unwed fathers or mothers) of high school age. Then the same procedure that was used in the earlier survey is used to determine whether each unwed parent had accurate and reasonably complete information regarding sex before becoming a parent. Since the earlier study indicated that 50 percent of the high school students had such information, the investigator assumes that the same percentage should be obtained for unwed parents if sex education is unrelated to being an unwed parent. The results of his investigation are presented in Table 9-2. The basic task was to sort the sample of 120 unwed parents into two categories: adequate sex education and inadequate sex education. If being an unwed parent is not related to adequate sex education, the expected frequency in each category should be 60.

The Chi Square Test is used to evaluate whether the obtained frequencies

TABLE 9-2

Obtained and Expected Frequencies of Adequate and Inadequate Sex Education for 120 Unwed Parents (fictitious data)

Sex education	
Adequate	*Inadequate*
Obtained = 40 Expected = 60	Obtained = 80 Expected = 60

Computation of the Chi Square value

$$\chi^2 = \Sigma \frac{(O - E)^2}{E}$$

$$\chi^2 = \frac{(40 - 60)^2}{E} + \frac{(80 - 60)^2}{E}$$

$$\chi^2 = \frac{(-20)^2}{60} + \frac{(20)^2}{60}$$

$$\chi^2 = 6.67 + 6.67$$

$$\chi^2 = 13.34$$

are significantly different from the expected frequencies. The level of measurement is nominal, and the subject variable is being an unwed parent or not being an unwed parent. The information from the earlier survey of high school students is used to predict the performance for the unwed parent. This is an instance of a subject variable manipulation since the purpose is to compare unwed parents with the general population of high school students.

Computation of Chi Square. The computation of the Chi Square is presented in Table 9-2. The expected frequency is subtracted from the obtained frequency for each category; the difference is squared and divided by the expected frequency. The same procedure is used for each category, and then the values obtained for each are summed. In this case the obtained Chi Square value is equal to 13.34. The next step is to evaluate this value.

Evaluation of Chi Square. The question is whether the Chi Square value of 13.34 is large enough so that the hypothesis that the observed results are attributable to chance can be rejected. If the Chi Square value is significant, then the results suggest that unwed parents differ from the general population of high school students with respect to the adequacy of their sex education. If the Chi Square value is not significant, then there is no reason to believe that this is so. The Chi Square value is assessed by referring to the table of Chi Square values in Appendix C-2.

There is one degree of freedom for the present example since there are two categories. An examination of the table reveals that a value of 3.841 is needed to reject the null hypothesis at the .05 level of significance with one degree of freedom. The use of the .05 level is somewhat arbitrary. Some investigators may prefer a more stringent (e.g., .01) or in rare cases a more lenient (e.g., .10) significance level. The factor to consider in adopting a significance level is whether you prefer to minimize the probability of making a Type 1 or a Type 2 error. If you decrease the probability of making one kind of error you increase the probability of making the other. Most investigators adopt the .05 significance level. Since the obtained Chi Square value of 13.34 is greater than the table value of 3.841, the null hypothesis is rejected. The results support the view that unwed parents are more likely to have had an inadequate sex education. Although investigators tend to select the .05 significance level, they usually report the highest significance level obtained simply because more information is conveyed when the highest level is reported. For example, if an investigator reports that a Chi Square is significant at the .01 level, it is, of course, also significant at the .05 level. The reverse is not true.

Interpretation of the Results. There are a few methodological weaknesses in the sex education study. It is necessary to assume that the unwed parents could accurately complete the survey using only knowledge they had at an earlier time and not rely on more recently acquired knowledge. It is also necessary to assume that demand characteristics are not an important factor. Unfortunately, this may not be a safe assumption. An unwed parent might reason that the only logical response to the survey is to claim an inadequate knowledge of sex; he might think that, otherwise, he would be taken for a fool to have gotten into this "predicament."

Even if these two assumptions are valid, it does not follow necessarily that an inadequate sex education increases the probability of becoming an unwed parent. Since a subject variable manipulation was made, it is incorrect to interpret the results in cause-effect terms. Inadequate sex education may be more common in the case of unwed parents than in the larger population of high school students, but this is not sufficient reason to infer a causal relationship. Yet, the attractiveness of the causal relationship hypothesis is increased by the fact that the subject variable manipulation data are consistent with it. The reader is reminded that the results in Table 9-2 are fictitious. They may not represent the true state of affairs.

Marital Adjustment Example

The Chi Square Test can be used to evaluate the relationship between two subject variables. Assume that you believe a satisfactory childhood has considerable influence on marital adjustment, and you decide to test your hypothesis. You develop one detailed questionnaire to assess the extent to which childhood experiences were pleasant and another to evaluate marital adjustment.

You do not have any elaborate theory about why the experiences of childhood should be related to marital happiness. Mostly it is gut level feeling you have about people. You believe that the child who has experienced such delights as playing mumbly peg, playing hopscotch, building a treehouse, collecting trading cards, flying a kite, chasing frogs, or tipping over a canoe is much better equipped for the problems of marriage than one who has spent a relatively dull childhood. A person who has had an enjoyable childhood has reason to be optimistic about the future. Perhaps you think back to the first time you "stole" cookies from the cookie jar, to your first trip to the circus, or to your first love. Surely, you reason, these experiences can be a continued source of pleasure in the adult years. Or, perhaps you believe that a person learns how to enjoy life early. You may believe that one has to learn how to laugh at oneself, how to relax, and how to turn an unpleasant event into a pleasant one by using wit — that a sense of humor is important and that its elements are acquired early. You test your view by classifying 450 people into nine different categories based on their early life experiences and marital adjustment.

The results of the experiment are presented in Table 9-3. The 450 individuals are placed in the nine mutually exclusive categories. Keep in mind that you are not concerned with the number of people who have poor, medium, or good marriages, nor with the number who have pleasant, average, or unpleasant childhoods. The number of people in each of these large categories is used as the starting point for assessing whether the two variables are related. That is, you are interested in the obtained, relative to the expected, frequencies in the nine categories in the body of the table, not in the frequencies in the margins (total for each row and column).

Calculating Expected Frequencies. In order to determine the expected frequency for each category in the body of the table, one needs to calculate the probability that an individual will be classified in each row *and* in each column, given that the row and column totals are determined. Rows go across the page; columns go down the page. If the two variables of interest are unrelated, then only chance should determine the obtained frequencies in each of the nine categories. There are two ways to compute the expected frequencies, a hard way and an easy way. The hard way is considered first.

TABLE 9–3

Obtained and Expected Frequencies for Each of the Nine Categories of Childhood Experiences and Marital Success. The Computation of the Chi Square Value Is Included (fictitious data)

Childhood experiences	***Marital success***			
	Poor	*Medium*	*Good*	***Row total***
Unpleasant	$O = 60$ $E = 33.33$	$O = 50$ $E = 50.00$	$O = 40$ $E = 66.67$	150
Average	$O = 30$ $E = 33.33$	$O = 60$ $E = 50.00$	$O = 60$ $E = 66.67$	150
Pleasant	$O = 10$ $E = 33.33$	$O = 40$ $E = 50.00$	$O = 100$ $E = 66.67$	150
Column total	100	150	200	450

Computation of the Chi Square value

$$\chi^2 = \Sigma \frac{(O - E)^2}{E}$$

$$\chi^2 = \frac{(60 - 33.33)^2}{33.33} + \frac{(50 - 50.00)^2}{50} + \frac{(40 - 66.67)^2}{66.67} + \frac{(30 - 33.33)^2}{33.33} + \frac{(60 - 50.00)^2}{50}$$

$$+ \frac{(60 - 66.67)^2}{66.67} + \frac{(10 - 33.33)^2}{33.33} + \frac{(40 - 50.00)^2}{50} + \frac{(100 - 66.67)^2}{66.67}$$

$$\chi^2 = 21.34 + 0 + 10.67 + .33 + 2.00 + .67 + 16.33 + 2.00 + 16.66$$

$$\chi^2 = 70.00$$

One way to compute each expected frequency is to use the fact that the probability of an event is the number of favorable events divided by the total number of possible events if only chance is operating. In this case the probability of an event in each of the three rows is equal to .333 (150 divided by 450); and the probabilities for the three columns are .222 (100 divided by 450), .333 (150 divided by 450), and .444 (200 divided by 450). Given the probability for each row and column, the probability for each category in the body of the table is obtained by multiplying the row probability by the column probability. That is, assuming that childhood experiences and marital success are unrelated, the probability that an individual will be placed in a particular category is equal to the probability of his being in the row of the particular category multiplied by the probability of his being in the column of the category. The interested reader can refer to Appendix A-1 for additional information about computing the joint probability of independent events. Finally, to get the expected frequency for each category, the probability for each is multiplied by the total frequency, in this case, 450.

The easy way to compute each expected frequency is simply to multiply the column total by the row total and divide by the total number of subjects. For example, to compute the expected frequency for the unpleasant childhood experiences and poor marital success cell, the row total of 150 is multiplied by the column total of 100 and the product is divided by 450, the total number of subjects. This way is far easier than the procedure discussed above and the result is exactly the same. The second procedure simply avoids the needless step of multiplying and dividing by the total number of subjects. Obviously, if one number (say, 50) is multiplied by another number (say, 150) and then divided by the same number (i.e., 150), the end result is the original number (i.e., 50). Thus, the second procedure saves needless computation. The more complicated procedure was presented to demonstrate that the expected frequencies are obtained by determining what is probable if only chance is operating. The student should, of course, use the simple way to obtain the expected frequencies in each cell.

Computing and Evaluating the Chi Square. The procedure for computing the Chi Square value is identical to that used for the earlier example. The computation is presented in Table 9-3. Following the computation of the Chi Square, the degrees of freedom should be determined, and then the table in Appendix C-2 should be used to obtain the appropriate table value. If the obtained Chi Square value is greater than the table value, then the null hypothesis should be rejected.

The problem of determining degrees of freedom for Chi Square causes little difficulty if you observe that the totals for the rows and columns are "fixed" (i.e., not free to vary). They do not provide information about the independence or dependence of the variables but, instead, are only the starting points for assessing independence or dependence. They are fixed. Therefore, it is easy to compute the number of degrees of freedom simply by counting the number of obtained category frequencies that are free to vary. In the present example, only four cell frequencies are free to vary; the others are determined. Therefore, there are four degrees of freedom. The reader who does not see that there are only four degrees of freedom should prepare a few Chi Square tables similar to the one in Table 9-3. Fill in the totals for each row and column and then fill in the "obtained" category frequencies. If you do this, you should soon prove to yourself that you have four degrees of freedom; i.e., once you have filled in obtained values for four of the cells, the values in the rest are determined. If you compute the degrees of freedom for tables having different numbers of categories, you should soon realize that the number of degrees of freedom for a Chi Square with two variables is always equal to the number of rows minus one times the number of columns minus one.

After computing the degrees of freedom and the Chi Square it is a simple matter to refer to the Chi Square table in Appendix C-2 to find that the obtained value of 70.00 is significant at the .01 level since it exceeds the table value of 13.28. Thus, the null hypothesis of independence is rejected. It appears that childhood experiences and marital success are related. Once again, since subject variables were manipulated, it is incorrect to conclude that the relationship is causal. If the variables of interest are subject variables then correlational techniques can also be used. For example, one could compute a correlation between marital success and childhood happiness using the scores on the questionnaires, or by performing the Chi Square Test that has just been presented.

Since the two examples demonstrating the use of Chi Square have involved classifying individuals on the basis of subject variables, let us consider examples which involve nonsubject variable manipulations. Chi Square is an extremely useful tool for many different purposes, so the student should not get the mistaken impression that its use is limited to subject variable manipulations.

CHI SQUARE AND NONSUBJECT VARIABLES

Political Views Example

The use of the Chi Square Test is essentially the same regardless of whether a subject or nonsubject variable is manipulated. Assume that an investigator with considerable wealth and resources wants to assess whether it is possible to persuade people to become socialists, moderates, or conservatives. He believes there are at least two important aspects to influencing political opinions and voting behavior: indoctrinating subjects in the arguments for a particular position and reinforcing them for holding it. He tests this view by investigating the effects on subsequent political behaviors of a two year indoctrination program. Three different programs are used, each designed to produce either socialists, moderates, or conservatives. The reader can decide what might be the best curriculum and reward structure for such programs and can wrestle with the ethical issues of whether such indoctrination should be undertaken.

Design and Procedures. A group of 300 adults is obtained, from all walks of life, between the ages of eighteen and forty. The subjects are randomly assigned to three groups with the restriction that there are 100 subjects in each group and that married couples are assigned to the same group. That is, a random-groups design is used. The subjects are well paid for serving in the experiment. During the two year experimental manipulation the investigator has virtually complete control over everything the subjects read, whom they are allowed to converse with, what they are praised for, and so on.

Following the indoctrination period the subjects do not receive any further monetary reward. Ten years after the termination of the program, judges unaware of the purpose of the experiment classify each subject as a socialist, moderate, or conservative. The principal concern is whether the political views that the subjects hold after ten years were influenced by the indoctrination program they received.

Calculating and Evaluating the Chi Square. The results of the experiment are presented in Table 9-4. The evaluation procedure is essentially identical to that used for the last example. It is necessary to compute an expected frequency for each category and then determine whether the obtained frequencies are significantly different. This is done, of course, by computing a Chi Square. The calculations for the Chi Square are also included in Table 9-4. To evaluate whether the Chi Square is statistically significant, the table in Appendix C-2 is used to determine whether the obtained value exceeds the table value for four degrees of freedom and the significance level (say, .05) that is adopted. In this case the Chi Square value of 2.72 is less than the table value of 9.488, so it is not possible to reject the null hypothesis. There is no support for the view that one can change political views over a ten year period with the indoctrination programs employed. If the Chi Square had been significant, the differences in political opinion could have been attributed to the independent variable.

The Median Test — Vitamin C Example

The Median Test can be used to evaluate between-subject designs when ordinal data are obtained. It requires, however, that the ordinal data be treated like nominal data since the Median Test is a special application of the Chi Square Test. A single example should be sufficient to familiarize the student with this test. Assume that an investigator is interested in the effect of Vitamin C on general health.

Experimental Method. The investigator is particularly concerned with

TABLE 9–4

The Number of Obtained and Expected Frequencies in Each Political Category for the Subjects Who Received Each Political Indoctrination Program (The computation of the Chi Square value is included – fictitious data)

Type of indoctrination program	*Ten years after indoctrination*			*Row total*
	Socialist	*Moderate*	*Conservative*	
Socialist	$O = 25$ $E = 30$	$O = 42$ $E = 40$	$O = 33$ $E = 30$	100
Moderate	$O = 35$ $E = 30$	$O = 36$ $E = 40$	$O = 29$ $E = 30$	100
Conservative	$O = 30$ $E = 30$	$O = 42$ $E = 40$	$O = 28$ $E = 30$	100
Column total	90	120	90	300

Computation of the Chi Square value

$$\chi^2 = \Sigma \frac{(O - E)^2}{E}$$

$$\chi^2 = \frac{(25 - 30)^2}{30} + \frac{(42 - 40)^2}{40} + \frac{(33 - 30)^2}{30} + \frac{(35 - 30)^2}{30} + \frac{(36 - 40)^2}{40}$$

$$+ \frac{(29 - 30)^2}{30} + \frac{(30 - 30)^2}{30} + \frac{(42 - 40)^2}{40} + \frac{(28 - 30)^2}{30}$$

$$\chi^2 = .83 + .10 + .30 + .83 + .40 + .03 + 0 + .10 + .13$$

$$\chi^2 = 2.72$$

whether or not Vitamin C helps to prevent colds, so cold symptoms are given a high weighting by the judges who assess the general health of each subject. Thirty army recruits in basic training, who volunteered for the experiment, are randomly assigned to two groups with the restriction that there be fifteen subjects in each group. Each subject in the Experimental Group takes massive doses of Vitamin C each day for a three month period. Each subject in the Control Group takes massive doses of a placebo.

The dependent measure is the general health of the subjects for the three months during which experimental subjects take Vitamin C. The judges, who are unaware of the condition each subject is in, rank order the subjects on the basis of general health for the entire three month period. The rank of 1 is assigned to the subject with the best health, the rank of 30 to the subject with the worst health. Initially, the experimenter hoped it would be possible to rank order the thirty subjects without allowing ties, but the judges, after several attempts to make fine discriminations, decide that ties are permissible.

Results. The rank ordering of the thirty subjects is presented in Table 9-5. Although each subject's score is a rank in this particular experiment, it is not necessary to rank order subjects directly on the dependent measure in order to use the Median Test. That is, one could obtain a score for each subject and then rank order the scores. In any case, it is necessary to arrive at one overall ranking of the thirty subjects. Given the results in Table 9-5, the problem is to decide whether the results should be attributed to chance or to the effect of the manipulation.

Computing and Evaluating the Chi Square. One way to assess the significance of the results is to use the Chi Square Test. The results can be analyzed in about the same way as if nominal data had been obtained. About the only difference is that it is necessary to categorize subjects on the basis of their group (experimental or control) and on whether they are above or below the median rank. Then there will be four categories for the thirty subjects. Each subject can be counted in only one of the four.

The obtained and expected frequencies in each category are presented in Table 9-6. The Chi Square value is computed in exactly the same way that it is for nominal data. After computing the Chi Square value and determining the degrees of freedom, the table in Appendix C-2 is used to assess whether the obtained value (with one degree of freedom) is large enough to reject the null hypothesis. In this case the Chi Square value of 6.53 is greater than

TABLE 9–5

The Rank for Each Subject in the Experimental (E) and Control (C) Conditions for the Vitamin C Experiment (fictitious data)

Subject	*Condition*	*Rank*	*Subject*	*Condition*	*Rank*
A. B.	E	1	R. M.	E	16
T. B.	E	2	C. B.	C	17
C. S.	C	3	P. D.	E	18
K. P.	E	4.5	C. W.	C	19
L. W.	E	4.5	G. C.	E	20
S. B.	C	6	D. H.	C	21
W. C.	E	7	R. F.	E	22
C. C.	E	8	K. Z.	C	23
J. K.	E	9	J. F.	C	24
F. S.	C	10.5	J. P.	C	25
E. T.	E	10.5	L. W.	C	26
J. D.	C	12	L. S.	C	27
B. B.	E	13	J. M.	C	28
A. D.	E	14	A. M.	C	29
G. D.	E	15	R. R.	C	30

TABLE 9–6

The Obtained and Expected Frequencies for the Four Categories in the Experiment on the Effect of Vitamin C on General Health (The computation of the Chi Square is included – fictitious data)

	General health		
Condition	*Above median*	*Below median*	***Row total***
Vitamin C (Experimental)	$O = 11$ $E = 7.5$	$O = 4$ $E = 7.5$	15
Control	$O = 4$ $E = 7.5$	$O = 11$ $E = 7.5$	15
Column total	15	15	30

Computation of the Chi Square value

$$\chi^2 = \Sigma \frac{(O - E)^2}{E}$$

$$\chi^2 = \frac{(11 - 7.5)^2}{7.5} + \frac{(4 - 7.5)^2}{7.5} + \frac{(4 - 7.5)^2}{7.5} + \frac{(11 - 7.5)^2}{7.5}$$

$$\chi^2 = 1.633 + 1.633 + 1.633 + 1.633$$

$$\chi^2 = 6.532$$

the table value (3.841) with one degree of freedom and the .05 level of significance, so the null hypothesis is rejected. It appears that Vitamin C has a tendency to improve health. The reader should remember that the results are fictitious.

Hopefully, the student now understands how to compute a Chi Square and evaluate it for statistical significance. If you do much research in the social sciences you are very likely to use the Chi Square sooner or later. It is probably used as much as any other single statistical tool. It is one of the few good tools for analyzing nominal data. Another reason for its popularity is that it is relatively easy to compute and evaluate. Even though the use of the Chi Square is generally straightforward, there are some pitfalls to be avoided in using this tool.

RESTRICTIONS ON THE USE OF CHI SQUARE

There are three restrictions to be aware of in using the Chi Square Test. First, the test is appropriate only if the frequency measures are independent.

In simplest terms this means that only one measure is obtained for each subject. Each individual can be placed in one and only one category. Secondly, the data must be in frequency form. There is little problem with this restriction as long as the Chi Square Test is understood to be appropriate when individuals are assigned to categories. The data of interest are the number of individuals assigned to each.

The third limitation is that the test should not be used if the expected frequencies are too small. What is considered too small will vary somewhat with the number of variables and the total number of subjects. In any case, the test can be used with confidence as long as none of the expected frequencies is equal to or less than five. If there are expected frequencies of less than five, then the number of subjects should be increased so that the expected frequencies increase. Or, it may be possible to combine categories so that those which have expected frequencies of less than five are eliminated. If neither of these options is suitable then another test of significance (e.g., Fisher-Yates Exact Probability Test) should be used. The student who wants to use another test should refer to other textbooks on statistics (e.g., Kolstoe, 1973). The next task is to consider the Wilcoxon-Mann-Whitney Test.

WILCOXON-MANN-WHITNEY TEST

A disadvantage to the use of the Chi Square Test (Median Test) when ordinal data are obtained is that all the available information is not used since the relatively crude classification of above versus below the median is employed. Any two ranks above the median count the same, and any two ranks below the median count the same. That is, ordinal data are treated like nominal data. The Wilcoxon-Mann-Whitney Test takes into account the differences between ranks on the same side of the median.

Computational Steps

Let us return to the example of the effect of Vitamin C on general health and use the Wilcoxon-Mann-Whitney Test. The first step is to obtain a rank ordering of the subjects similar to that in Table 9-5. The principal concern is the sum of the ranks for the experimental subjects and for the control subjects. The sum of each of these ranks is presented in Table 9-7. You should compute the sum of the ranks for each group and then select the smaller sum. In this case the sum of the ranks for the Experimental Group is selected because it is less than the sum for the Control Group.

The two groups have the same number of subjects so it is reasonable to expect that the sums should be about the same if only chance is operating. As one sum decreases the other must increase because together they must equal the sum for all the subjects regardless of group. Since the two sums are directly related, the results of a two-group experiment can be evaluated by considering the sum of ranks for just one group. That is, the effect of the

TABLE 9–7

The Sum of the Ranks for the Experimental and Control Subjects for the Results Presented in Table 9–5

	Experimental	*Control*
	1	3
	2	6
	4.5	10.5
	4.5	12
	7	17
	8	19
	9	21
	10.5	23
	13	24
	14	25
	15	26
	16	27
	18	28
	20	29
	22	30
Sum	164.5	300.5

manipulation can be assessed by considering the magnitude of the sum of ranks for one group. The issue is whether the smaller sum is small enough that the obtained results would be a rare event if only chance were operating.

To reiterate, the task is to obtain a rank ordering of the subjects and compute the sum of the ranks for each group and then take the smaller sum. The next step is to evaluate this sum to see whether it is small enough that it is reasonable to conclude that something other than chance is operating.

Evaluating the Test

The smaller sum is evaluated by referring to Appendix C-3. In order to determine the appropriate table value you must decide on a level of significance (say, .05) and determine the number of subjects in each group (in this case fifteen). If the two groups are of unequal size, then you must refer to the appropriate *column* for the smaller group and the appropriate *row* for the larger group. If the groups are the same size then, of course, it doesn't make any difference. For the present example the correct table value is 184 for the .05 level of significance and fifteen subjects per group.

If the smaller of the two group sums is *equal to or less than* the table value, the null hypothesis is rejected. In this case the null hypothesis is rejected since the obtained sum of 164.5 is less than 184. Thus, the Wilcoxon-Mann-

Whitney Test is consistent with the Median Test in revealing that the probability of obtaining these results by chance is less than .05. On the basis of chance a value smaller than the table value should be obtained about five times in one hundred attempts. Since this is an unlikely event, it is reasonable to conclude that the results are not attributable to chance. The investigator can conclude that the manipulation was responsible for the obtained difference between groups.

Characteristics of the Test

The Wilcoxon-Mann-Whitney Test is relatively easy to compute and evaluate for significance. The table which is used to evaluate the obtained sum of ranks for the smaller of the two samples is appropriate only if each group has twenty or fewer subjects. This should not be a problem, however, because it is unlikely that you will have more than twenty subjects in one group. If you do, you can refer to Kruskal and Wallis (1952) to learn how to evaluate the sum of ranks for larger groups. Also, note that the obtained value must be smaller than the appropriate table value in order to be significant. This is unusual as in most significance tests the obtained value has to be larger than the table value to be significant.

If there are many tied scores the value of the sum of ranks may be affected. Obviously, tied scores will not have any effect when the subjects with the tied scores are in the same group, since the ranks are summed for each group. However, when the ties are between groups, this tends to decrease the smaller sum of ranks and, therefore, increases the likelihood of rejecting the null hypothesis. When there are many tied ranks between groups you may want to adopt a more stringent significance level (say, the .01 instead of the .05) or resolve the ties in the way that affords a more conservative test of the research hypothesis. For example, if you have predicted that the experimental subjects will have lower ranks than the control subjects, in the case of a between-group tie you should give the control subject the lower of the two ranks and the experimental subject the higher, instead of giving both subjects the average.

If there are more than two treatments to be compared and each subject obtains a score on some ordinal measure, it is possible to use the Wilcoxon-Mann-Whitney Test. However, only two conditions can be compared at the same time. If there are a number of treatments to compare (e.g., five separate comparisons), it is usually a good idea to adopt a stringent significance level so that the significance level per experiment is not too lenient. For example, if five comparisons are made and the .05 level is used for each, then the significance level for the entire experiment is five times .05 or .25, whereas if the .01 level is used for each comparison, then the significance level for the entire experiment is still only .05. Many investigators prefer to use the more stringent significance level when making multiple comparisons.

At this point you have the tools to evaluate between-subject design experiments yielding nominal and ordinal data. The next task is to consider the evaluation of between-subject design experiments yielding interval data.

SUMMARY

The type of statistical test that is appropriate depends on the type of design and the level of measurement obtained. Appropriate tests for the six major combinations of measurement level and design type are presented in Table 9-1.

The Chi Square Test is used to analyze between-subject designs in which nominal data are obtained. The basic task is to determine whether the obtained frequencies in a set of categories differ significantly from the expected frequencies. Expected frequencies are calculated by assuming the null hypothesis is true.

Chi Square value is computed by subtracting the expected frequency from the obtained frequency for a category, squaring the difference, and dividing by the expected frequency. This is done for each category. The Chi Square value is the sum of the values obtained for each category. The obtained Chi Square is evaluated by comparing it with the appropriate value in the Chi Square table. If the obtained value exceeds the table value, the Chi Square is significant.

The Median Test is a special application of the Chi Square Test. All subjects are rank ordered and then split into two categories, above the median and below the median. A Chi Square Test is used to determine whether the number of experimental subjects above the median is greater or less than what can be expected on the basis of chance.

There are three restrictions on the use of the Chi Square Test. The test is appropriate only if frequency measures are independent. The data must be in frequency form. And the test should not be used if the expected frequencies are too small.

The Wilcoxon-Mann-Whitney Test is appropriate for between-subject designs in which ordinal data are obtained. Like the Median Test, this test is only appropriate for evaluating two conditions at a time. All subjects are rank ordered and the sum of ranks for both groups is obtained. The smaller sum is then evaluated by comparing it with the appropriate table value. If the obtained sum is smaller than the table sum, the results are significant.

QUESTIONS

1. Determine the expected frequency for each category (cell) in the table on the next page. In determining the expected frequencies you assume, of course, that the two variables are unrelated. There are 400 subjects in this experiment.

Variable #2	*Variable #1* Poor	Good	
A			100
B			150
C			150
	100	300	

2. A sample of fifty Democrats, fifty Republicans, and fifty Independents is obtained to check the view that wealth and political preference are related. An annual income of $18,000 is used as the criterion of wealth. It is possible to classify each individual according to political party and income. Each can be placed in one category only. Do a Chi Square Test to determine if the two variables are related.

Wealth	*Political Party* Republicans	Democrats	Independents
Below $18,000	$O = 15$	$O = 30$	$O = 25$
Above $18,000	$O = 35$	$O = 20$	$O = 25$

3. Is there any similarity between deciding whether two subjects variables are related by using a Chi Square Test and computing a correlation between the two subject variables?
4. Let us assume you assess the effects of violence in films on aggression for males and females. You select a sample of 100 males and 100 females. You randomly assign subjects to the violent film and nonviolent film conditions such that there are 50 males and 50 females in the two treatment conditions. You obtain the results given below. Do a Chi Square to determine if the treatment has an effect. Since you are only interested in the effect of the treatment, you should combine the results for males and females before computing the Chi Square. Thus, the obtained values in the four cells are 55, 45, 10, and 90.

	Sex *Males* *Aggression*		*Females* *Aggression*	
	Increased	*No change*	*Increased*	*No change*
Violent Film	$O = 45$	$O = 5$	$O = 10$	$O = 40$
Nonviolent Film	$O = 5$	$O = 45$	$O = 5$	$O = 45$

5. Do a Chi Square for the male subjects only. Does the treatment have an effect? Do a Chi Square for the female subjects only. Does the treatment have an effect?

6. What are the limitations of the Chi Square Test?
7. Let us assume that you want to evaluate a new program of instruction. You randomly assign twelve subjects to the treatment (experimental) condition and twelve to the control condition. After the treatment, judges who are not aware of the treatment manipulation rank order the subjects according to their performance on a criterion test. You obtain the results given below. Did the treatment have an effect? Use the Median Test to evaluate your results.

Subject	*Condition*	*Rank*
a	E	1
b	E	2
c	E	3
d	C	4
e	E	5
f	C	6
g	E	7
h	E	8
i	C	9
j	C	10
k	E	11
l	E	12
m	E	13
n	E	14
o	E	15
p	C	16
q	E	17
r	C	18
s	C	19
t	C	20
u	C	21
v	C	22
w	C	23
x	C	24

8. Repeat the above analysis, but this time use the Wilcoxon-Mann-Whitney Test.

statistical analysis of between-subject designs: interval data

The purpose of this chapter is to consider the analysis of experiments in which interval data are obtained and between-subject designs are used. The logic of analysis of variance is presented. Then there is a discussion of the steps involved in computing an analysis of variance for an experiment in which one independent variable is manipulated. The same procedure is used for an experiment in which two independent variables are manipulated. The chapter ends with a discussion of the assumptions of the analysis of variance test.

The major goal of this chapter is to explain how analysis of variance can be used with experiments in which interval data are obtained and between-subject analysis is appropriate. The analysis of variance is a particularly useful tool at both a methodological and a statistical level. The student who knows the logic of the analysis of variance is better able to understand the consequences of particular design and procedural decisions.

It is unfortunate that the approach in many introductory statistics courses is to introduce students to the *t*-test. After students have some understanding of this test, they may be exposed to the analysis of variance. The fact is, however, that analysis of variance can be used to perform all the functions of the *t*-test and many more. The student who understands the analysis of variance with relatively simple designs should have little difficulty learning the few additional steps necessary to handle more complicated designs. This is not true for the *t*-test. The *t*-test is a dead end in the sense that it is not useful for analyzing complex designs. It should be helpful to repeat the logic of the analysis of variance before we consider the steps involved in using this test.

LOGIC OF THE ANALYSIS OF VARIANCE

Obtaining Two Estimates of Population Variance

The crux of the analysis of variance with a random-groups design is to obtain two independent estimates of population variance. The subjects who are tested or observed comprise the sample. The sample is usually a small portion of the subjects that could have been selected. The larger group of potential subjects is called the population. Variance is a measure indicating the extent to which scores differ. One estimate of population variance is based on within-group variance, the other on between-group variance.

Within-Group Variance. The variance of each group is an estimate of population variance so there are as many estimates as there are groups. However, it is necessary to obtain a single estimate based on the variance within each sample. Therefore, an average of the sample variances is the best within-group estimate of population variance. The within-group variance measure increases as the fluctuations between subjects in the same group increase.

Between-Group Variance. The other estimate of population variance is based on group means. If the null hypothesis is true, then the group means can be considered a distribution of sample means from the same population. This distribution of sample means can be used to obtain another estimate of population variance. Since the second estimate is based on group means, it is a between-group estimate. That is, the first estimate of population variance is influenced by fluctuations *within* each group and the second, which is based on means, by fluctuations *between* groups (between means). A proof that two independent estimates of population variance can be obtained, one based on within-group and the other on between-group variance, is presented in Appendix A-2. The interested reader should read this chapter first as a prerequisite for understanding the proof.

Comparing the Two Variance Estimates

The two estimates of population variance can be compared to assess the effect of the independent variable. If only chance is operating, i.e., if the null hypothesis is true, the two estimates should be about the same. However, if the independent variable has an effect, then there should be greater differences between the group means than if there were no effect. The reason for this is simple enough. If the independent variable does not have an effect, then the group means are all estimates of the same population mean. However, if it does have an effect, the group means will not all be estimates of the same mean because the manipulation will result in an increase or decrease in the Experimental Group mean. Thus, the between-group fluctuations will increase when the independent variable has an effect, but there is no reason to expect within-group fluctuations to increase.

The crux of the analysis of variance test is to compare the between-group and within-group estimates of population variance. If the two are about the same, then there is no reason to reject the null hypothesis. If the between-group is considerably larger than the within-group estimate, then the null hypothesis can be rejected.

ANALYSIS OF VARIANCE WITH ONE INDEPENDENT VARIABLE

The steps involved in using the analysis of variance to evaluate the effect of an independent variable can be demonstrated by considering an example. Assume that an investigator is interested in how a person's willingness to buy is influenced by the aggressiveness of the salesman. The investigator plays the role of a salesman and measures the effect of his degree of assertiveness on sales. The independent variable is whether he plays his role with a low, medium, or high degree of aggressiveness when making the sales pitch (with "information content" of the sales pitch equated for the three roles). Thirty prospective customers are randomly assigned to the three conditions with the restriction that there be ten subjects in each group. The effectiveness of each treatment is measured by the total dollar value of the sales to each customer.

The results of the experiment are presented in Table 10-1. The task is to

TABLE 10–1

The Total Dollar Value of Each Sale for the Ten Subjects in the Three Experimental Conditions (fictitious data)

	Low aggressiveness	Medium aggressiveness	High aggressiveness
	9	21	36
	11	23	32
	5	24	30
	17	15	25
	13	22	32
	10	26	37
	12	19	27
	11	20	33
	15	18	29
	12	21	31
ΣX	115	209	312
ΣX^2	1419	4457	9858

determine whether the different sales pitches influenced sales. The analysis of variance is an appropriate statistical test. A random-groups design was used and interval data were obtained. We will consider some basic terminology before doing the actual computation.

Sum of Squares

The basic task in performing an analysis of variance for this type of experiment is to compute the sum of squares total (SS_{tot}), the sum of squares between groups (SS_{bg}), and the sum of squares within groups (SS_{wg}). The task is simplified somewhat in that the SS_{tot} is equal to the SS_{bg} plus the SS_{wg}. Thus, given two values, the third can be obtained by subtraction. The term *sum of squares* is a short form of the term *sum of squared deviations from the mean.* There are two ways to obtain the values we are interested in. One way is to use the deviation formulae. For example, in order to obtain the SS_{tot} by the deviation method, the overall mean is subtracted from each score, each difference is squared, and all of the squared difference scores are added. Another way is to use computational formulae to obtain the three values.

The use of the deviation method is a good way to understand what the computation of the analysis of variance is all about in that the deviations are obtained directly. However, this method is cumbersome in that the means are rarely whole numbers, and, therefore, the computation of squared deviation scores is usually laborious. We will use the computational formulae, which are much easier to handle, particularly if a calculator is available. If, after reading this chapter, you want to work through an example with the deviation formulae, refer to Appendix A-4. If you want to convince yourself that the deviation and computational formulae are comparable, refer to Appendix A-5. Or, if you want to examine the proof for the assertion that the $SS_{tot} = SS_{bg} + SS_{wg}$, refer to Appendix A-3.

Let us now perform an analysis of variance on the data in Table 10-1. Again, the basic task is to compute the SS_{tot}, the SS_{bg} and the SS_{wg}. Since we will be working with group totals and the sum of the squared scores, you may prefer to obtain these values before considering the three formulae. If you refer to Table 10-1, you will see that the total for each group and the sum of the squared scores for each group have been calculated. The overall total can be obtained by adding the group totals.

Computation of the Sum of Squares Total. The first step is to compute the SS_{tot}. The formula for the computation of SS_{tot} is:

$$SS_{tot} = \Sigma\Sigma X^2 - \frac{(T)^2}{N}$$

The summation signs mean that you perform the adding operations; the numbers denoted by the symbol following the summation signs are added. The X in the formula refers to any score. In this case each score is squared and then all the squared scores are added. It is important to note that the scores are squared *before* they are added. There are two summation signs because the squared scores in each group are added and then the group totals are added (i.e., this can be regarded as two separate adding operations). If all the scores are squared and added, the obtained value is 15,734. The T in the formula refers to the total for all the scores. The total is squared and then divided by N. The N in the formula refers to the total number of scores, in this case 30. The computation of the SS_{tot} is presented in Table 10-2. The next step is to compute the SS_{bg}.

Computation of the Sum of Squares Between Groups. The formula for the SS_{bg} is:

$$SS_{bg} = \Sigma \frac{(\text{group total})^2}{n} - \frac{(T)^2}{N}$$

The small n is the symbol for the number of scores in each group. In words, the formula means that each group total is squared and divided by the number of scores in that group. Since the formulae presented are appropriate only for analyzing experiments in which there are the same number of subjects in each group, each total can be squared, the obtained values summed, and the sum divided by the number of subjects in each group. The last term in the formula is identical to the last term in the formula for the SS_{tot}. Since this value has already been computed, it is not necessary to do it again. The computation of SS_{bg} for our example is presented in Table 10-2.

Computation of the Sum of Squares Within Groups. The computation of the

TABLE 10–2

Computation of the Analysis of Variance for the Data Presented in Table 10–1

$$SS_{tot} = \Sigma\Sigma X^2 - \frac{(T)^2}{N}$$

$$SS_{tot} = 15,734 - \frac{(636)^2}{30}$$

$$SS_{tot} = 2,250.80$$

$$SS_{bg} = \Sigma \frac{(group\ total)^2}{n} - \frac{(T)^2}{N}$$

$$SS_{bg} = \frac{(115)^2 + (209)^2 + (312)^2}{10} - \frac{(636)^2}{30}$$

$$SS_{bg} = \frac{154,250}{10} - \frac{(636)^2}{30}$$

$$SS_{bg} = 1941.80$$

$$SS_{wg} = SS_{tot} - SS_{bg}$$

$$SS_{wg} = 2,250.80 - 1941.80$$

$$SS_{wg} = 309.00$$

or

$$SS_{wg} = \left[1,419 - \frac{(115)^2}{10}\right] + \left[4,457 - \frac{(209)^2}{10}\right] + \left[9,858 - \frac{(312)^2}{10}\right]$$

$$SS_{wg} = 96.5 + 88.9 + 123.6$$

$$SS_{wg} = 309.00$$

SS_{wg} is very easy since the value can be obtained by subtracting the SS_{bg} from the SS_{tot}. This follows because the $SS_{tot} = SS_{bg} + SS_{wg}$. You may object to this procedure because you lack confidence that the SS_{tot} and SS_{bg} were computed correctly. Obviously, if a mistake is made in computing the SS_{tot} or the SS_{bg} it is not possible to obtain the correct SS_{wg} by subtraction. Thus, it is a good idea to compute the SS_{wg} directly as well. If the results are the same with both methods, you can proceed with confidence. To compute the SS_{wg} directly, each group is taken individually and a SS_{tot} is computed for that group only. After this is done for all the groups, the values that were obtained are summed. The total is equal to the SS_{wg}. If the work is done correctly, the SS_{tot} will be equal to the SS_{bg} plus the SS_{wg}. The computation of the SS_{wg} by the subtraction method and the direct method is presented in Table 10-2. The reader should note that the sum of squares can be zero (e.g., all groups have identical means), but never negative. A negative sum of squares indicates a mistake.

Analysis of Variance Table

Source of Variance. The next step is to prepare the analysis of variance table. This provides a convenient way to arrive at the estimates of population variance and compare the estimates. An analysis of variance table for our example is presented in Table 10-3. The first column is labeled *source.* This is shorthand for *source of variance.* Recall that there are two independent estimates of population variance, one based on within-group variance, the other on between-group variance; these are the two sources.

Degrees of Freedom. The second column is labeled *degrees of freedom (df).* The degrees of freedom for analysis of variance can be understood in about the same way as degrees of freedom for the Chi Square. The task is to determine the number of scores that are free to vary given that the total is determined. To determine the degrees of freedom for between groups, each group total and the overall total are considered. Given that the overall total is fixed, all the group totals except one are free to vary. Thus, the degrees of freedom between groups is one less than the number of groups. Since the symbol k is used to denote the number of groups, the degrees of freedom for between groups is $k-1$.

To compute the degrees of freedom for within groups, it is necessary to consider the number of scores in each group and the group total. Given that the group total is fixed, all the scores in each group except one are free to vary. Thus, the degrees of freedom for each group is one less than the number of

TABLE 10-3

Analysis of Variance Table for the Experiment in Which the Effect of Aggressiveness on Selling Was Assessed

Source	df	SS	MS	F
Between-groups	2	1,941.80	970.90	84.87
Within-groups	27	309.00	11.44	
Total	29	2,250.80		

subjects in each group. If n is used to denote the number of subjects in each group, then the degrees of freedom for each group is equal to $n-1$. Since there are k different groups, the number of degrees of freedom for within groups is equal to $k(n-1)$, given that there are the same number of subjects in each group. The degrees of freedom for SS_{tot} is equal to the total number of scores minus one. The degrees of freedom for between groups plus within groups should equal the degrees of freedom for SS_{tot}.

The SS, MS, *and* F *Columns.* The third column is for the sum of squares. Since these values have already been determined, it is only necessary to record them in the table.

The fourth column is labeled *mean square* (MS). The mean square is obtained by taking the SS for each effect, in this case the between groups and within groups, and dividing by the degrees of freedom for that effect. Assuming that only chance is operating, each mean square is an independent estimate of population variance. If the independent variable manipulation had an effect, the between-group mean square should be larger than the within-group mean square.

The two are compared by dividing the between-group mean square by the within-group mean square. The value obtained is called an F value. The F value is recorded in the fifth column of the analysis of variance table. (The value is labeled F after Sir Ronald Fisher who is largely responsible for developing the analysis of variance significance test.) In this case the F value is recorded in the between-group row because the size of the F is used to assess whether the differences between groups are greater than should be expected if only chance is operating. After completing the analysis of variance table, there is only one more step. It is necessary to determine whether the obtained F value is statistically significant.

Evaluating the Obtained F Value

By now the reader has probably guessed, correctly, that the obtained F value is evaluated for statistical significance by comparing it with a table value. If the between-group estimate is so much larger than the within-group estimate that the obtained F value is a rare event if only chance is operating, the results can be attributed to the independent variable. The table in Appendix C-4 is used to assess the likelihood of the obtained F value occurring if only chance is operating.

In order to find the appropriate table value for comparison it is necessary to know the number of degrees of freedom for each variance estimate and to select a significance level. Assume that the .05 level of significance is selected. The number of degrees of freedom for the between-group estimate indicates the appropriate column to refer to in the table, and the number of degrees of freedom for the within-group estimate indicates the appropriate row. In this case there are two degrees of freedom for the between-group and twenty-seven degrees of freedom for the within-group estimate. The table in Appendix C-4 does not have a value for two and twenty-seven degrees of freedom so it is necessary to use the next *smaller* degree of freedom for the within-group estimate. An examination of Column 2 and Row 26 reveals a table value of 3.37 corresponding to the .05 significance level. Thus, in order to reject the null hypothesis at the .05 level of significance, the obtained F value has to be equal to or greater than 3.37. Since the obtained F value of 84.87 is greater than 3.37, the null hypothesis is rejected. The results of this experiment are very unlikely if only chance is operating. Therefore, it appears that the level of aggressiveness influenced the dollar value of the sales.

Follow Up Tests

Need for Follow Up Tests. The previous analysis reveals that the level of aggressiveness influenced the dollar value of the sales, but it does not indicate whether medium aggressiveness differs significantly from high aggressiveness or from low aggressiveness. It is clear that there is a significant difference between low and high aggressiveness. Thus, if an independent variable with more than two levels produces a significant effect it is possible to conclude that the groups that do the best and the worst differ significantly, but it is not possible to make statements about comparisons between the other groups.

The relative effectiveness of different levels of the independent variable is usually not a major concern if a quantitative manipulation is made and a monotonic relationship is observed. In the present example, the major interest is in whether aggressiveness has an effect, not in the relative effectiveness of different levels of aggressiveness. Assessing the relative effectiveness may have much practical importance but has little theoretical importance. However, if a qualitative manipulation is made, e.g., three different instructional techniques, then one should compare the levels of the independent variable. It is important to know whether the groups differ significantly and *which* groups differ significantly. In order to obtain the information one must perform follow up tests.

Analysis of Variance as a Follow Up Test. An appropriate follow up test is to repeat the analysis of variance for the comparisons of interest. For example, if three different instructional techniques (A, B, and C) were tested, it may be interesting to know if A and B differ, if B and C differ, and if A and C differ. If the overall analysis is significant then at least one, and maybe all, of these comparisons will be significant. To make each comparison, it is necessary to consider two groups at a time, not three. For example, to make the A versus B comparison, the investigator should ignore Group C entirely.

It is a good idea to use the mean square and degrees of freedom from the overall analysis when making a follow up comparison because the within-group estimate of population variance is not likely to be affected by the treatment manipulation. Therefore, the best within-group estimate is obtained when all groups are considered. For instance, in the previous example of aggressiveness and dollar value of sales, it is possible to do an analysis of variance for the low and medium conditions only. The high aggressiveness condition is ignored completely. The between-group estimate of population variance is based only on the low and medium groups. However, the overall within-group estimate of population variance (i.e., 11.44 with twenty-seven degrees of freedom) can be used to evaluate the low versus medium comparison. The degrees of freedom for the obtained F value would be one and twenty-seven.

Multiple Comparisons and Significance Level. It is usually a good idea to adopt a more stringent significance level (e.g., .01 instead of .05) if a number of comparisons are to be made. Adopting a more stringent level keeps the significance level per experiment from becoming too high. What is too high will, of course, depend on the goals of the investigator. If he is interested in keeping the probability of making a Type 1 error low for the entire experiment, then he should adopt a stringent significance level for each comparison. For example, if five comparisons are made and the .01 level is adopted then the significance level for the experiment will be .05.

On the other hand, when there are a number of comparisons it is more likely that one or more will be effective than when there is only one comparison. Therefore, it can be argued that investigators should not adopt a stringent significance level for the entire experiment because this will increase the probability of making a Type 2 error. Thus, the question comes down to which type of error the investigator would rather avoid. Many investigators adopt a more stringent significance level when making multiple comparisons; some do not.

The discussion of analysis of variance in which one independent variable is manipulated is now concluded. A random-groups design was used in the above example, but a subject variable manipulation could also have been used. The steps involved in performing the analysis of variance are identical in both cases. Before going on to the next example it is very important for the student to have a firm understanding of the steps used in the first example.

In order to master the steps you should do the actual computation with a number of different examples. If a calculator is available, compute the analysis of variance by just referring to the text material and Table 10-1. If you can do it without referring to Table 10-2, then you should be ready to continue on to the next example. This is also a good point at which to turn to the problems at the end of the chapter and work those which require that an analysis of variance be performed with just one independent variable. The reader who spends an hour or so working examples will find the next section, which is concerned with a more complex example involving two independent variables, much easier to follow.

ANALYSIS OF VARIANCE WITH TWO INDEPENDENT VARIABLES

An example will illustrate the steps involved in using the analysis of variance to evaluate experiments in which two independent variables are manipulated. Assume that an investigator is interested in the quality of instruction and the quality of the student body at a particular institution. He has witnessed both outstanding and abysmal examples of instruction and has had contact with students who take their course work very seriously and with students who consider higher education a farce. He wonders what can be done to improve the quality of instruction.

In some cases the problem may lie in the nature of the course content. For example, many students in introductory courses in the social sciences expect to learn a set of principles that will afford them insight into social behavior. They soon find out, however, that there are few generally accepted principles that are "relevant" to their practical problems, and that there is much controversy. In the face of such ambiguity, a student may conclude that the course is a farce. Students who want to learn the general principles governing behavior find out, instead, that behavior is extremely complex. Simpleminded explanations (e.g., one variable as the crucial determiner of a particular behavior) are just not adequate. The effect that one variable has may, in fact, depend on the particular condition being examined. Moreover, it is generally better to seek probability statements rather than all-or-none predictions. Let us digress from our quality of instruction problem long enough to clarify this point.

Probability, Multiple Determiners, and Interactions

A number of theorists have something to say about the effect of birth order on personality. Toman (1970) studied the effect of birth order on marital adjustment, as measured by the incidence of divorce. Birth order is believed to be important because it generally influences which type of behavior will be reinforced. Firstborn children are likely to be reinforced for taking charge of their younger siblings. The oldest child tends to become the leader even though the parents may chide him about bossing the younger brother or sister. The youngest gets used to being a follower. Children in the middle tend to learn to be both leaders and followers. Another factor believed to be important is the experience of living with peers, particularly with peers of the opposite sex. An only child usually does not have much experience living with peers before marriage.

In order to test the view that birth order and experience living with peers are related to marital adjustment, Toman considered different kinds of marriages. If the older brother of a sister marries the younger sister of a brother, this should, according to the theory, be a good match. They both have had experience living with peers of the opposite sex, and there is no conflict over the dominance role. Similarly, the match of a younger brother of sisters with the oldest sister of brothers is also likely to be a good match. The wife will tend to be dominant and the husband dependent. If the older brother of a sister marries an oldest sister of sisters, they are likely to have some dominance problems. Both have learned to expect "seniority" rights. If the youngest brother of brothers marries the youngest sister of sisters, they are likely to have dominance problems (i.e., both are dependent) and lack of experience in getting along with the opposite sex (see Toman, 1970).

Toman compared the divorce rate of good matches and poor matches, as defined by this view, and found that the rate is lower than expected (obtained = 21, expected = 33) for the good matches, and higher than expected (obtained = 63, expected = 49) for the poor matches. The obtained Chi Square computed from Toman's data is equal to 8.36. The reader who checks this value in Appendix C-2 will find that the obtained value, with one degree of freedom, is significant at the .01 level. Thus, it is reasonable to conclude that birth order and experience living with peers are related to marital adjustment. However, it is not possible to predict divorces accurately solely on the basis of these variables. Some of the "good matches" ended in divorce and many of the "poor matches" did not.

It seems safe to conclude that many other variables are also related to marital adjustment. Workers in the social sciences have to accept the fact that there are multiple determiners of behavior. Yet, one should not minimize the finding that birth order and experience living with peers are related to marital adjustment. The *probability* of divorce appears to be greater with "poor matches." Someone who considers marriage in a very rational manner, if there is such a person, may want to consider these factors before selecting a mate.

The previous example was a rather long-winded way of pointing out that social scientists usually have to settle for finding variables which influence the probability of particular behaviors. Even if it were possible to delineate all the variables, it is doubtful that perfect predictions could be made. The problem is that the effect of one variable may be determined by the effect of another. For example, a particular variable may have an effect for one type of person but not for another. To assess such effects, it is necessary to utilize designs involving more than one variable. Let us return to the problem of improving the quality of instruction.

Combination of Subject and Nonsubject Variable Manipulations

The investigator is convinced that learning is a very complicated phenomenon. He has rejected the view that there is a single best way to present material because he has witnessed various styles that appear to be effective. Moreover, the emphasis on the quality of instruction, although important, is only one side of the problem. After all, regardless of the quality of instruction, the student still has complete veto power over all learning. If he decides not to learn, there is no way that an instructional program of whatever quality will succeed. Thus, it is also necessary to consider the quality or state of the learner. A particular instructional program may be effective for one kind of learner but not for another. The investigator decides to test this view by conducting an experiment.

Nonsubject Variable Manipulation. There are many different models of instruction, and each approach has its advocates and critics. The investigator decides to study the effect of the instructor's style. A content-oriented formal approach is selected for one style, and a motivation-oriented informal approach for the other. For the formal approach the material is presented with few examples, and little or no attempt is made to entertain the students or relate the material to "real life" situations. The instructor does not take any responsibility for motivating the student. If the student is not self-motivated, that is his own problem. The instructor's role is to present the material in a well-organized manner without garnishment; the student's role is to learn it. The instructor does not encourage the students to relate to him on a personal basis.

For the informal approach the instructor uses many examples. If possible, the examples are amusing or help the student relate the material to real life situations. The instructor tries to motivate the students to learn, and encourages them to be very informal with him both inside and outside of the classroom. In short, he attempts to relate to them personally.

Subject Variable Manipulation. The investigator believes that the effectiveness of each instructional approach may depend on the characteristics of the students. Some students may want to relate to their instructors on a personal basis and have the instructor attempt to motivate them. Others, however, may have little or no interest in a personal relationship with the instructor. They do not want the instructor to attempt to motivate them because they believe they are able to cope with their motivational problems. In short, the investigator believes that students can be placed in two large categories, which can be labeled, for convenience in exposition, Low Academic Motivation and High Academic Motivation. A questionnaire is designed to determine motivation level. Assume that the questionnaire is reliable and valid.

Method. The two independent variables are the instructional approach and the type of student. The dependent variable is course performance as assessed by the total number of points each student accumulates. The final grade is based on the number of points. The behavioral objectives are the same for both instructional techniques, and the students are informed of these objectives. The evaluation process is consistent with the stated objectives. Every level of each independent variable is combined with every level of every other independent variable, and the number of observations are the same for each combination of treatments. In this case there are two levels of instruction and two kinds of students so there are four different conditions. This is called a 2 by 2 factorial design, indicating that there are two levels of each of two independent variables.

A questionnaire designed to assess academic motivation is presented to a group of 200 students. Then the top thirty-two students (high motivation) and the bottom thirty-two (low motivation) are selected. The top thirty-two are randomly assigned to the two instructional conditions with the restriction that there be sixteen subjects in each group. The same procedure is used for the bottom thirty-two. It is important that there are the same number of subjects in each of the four conditions. The two groups of high motivation students differ with respect to the instructional manipulation, as do the two groups of low motivation students. Assume that all methodological or procedural problems are handled properly and that the data are collected with a minimum of difficulty.

Results. The total number of points each student accumulated in the four different experimental conditions is presented in Table 10-4. The task is to determine whether the independent variables had an effect on course performance. The analysis of variance is an appropriate statistical test. The level of measurement is interval, and a combination random-groups design and subject variable manipulation was used.

Computation of Analysis of Variance

The procedure for analyzing this experiment is very similar to that used for the previous example. In fact, the initial steps are identical to the steps used when only one independent variable is manipulated. The basic task is to compute the SS_{tot}, SS_{bg}, and SS_{wg}, in that order. The reader probably remembers that it is necessary to compute the sum of the scores for each group and the sum of the squared scores for each group in order to compute the three sums of squares.

Computing the SS_{tot}, SS_{bg}, *and* SS_{wg}. The formula for the computation of the SS_{tot} is:

$$SS_{tot} = \Sigma\Sigma X^2 - \frac{(T)^2}{N}.$$

As we know, the first term is obtained by squaring the score for each subject and then adding all the squared scores. To obtain the value for the second term, the total for all the scores is squared and then divided by the total number of scores (in this case sixty-four). The formula for the SS_{bg} is:

$$SS_{bg} = \Sigma \frac{(group\ total)^2}{n} - \frac{(T)^2}{N}.$$

TABLE 10-4

The Total Number of Points for Each Student in the Four Experimental Conditions (fictitious data)

	Instructional approach			
	Content-oriented formal		*Motivation-oriented informal*	
	Academic motivation		*Academic motivation*	
	High	*Low*	*High*	*Low*
	189	102	132	164
	168	112	94	165
	137	95	118	175
	175	100	153	181
	165	117	109	140
	173	76	100	138
	162	128	127	160
	198	81	104	156
	150	109	120	133
	158	88	135	154
	147	111	107	159
	173	93	110	152
	156	124	103	113
	177	84	108	185
	129	135	121	146
	151	105	128	159
ΣX	2,608	1,660	1,869	2,480
ΣX^2	430,050	176,660	221,891	389,468

Thus, to obtain the first term each group total is squared and the squared group totals are added and then divided by the number of subjects in each group (in this case sixteen). The second term was already computed when the SS_{tot} was computed. Since the SS_{tot} is equal to the SS_{bn} plus the SS_{wg}, the SS_{wg} can be obtained by subtraction (or by computing a SS_{tot} for each group separately and then adding these values). The computation of the analysis of variance for this example is presented in Table 10-5.

After these three sums of squares are obtained an analysis of variance table could be prepared and an F value obtained in exactly the same way as for the previous example. Then the F value could be evaluated to determine whether the differences among the four groups are a rare outcome if only chance is operating. Although the approach is possible, it would not be satisfactory. The experiment was conducted to assess the effects of two independent variables. Assessing whether there are differences among the four groups would not allow the experimenter to determine the independent variable(s) responsible for any obtained differences. In order to assess each independent variable

TABLE 10–5

Computation of the Analysis of Variance for the Data Presented in Table 10–4

$$SS_{tot} = \Sigma\Sigma X^2 - \frac{(T)^2}{N}$$

$$SS_{tot} = 1{,}218{,}069 - \frac{(8{,}617)^2}{64}$$

$$SS_{tot} = 57{,}870.73$$

$$SS_{bg} = \Sigma \frac{(group\ total)^2}{n} - \frac{(T)^2}{N}$$

$$SS_{bg} = \frac{(2{,}608)^2 + (1{,}660)^2 + (1{,}869)^2 + (2{,}480)^2}{16} - \frac{(8{,}617)^2}{64}$$

$$SS_{bg} = \frac{19{,}200{,}825}{16} - \frac{(8{,}617)^2}{64}$$

$$SS_{bg} = 39{,}853.29$$

$$SS_{wg} = SS_{tot} - SS_{bg}$$

$$SS_{wg} = 57{,}870.73 - 39{,}853.29$$

$$SS_{wg} = 18{,}017.44$$

$$SS_{instruction} = \Sigma \frac{(group\ total)^2}{n} - \frac{(T)^2}{N}$$

$$SS_{instruction} = \frac{(4{,}268)^2 + (4{,}349)^2}{32} - \frac{(8{,}617)^2}{64}$$

$$SS_{instructuon} = 102.51$$

$$SS_{type\ of\ student} = \Sigma \frac{(group\ total)^2}{n} - \frac{(T)^2}{N}$$

$$SS_{type\ of\ student} = \frac{(4{,}477)^2 + (4{,}140)^2}{32} - \frac{(8{,}617)^2}{64}$$

$$SS_{type\ of\ student} = 1{,}774.51$$

$$SS_{I \times S} = SS_{bg} - SS_{instruction} - SS_{type\ of\ student}$$

$$SS_{I \times S} = 39{,}853.29 - 102.51 - 1774.51$$

$$SS_{I \times S} = 37{,}976.27$$

separately, we must look at the experiment in a slightly different manner. One independent variable has to be ignored while the other is evaluated.

Computing a Sum of Squares for Each Independent Variable. This step in the analysis requires a little flexibility or imagination on the part of the student. The formula for the SS_{bg} is used extensively, but the definition of a group changes as the effect of each independent variable is assessed. That is, the first term in the SS_{bg} formula is obtained by squaring each group total, adding the squared scores, and dividing by the number of scores in each group. The same procedure is used to evaluate the effect of each independent variable separately, but the way the groups are defined changes. Therefore, the student has to look at the experiment from a number of different points of view. The way the groups are defined will also determine the label given to the SS_{bg}. The SS_{bg} is very useful since it can be used to evaluate the effect of each independent variable separately. These points should shortly become clear.

The effect of the instructional manipulation can be evaluated by viewing the experiment as a two-group experiment. There are low and high motivation students in each of the instructional groups. The type of student variable is collapsed in order to evaluate the effect of instruction. If the type of student variable is ignored, then there are thirty-two students in one instructional group and thirty-two in the other. That is, imagine that academic motivation was not manipulated and that thirty-two students were tested with each instructional approach. The SS_{bg} can be obtained for each of the two instruction groups to assess the effect of the instructional manipulation. If these two groups differ markedly the difference can be attributed to the instructional manipulation. It is not reasonable to attribute these group differences to the type of student manipulation since there are low and high motivation students in each group.

Although the SS_{bg} formula is used to assess the instructional effect, it is more appropriate to label the sum of squares obtained the $SS_{instruction}$ in order to minimize confusion. A between-group sum of squares is obtained, but it is of a particular kind. It is the sum of squares obtained by comparing the subjects who had one instructional technique with the subjects who had the other. Thus, it makes good sense to label it the $SS_{instruction}$. The computation of the $SS_{instruction}$ is presented in Table 10-5.

A similar procedure is used to obtain a sum of squares for the type of student effect. In this case, one group consists of thirty-two low motivation students and the other of thirty-two high motivation students. Once again, the SS_{bg} formula is used. A total is obtained for each of the two groups. These totals are squared, then added, and then divided by the number of subjects in each group (thirty-two). The resultant value is labeled the $SS_{type\ of\ student}$. Now consider the differences among all four groups.

Computing the Sum of Squares for the Interaction. Let us consider the factors, besides chance, which might cause the four group totals to differ. If the instruction and type of student manipulations influence course performance, these manipulations will cause the four group totals to vary. Yet, the $SS_{instruction}$

and the $SS_{type\ of\ student}$ may not account for all the differences among the groups. Determining the "overall" effect of instruction or type of student does not afford an assessment of the extent to which the effect of one of the manipulations (say, instruction) depends on the level of the other independent variable (type of student). If the effect of one depends on the level of the other, the two variables are said to *interact.*

The interaction effect is assessed by determining the extent to which the $SS_{instruction}$ and $SS_{type\ of\ student}$ effects account for all the differences among the four groups. That is, the sum of squares for the instruction-by-type-of-student interaction is computed by subtracting the $SS_{instruction}$ and $SS_{type\ of\ student}$ effects from the SS_{bg}. The interaction effect is the difference among the four groups which is not accounted for by the instruction effect and the type of student effect. This computation is also presented in Table 10-5. Interaction effects are considered in greater detail following the completion of the computations for this example. Now that all the sums of squares have been computed, the analysis of variance table can be considered.

The Analysis of Variance Table

Source of Variance. The analysis of variance table for this example appears in Table 10-6. The principal difference between this table and the one for the earlier example is that the between-group source of variance is replaced with an instruction, a type of student, and an instruction-by-type-of-student interaction effect. It is necessary to consider the between-group differences in terms of these three *independent* effects rather than in terms of an overall between-group effect. The effects are independent in that the statistical significance of any one of them does not depend on the significance, or lack of it, of any other. The within-group variance is used in the same way that it was when only one independent variable was considered.

Degrees of Freedom. The degrees of freedom are determined in essentially the same way as when there is only one independent variable. The

TABLE 10–6

Analysis of Variance Table for the Experiment Investigating the Effect of Type of Instruction and Type of Student on Course Performance

Source of variance	df	SS	MS	F
Instruction (*I*)	1	102.51	102.51	.34
Type of student (*S*)	1	1,774.51	1,774.51	5.91
I × *S*	1	37,976.27	37,976.27	126.47
Within-group	60	18,017.44	300.29	
Total	63	57,870.73		

degrees of freedom for the instruction effect is equal to one because there are only two different instruction groups. That is, when calculating the instruction effect, the type of student variable was collapsed. This leaves two groups of thirty-two subjects each. Given that the overall total is fixed, only one group total is free to vary. By the same reasoning, the degrees of freedom for the type of student effect is also equal to one.

A simple way to remember how to compute the degrees of freedom for any interaction is to keep in mind that a multiplication sign is used to label an interaction (e.g., *instruction* × *type of student*). The degrees of freedom for any interaction effect can be obtained by multiplying the degrees of freedom for the variables involved. In this case there is one degree of freedom for the interaction because the product of the degrees of freedom for the two variables is equal to one.

Note that the sum of the degrees of freedom for the three effects is equal to that which would have been obtained if the overall between-group effect had been assessed. Since there were four independent groups there would be three degrees of freedom for the between-group effect. The degrees of freedom for the SS_{wg} is sixty since there are four groups and sixteen subjects per group, i.e., $k(n-1) = 4(15) = 60$.

The SS, MS, *and* F *Columns.* The column for *SS* should not cause any difficulty because the sum of squares for each effect has been computed. The task is simply to record the values in the table. The values for the *MS* column are obtained by dividing the *SS* values for each effect by the degrees of freedom for that effect. The *F* value for each effect is obtained by dividing the mean square for the effect by the within-group mean square. In this case there are three separate effects. Each effect is evaluated by comparing the obtained *F* value with the appropriate table value. You will recall that in this case there are one and sixty degrees of freedom for each effect. If the .05 significance level is adopted, an obtained *F* value of 4.00 or greater (see Appendix C-4) is needed in order to have a statistically significant effect. We find that the type of student effect and the instruction-by-type-of-student interaction are significant, but the instruction effect is not significant.

INTERACTIONS

Let us look at the results of this experiment in greater detail. The interpretation of the effect of a single variable (main effect) is usually straightforward. The particular manipulation either produces a statistically significant effect or it does not. In this case, the type of student manipulation produced a statistically significant effect and the instruction manipulation did not. Since the type of student manipulation is a subject variable, one cannot be confident that the obtained difference between the groups was due solely to motivational differences. Perhaps some other subject variable, which is correlated with academic motivation, was actually responsible. For example, the two motivational groups may have differed in intelligence.

At this point the reader may be ready to conclude that the results of the experiment are not very interesting. The instruction manipulation did not result in a statistically significant effect, and the one significant main effect is difficult to interpret because it involved a subject variable manipulation. Perhaps the experimenter wasted a lot of time. It would have been much simpler to correlate the academic motivation measure with course performance, instead of conducting an elaborate experiment. Of course, one could argue that there was no way of knowing that the instruction manipulation would not have an effect. Obviously, investigators should be prepared to accept the fact that their notions may be incorrect. In this case, however, there is little reason for gloom. The interaction is statistically significant, *and* it has practical and theoretical importance.

Definition of an Interaction

Some people have a difficult time understanding interactions so a brief review may be useful. An interaction between two independent variables means that the effect of one depends on the level of the other. In our example, the effect of instruction proved to depend on the type of student. In simple terms, the content-oriented formal approach produced better results with the highly motivated students, and the motivation-oriented informal approach produced better results with the less motivated students. (Remember that these results are fictitious; they may not represent the true state of affairs.) Thus, the instruction effect would have been different if only high motivation or only low motivation students had been used. Even though the *overall* instructional manipulation did not have an effect, the finding indicates that the effectiveness of a particular instructional approach depends on the type of student.

Importance of Interactions

It is extremely unlikely that one can attain a satisfactory understanding of behavior without considering how variables interact. It is, of course, important to determine the main effects of particular independent variables upon performance, but it is also important to determine the conditions under which the independent variable manipulation is effective or ineffective. If the student can see that interactions are important, then he should also be able to see the importance of understanding the procedures for assessing interactions.

The investigation of interactions is one way to circumvent some of the interpretational difficulties in studying subject variables. The fact that the effectiveness of a particular variable depends upon the type of subject is important even if there is no way to be confident that the right label is used for the subject variable. If it is possible to separate subjects into categories and then find a nonsubject variable manipulation which is differentially effective depending on the category of subjects considered, the finding is easy to interpret. It is essentially irrelevant what label is used for the categories. The important point is that the sorting is *useful* if the effectiveness of a nonsubject variable manipulation depends on the type of subject.

A common misconception about interactions is that one or more of the variables must be significant in order to obtain a significant interaction. This is simply not true, particularly when only two independent variables are manipulated. Main effects are independent of each other and they are independent of interactions. One can assess whether variables are independent of each other by determining whether they interact, but they can interact without producing main effects and vice versa. Let us consider a few pictorial examples in order to clarify the relationship between main effects and interactions.

Relationship Between Interactions and Main Effects

Let us assume an experiment is conducted in which instructional method (Method 1 and Method 2) and type of student (social science major and natural science major) are varied. Course performance is the dependent variable. Four possible outcomes of the experiment are presented in Figure 10-1. Assume that the within-group mean square is quite small so that the differences which appear to be significant *are* significant. In the first three cases, the method-by-type-of-student interaction is significant. That is, the effectiveness of the method depends on the type of student. Yet, in one case (Figure 10-1A) both main effects are not statistically significant; in another case (Figure 10-1B), one main effect (the method effect) is significant; and in the third case (Figure 10-1C), both main effects are significant. In the fourth case (Figure 10-1D), both main effects are significant but the interaction is not. The figures are drawn as bar graphs because it is unlikely that there is a single quantitative dimension underlying the independent variable of type of student. The type of student manipulation is more accurately classified as a qualitative manipulation.

The same results presented in Figure 10-1 are presented in Figure 10-2 in line graph form. The type of student manipulation has been changed to quantitative ability. Once again, for the first three cases the interaction is significant and the main effects may or may not be significant. In the fourth case both main effects are significant, but the interaction is not.

At this point the reader has almost enough information to compute an analysis of variance for a random-groups design with an unlimited number

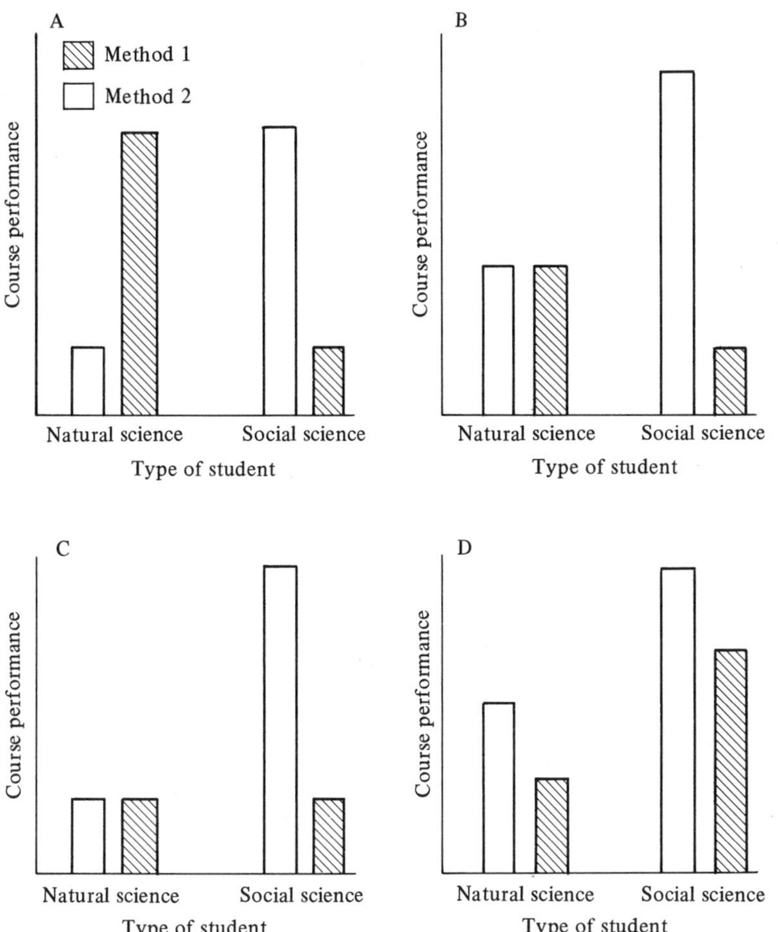

FIGURE 10–1

Course performance as a function of the type of student and instruction method (fictitious data).

of independent variables. Obviously, as the number of independent variables increases, the number of groups and, therefore, the number of subjects also increases. If there are four or more independent variables, it is probably better to use a computer to do the analysis. In principle, however, the same procedure that was used for the first two examples can be used to analyze a more complex design. The basic strategy is to collapse the variables that are not being analyzed.

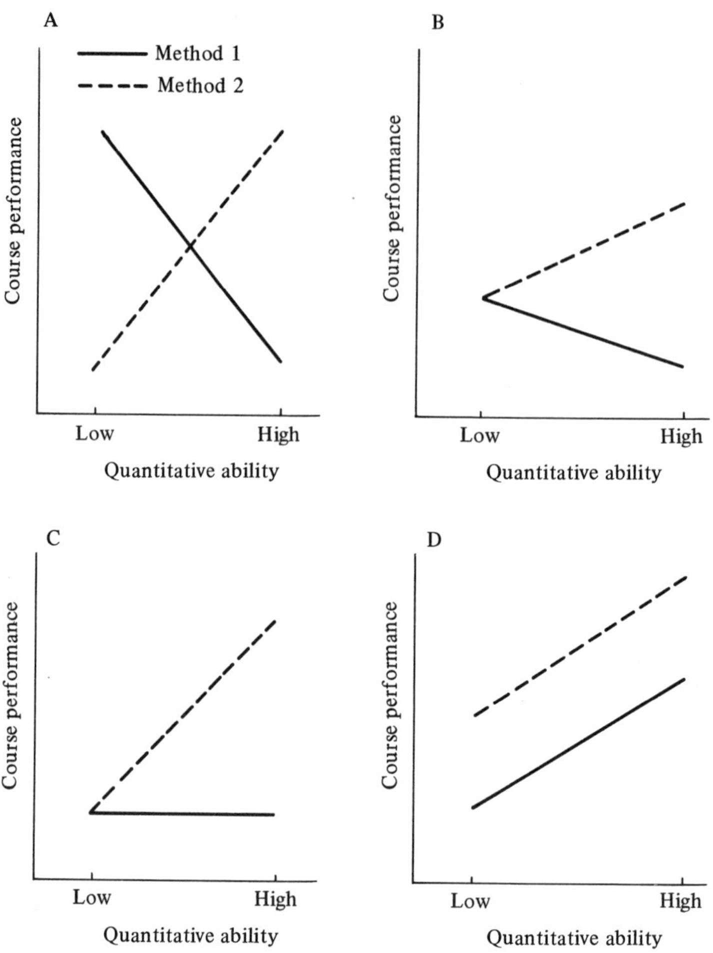

FIGURE 10–2

Course performance as a function of the instructional method and the quantitative ability of the students (fictitious data).

ASSUMPTIONS OF THE ANALYSIS OF VARIANCE

The assumptions underlying the analysis of variance depend on the particular model used. Only the fixed effects model is considered in this text. That is, conclusions are drawn only about the levels of the independent variable actually manipulated. The reader who is interested in other uses of analysis of variance should consult more advanced texts such as Hays (1963) or Winer (1971). For the fixed effects model, one makes two assumptions:

that the variances of the samples are homogenous and that the distributions within each sample are normal.

Homogeneity of Variance

The independent variable is expected to influence the extent to which the groups differ but not the fluctuations within a particular group. The within-group fluctuations are expected to be about the same regardless of the treatment. If, however, the manipulation influences the within-group variance (i.e., there is significantly greater fluctuation within one group than within another), the assumption of homogeneity of variance has been violated. The task is to assess whether the within-group fluctuations (variance) are greater than should be expected on the basis of chance. This can be accomplished by dividing the variance of the group having the greatest variance by that of the group having the smallest variance. The resultant quotient is called the F_{max} value.

The F_{max} value can be evaluated by referring to Appendix C-5. In order to find the correct table value, the number of groups and the size of each group must be considered. The number of groups is used to determine the correct column, and the degrees of freedom for each group (i.e., the number of subjects minus one) is used to determine the correct row. The values are given for both the .05 and .01 level of significance. For example, if there are six groups and sixteen subjects in each group, the F_{max} value has to be equal to or greater than 4.68 in order to conclude that the variances are heterogeneous. If the table does not include the value for your degrees of freedom, you should use the next lower value (e.g., 10 instead of 12) if you are interested in obtaining a significant F_{max} value, and the next highest (e.g., 12 instead of 10) if you are interested in obtaining a nonsignificant F_{max} value. Since investigators are usually interested in obtaining a nonsignificant F_{max} value, the next highest degree of freedom is usually used whenever the table does not include the value for your degrees of freedom. If the variances are heterogeneous, i.e., if a significant F_{max} value is obtained, then the assumption of homogeneity of variance has not been met.

Assume that an investigator performs the F_{max} test and obtains a significant value. There is good reason to believe that the sample variances are not homogeneous. The question then is what investigators should do when heterogeneous variances are obtained. Although there is some disagreement on this point, most statisticians think that violating the assumption of homogeneity of variance is not too serious a problem. If this assumption is violated, the experimenter is likely to reject the null hypothesis more often than is justified. The likelihood of error is a function of the size of the sample and the extent of the heterogeneity of the variances. Yet, there is usually little cause for concern in that the violation of this assumption tends to have very little effect on the accuracy of the analysis of variance test. If the assumption has been violated, a more stringent significance level (say, .01 instead of .05) should probably be used.

On the other hand, the significant F_{max} value may be a very interesting finding. If the independent variable influenced the within-group variance for some groups and not others, this suggests that subjects in the group(s) with the high variance were influenced differentially by the treatment. If the performance of some subjects and not of others is influenced, then the task for the experimenter is to determine why. In short, the fact that a treatment influences variance can be viewed as a finding *to be explained,* not merely as a failure to meet the assumption of the analysis of variance test.

Normality of Each Sample Distribution

The fact that the analysis of variance is so robust (i.e., insensitive) with respect to violations of homogeneity of variance has led many investigators to ignore the assumption and not to test for homogeneity of variance. Since the analysis of variance test is also robust with respect to the assumption of the normality of the distribution within each sample, many investigators tend to ignore this assumption as well. Violations of the normality assumption do not have much effect on the validity of the test. However, some readers may want to know how to determine whether this assumption has been met.

The assumption can be evaluated by plotting the deviation of each score from its *group* mean. If the frequency distribution of these deviation scores for all groups combined is relatively normal (symmetrical and mesokurtic), the assumption is satisfied. If the assumption is not satisfied (i.e., if the distribution is markedly skewed), the investigator may elect to use a statistical test which does not require this assumption (see Siegel, 1956). The student who is interested in learning more about the assumptions of the analysis of variance should refer to a more advanced statistical text (e.g., Winer, 1971).

SUMMARY

The crux of the analysis of variance is to obtain two independent estimates of population variance. One estimate is based on within-group variance and one on between-group variance. The two estimates can be compared to assess the effect of the independent variable. If the null hypothesis is true, the two estimates should be about the same. If the null hypothesis is not true, the between-group should be larger than the within-group estimate.

The computation of the analysis of variance for an experiment with one independent variable consists primarily of obtaining two estimates of population variance. These are obtained by first computing the sum of the squared deviations from the mean. The sum of squares total is the sum of the squared deviations of each score from the overall mean. The sum of squares between groups is the weighted sum of squares of each group mean from the overall mean; that is, the difference between each group mean and the overall mean is multiplied (weighted by) the number of subjects in the group. The sum of squares within groups is the sum of the squared deviations of each score from the group mean.

The between-group estimate of population variance (mean square) is obtained by dividing the sum of squares between groups by its degrees of freedom. The within-group estimate of population variance (mean square) is obtained by dividing the sum of squares within groups by its degrees of freedom. The mean square between groups is divided by the mean square within groups to obtain an F value for the effect of the independent variable. The F value is evaluated by comparing it to the appropriate table value. If the obtained value exceeds the table value, the null hypothesis is rejected.

A similar procedure is used to evaluate experiments in which more than one independent variable is manipulated, except that the sum of squares between groups is broken up to assess the effect of each independent variable and the interaction of the independent variables separately. It is not necessary to obtain a significant main effect in order to obtain a significant interaction.

The two major assumptions of the analysis of variance are homogeneity of variance and normality of each sample distribution. Slight violations of these assumptions do not have much effect on the accuracy of the analysis of variance test.

QUESTIONS

1. What is the logic of the analysis of variance — why is it important to obtain two independent estimates of population variance?
2. Do an analysis of variance to determine if the effect of the independent variable influenced performance. Present the analysis of variance table. A random-groups design was used and interval data were obtained.

Group I	*Group II*	*Group III*
16	26	21
2	19	6
18	31	12
3	6	18
14	22	2
25	3	24
9	16	5
20	22	19

3. Do an analysis of variance to determine if the effect of the independent variable influenced performance. Once again, a random-groups design was used and interval data obtained.

Group I	*Group II*
19	25
22	26
16	27
25	24
19	24
23	28

4. The investigator was interested in whether the attitude of the experimenter toward a child would affect the child's ability to perform a manual dexterity task. While meeting the child and introducing him to the task, the experimenter was either very friendly to the child or very businesslike. The child's task was to drop as many marbles as possible into a jar. The dependent measure was the number of marbles in the jar after a one minute period. A random-groups design was used. Analyze the results of the experiment and state the conclusions.

Friendly experimenter	*Businesslike experimenter*
20	34
30	35
36	29
26	31
22	27
23	33
32	26
28	30
24	24
25	33

5. Do an analysis of variance to determine if the level of the independent variable influenced performance. Present the analysis of variance table. A random-groups design was used and interval data were obtained.

Group I	*Group II*	*Group III*
42	47	40
39	49	41
36	45	35
44	51	39
40	53	36
41	44	40
38	52	38
42	49	37
35	47	35
41	53	37
40	51	39

6. Do the follow up tests for the data in Question 6 to determine which groups differ significantly. How many degrees of freedom are there for the within-group mean square?
7. An investigator was interested in the amount of money different types of people would give to help free George Grimley from prison after an unfair trial. The two types of subjects used were humanitarians and lawyers. (Those who qualified for both categories were not used in the study.) The investigator also used two approaches: an emotional approach, based on the plight of poor George Grimley and his family of fifteen children, and a judicial approach, based on the legal precedents which could be set by the case. The dependent measure was the amount of money given. Random assignment was used to assign people to the type of approach. Present the analysis of variance table.

Humanitarian		*Lawyer*	
Emotional appeal	*Judicial appeal*	*Emotional appeal*	*Judicial appeal*
26	19	20	28
24	17	19	26
23	18	16	24
27	14	19	27
25	16	18	26
25	17	17	22
24	15	16	24
26	16	15	25

8. Do an analysis of variance to determine if the effect of the two independent variables, type of task and anxiety level, influenced performance. Do the two variables interact? A combination random-groups design and subject variable manipulation was used, and interval data were obtained.

Type of task			
Easy Anxiety level		*Difficult Anxiety level*	
Low	*High*	*Low*	*High*
9	10	6	2
10	11	5	3
8	9	7	4
7	10	8	3
9	12	6	4
10	13	5	3
11	14	6	5
9	12	7	4

9. Draw a figure for the results obtained in Question 9.
10. What are the assumptions of analysis of variance?
11. Is the assumption of homogeneity of variance satisfied for the results presented in Question 9?

analysis of within-subject and matched-groups designs

The purpose of this chapter is to present statistical tests for within-subject designs. The significance tests considered are also applicable for matched-groups designs in which matching is done on a subject by subject basis. Statistical tests are considered for experiments in which nominal, ordinal, and interval data are obtained. The Cochran Q Test is appropriate for nominal data, the Friedman Test for ordinal data, and the analysis of variance for interval data. Two topics given special attention are the treatment-by-subject interaction in analysis of variance, and the question of whether to manipulate or match on a variable.

A few words need to be said about matched-groups designs and between-subject analyses before we consider statistical tests for within-subject and matched-groups designs. A matched-groups design can be considered a half-way step between a within-subject and a between-subject design. The way the matching is carried out determines which type of analysis is appropriate. If groups are matched by equating the group means and variances on the matching variables, then the between-subject analyses discussed in Chapters 9 and 10 should be used. If they are matched on a subject by subject basis, then the analyses discussed in this chapter are appropriate.

The major purpose of this chapter is to acquaint the student with statistical tools for analyzing experiments in which related samples are obtained. The samples may be related in that each subject is tested under each treatment condition (within-subject design), or the subjects in each treatment condition may be matched with subjects in the other treatment conditions on a subject by subject basis. As in the previous two chapters, the type of statistical tool will depend on the level of measurement of the dependent measure. The levels of measurement are examined in the same order as before, namely, nominal, ordinal, and interval. The steps in computing each test are considered in the context of an example.

NOMINAL DATA

Nominal Data Example

Imagine that an experimenter is interested in how to persuade people to stop smoking. An experiment is conducted to test the effectiveness of two different treatments relative to no treatment. For one treatment condition an aversive stimulus is paired with smoking in an attempt to make smoking unpleasant. The stimulus is an electric shock of sufficient intensity to be annoying but weak enough that no physical damage is done. The second treatment condition combines emotional and intellectual appeals intended to convince subjects that it would be in their own best interest to stop smoking. This approach involves presenting the evidence that smoking causes lung cancer, familiarizing subjects with the consequences of lung cancer, and so on. The third is a no treatment condition. The three conditions are labeled shock, verbal, and control, respectively.

The two treatment conditions are administered for a two-hour period, four times a week for one month. The control subjects are also seen for the same amount of time, but their sessions are spent discussing issues unrelated to smoking, such as community problems. At the conclusion of the treatment period, the experimenter checks periodically with the subjects and with their associates to determine whether they have, in fact, quit smoking. Success is defined as smoking a mean of five or fewer cigarettes a day for two months. The dependent measure requires classifying each person into the success or failure category. Assume that the experimenter has little difficulty classifying the subjects. For our purposes, the success and failure categories are qualitatively different. That is, the dependent measure is to be treated as an instance of nominal data even though it could be viewed as an instance of a higher level of measurement.

The experimenter believes that the length of time a person has been smoking prior to treatment and the amount of smoking per day prior to treatment are likely to be related to the difficulty of breaking the cigarette habit. Therefore, he decides to match the three groups on the basis of prior smoking habits. From the sample of smokers, he identifies groups of three persons who have essentially the same smoking history. He then *randomly assigns* them to the three conditions such that one subject is in each condition. This process is repeated until three groups of twenty subjects each are obtained.

Results. The results of the experiment are presented in Table 11-1. Note that there are twenty subjects in each condition and that the three subjects in the same row are matched with respect to prior smoking history. Each subject has a score of 0 (failure) or 1 (success). The issue is whether the three groups differ significantly in the number of successes. A significance test is used to assess whether the obtained differences are greater than can reasonably be expected on the basis of chance. In this case, a test is needed that can be performed with a matched-groups (or within-subject) design which yields nominal data. The Cochran Q Test (Cochran, 1950) is suitable.

Cochran Q Test

Computing the Q *Value.* The data in Table 11-1 are in the correct form for the use of the Cochran Q Test in that each subject is placed in either a success or failure category. To make possible the use of the Cochran Q Test, the dependent measure must be dichotomous (e.g., success or failure, yes or no, pass or fail, consent or refuse). A zero is always assigned to individuals in one category and a one to individuals in the other. Also, the data in Table 11-1 are in correct form in that the treatment conditions are represented in the columns, and the number of observations in each condition is equal to the number of rows.

The value of Q can then be computed by the formula:

$$Q = \frac{(k-1)\ [k\ \Sigma(group\ total)^2 - (T)^2]}{k\ (\Sigma\ row\ totals) - \Sigma(row\ totals)^2}.$$

As in earlier examples, k is equal to the number of conditions (groups) and

TABLE 11-1

The Results of an Experiment Investigating the Effect of Two Treatments, Relative to a Control, in Reducing the Incidence of Smoking (fictitious data)

Row	Control	Verbal approach	Shock approach	Total
a	0	1	1	2
b	1	1	0	2
c	0	0	1	1
d	0	1	1	2
e	0	0	0	0
f	1	1	1	3
g	0	0	0	0
h	1	1	1	3
i	0	1	1	2
j	0	0	1	1
k	1	0	1	2
l	0	1	0	1
m	1	1	0	2
n	0	0	0	0
o	0	1	1	2
p	0	0	0	0
q	1	1	1	3
r	0	0	0	0
s	0	1	1	2
t	1	1	1	3
group total	7	12	12	$T = 31$
(group total)^2	49	144	144	Σ *(row total)*$^2 = 71$

$$Q = \frac{(k - 1)\,[k\,\Sigma(\text{group total})^2 - (T)^2]}{k\,(\Sigma\,\text{row totals}) - \Sigma\,(\text{row totals})^2}$$

$$Q = \frac{2\,[3\,(49 + 144 + 144) - (31)^2]}{3\,(31) - 71}$$

$$Q = 4.55$$

T is equal to the total of all the scores. The group totals refer, of course, to the totals for each condition. The computation of the Q value is presented in Table 11-1. Following the computation of Q, the next step is to evaluate Q to determine whether the obtained value is statistically significant.

Evaluating the Q *Value.* The obtained Q value is evaluated for significance in essentially the same way as the Chi Square. That is, since the two are essentially equal, the Chi Square distribution can be used to evaluate Q.

The number of degrees of freedom for the Q test is equal to $k - 1$. The value in the Chi Square table with $k - 1$ degrees of freedom is the appropriate table value with which to evaluate the obtained Q value. If the .05 significance level is adopted, then a Q value of 5.991 or higher (see Appendix C-2) is needed in order to reject the null hypothesis. In this case the obtained value of 4.55 is less than the value needed so it is not possible to reject the null hypothesis. The probability of this particular outcome is greater than 5 percent if only chance is operating.

Uses of the Cochran Q Test. To use the Cochran Q Test, the number of observations per condition should not be too small (less than, say, ten). Note also that the Cochran Q Test can be used with a within-subject as well as a matched-groups design. For example, a perception experiment could be performed in which each subject receives three different conditions of illumination. The condition of illumination is the independent variable. The task is to determine whether the subject is a success or failure under each of the three conditions. In this case, there would be three observations from each subject so the observations in each row would be one subject's data. The Cochran Q Test could be used to analyze this experiment in the same way that it was used to analyze the matched-groups experiment. However, if it is possible to do more than classify subjects into one of two categories, information is wasted by classifying them into two categories and using the Cochran Q Test. This point can be demonstrated by considering the smoking example again — this time reconstructed so as to yield ordinal data.

ORDINAL DATA

Ordinal Data Example

Let us assume that the experimenter decided to rank subjects instead of classifying them. The three subjects in each group with similar prior smoking histories are ranked with respect to improvement. The person who reduced his smoking the most is given the rank of 1; the person who is second is given the rank of 2; and the person who reduced his smoking the least is given the rank of 3. It does not matter which way the ranks are numbered, 1 for best or 1 for worst, as long as the assignment is consistent. When a tie occurs the tied subjects are assigned the average of the disputed ranks. For example, if two subjects in one group stop smoking entirely, the disputed ranks of 1 and 2 are averaged and both subjects given the rank of 1.5.

The results of this experiment, viewed in terms of ranks, are presented in Table 11-2. Since ordinal data are obtained, a test for related samples and ordinal data is needed. The Friedman Test is appropriate. Like the Cochran Q Test, the Friedman Test can be used to analyze within-group as well as matched-groups designs. Keep in mind, however, that matched-groups

TABLE 11-2

The Results of an Experiment Investigating the Effectiveness of Two Treatment Conditions Relative to a Control, in Reducing the Incidence of Smoking (The subjects in each row are rank ordered according to the amount [1 = most, 3 = least] that they decreased their smoking – fictitious data)

Row	*Control*	*Verbal approach*	*Shock approach*
a	3	1	2
b	2	1	3
c	3	2	1
d	3	2	1
e	3	1	2
f	3	1	2
g	3	2	1
h	2	1	3
i	3	1	2
j	3	2	1
k	2	3	1
l	3	1	2
m	2	1	3
n	3	2	1
o	3	1	2
p	3	1	2
q	3	2	1
r	3	1	2
s	3	1	2
t	2	1	3
ΣX	55	28	37
(sum of column ranks)^2	3025	784	1369

$$X_r^2 = \frac{12\ \Sigma\ (\textit{sum of column ranks})^2}{k\ (\textit{number of rows})\ (k+1)}$$

$$-3(\textit{number of rows})\ (k+1)$$

$$X_r^2 = \frac{12(3025 + 784 + 1369)}{3(20)(4)} - 3(20)(4)$$

$$X_r^2 = 18.9$$

designs can only be analyzed as within-subject designs if the matching is done on a subject by subject basis.

Friedman Test

Computing the X_r^2 *Value.* The data in Table 11-2 are in the correct form for the use of the Friedman Test. The three subjects in each row have been ranked according to the amount that they reduced their smoking. The conditions are represented in columns, and the subjects with similar prior smoking histories are presented in the same row. If this experiment were a within-subject instead of a matched-groups design, then the three scores in each row would be obtained from the same subject.

The formula for the Friedman Test is:

$$X_r^2 = \frac{12\ \Sigma(\textit{sum of column ranks})^2}{k(\textit{number of rows})(k+1)} - 3(\textit{number of rows})(k+1).$$

The reader may prefer to think of the X_r^2 symbol as indicating a "related" Chi Square since the groups are related when a matched-groups or within-subject design is used. Once again, the k refers to the number of conditions. The computation for this test is presented in Table 11-2. After completing the computation, the next step is to determine whether the obtained value is statistically significant.

Evaluating the X_r^2 *Value.* To evaluate the obtained value it is necessary to refer to the Chi Square table in Appendix C-2. The number of degrees of freedom for the Friedman Test is exactly the same as it is for the Cochran Q Test, namely $k - 1$. If the .05 significance level is adopted, a value of 5.991 is needed since there are two degrees of freedom. In this case, the obtained value is greater than 5.991 so the null hypothesis is rejected. It is safe to conclude that the verbal approach is superior to no treatment, but the effect of the shock approach relative to the other two conditions is not clear. It appears that the two treatment conditions are about equally effective. Sometimes it is necessary to repeat the test with fewer conditions (e.g., eliminate the verbal condition and use only two ranks) in order to determine whether two of the conditions differ significantly.

The Chi Square table is only appropriate for evaluating the obtained value if the number of rows is greater than nine *or* the number of conditions is more than four. Since it is unlikely that you will conduct an experiment in which you have fewer than ten rows, the Chi Square table should usually be sufficient. If there is not enough data to justify its use, you can refer to another statistics text (e.g., Kolstoe, 1973) to find out how to evaluate a Friedman Test performed on a small amount of data.

INTERVAL DATA AND ANALYSIS OF VARIANCE

Interval Data Example

The same example that we used for nominal and ordinal data will serve for interval data. Let us assume that the experimenter is not completely satisfied with the dependent measure used in the previous example. It is possible to do more than rank order the subjects with similar smoking histories with respect to their decreases, if any, in smoking. The number of cigarettes a person smokes per day is an interval measure. Therefore, it is possible to determine the average decrease in the amount of smoking for each subject and perform a statistical test which requires interval data. In all other respects, the experiment remains the same.

Note that an experiment is not normally analyzed at more than one level of measurement. The present example is considered at three different levels for pedagogical purposes. An experiment should be analyzed at the highest level of measurement possible (i.e., interval, then ordinal, then nominal) because information is wasted when a dependent measure is analyzed at a lower level than necessary.

The data for the smoking experiment are presented again in Table 11-3. This time the data obtained are interval, whereas in Tables 11-1 and 11-2 the data were nominal and ordinal, respectively. The fact that a different level of measurement is obtained means, of course, that it is appropriate to use a different kind of statistical tool for the significance test. The tool for interval data will be analysis of variance.

Incidentally, in some cases there may be subjects with positive and subjects with negative scores. This should not be of any concern since the presence of both positive and negative numbers will have no effect on the analysis. Yet, if the negative numbers bother you, they can be eliminated by adding a constant greater than the largest negative number to every score. Adding a constant to each score has no effect on the analysis of variance significance test.

Computation of Analysis of Variance

Computing the Sums of Squares. The computation of the analysis of variance is presented in Table 11-4. Note that the analysis differs somewhat from that performed for a between-subject design. The first step is to obtain the SS_{tot}. This value is obtained in exactly the same way as for a between-subject design. Next the $SS_{conditions}$ is obtained. *Conditions* is a label for the independent variable. For example, if the independent variable is type of therapy, then *therapy* could be substituted for *conditions.* This value is ob-

TABLE 11-3

The Results of an Experiment Investigating the Effectiveness of Two Treatment Conditions, Relative to a Control, in Reducing the Incidence of Smoking (The score for each subject indicates the mean daily decrease in the number of cigarettes [rounded to the nearest whole number] smoked each day for the two months following the experimental manipulation – fictitious data)

Row	*Control*	*Verbal approach*	*Shock approach*	*Total*
a	8	15	11	34
b	18	20	16	54
c	7	11	12	30
d	4	5	7	16
e	3	8	6	17
f	11	22	16	49
g	6	10	12	28
h	15	17	14	46
i	0	7	4	11
j	5	10	11	26
k	14	13	15	42
l	15	25	19	59
m	10	13	8	31
n	2	5	7	14
o	6	14	11	31
p	6	10	7	23
q	7	9	12	28
r	7	13	9	29
s	8	17	13	38
t	10	16	9	35
ΣX	162	260	219	641
ΣX^2	1,728	3,936	2,683	23,801

tained in the same way that the main effects for the independent variables were obtained for the between-subject design. The SS_{rows} is obtained after the $SS_{conditions}$, and it is obtained in the same way, except that the row totals are used instead of the column totals. After the squared row totals are added, the sum is divided by three because there are three observations in each row. The next step is to obtain the sum of squares for the conditions-by-rows interaction by subtracting the $SS_{conditions}$ and the SS_{rows} from the SS_{tot}. It is not possible to obtain an SS_{wg} because there is only one subject in each row and column combination.

The Analysis of Variance Table. The analysis of variance table for the present example is given in Table 11-5. The degrees of freedom and mean square values are obtained in the same manner as for a between-subject

TABLE 11–4

Analysis of Variance for the Data Presented in Table 11–3

$$SS_{tot} = \Sigma\Sigma X^2 - \frac{(T)^2}{N}$$

$$SS_{tot} = 8347 - \frac{(641)^2}{60}$$

$$SS_{tot} = 1{,}498.98$$

$$SS_{conditions} = \Sigma \frac{(group\ total)^2}{n} - \frac{(T)^2}{N}$$

$$SS_{conditions} = \frac{(162)^2 + (260)^2 + (219)^2}{20} - \frac{(641)^2}{60}$$

$$SS_{conditions} = 242.23$$

$$SS_{rows} = \Sigma \frac{(row\ total)^2}{n} - \frac{(T)^2}{N}$$

$$SS_{rows} = \frac{23{,}801}{3} - \frac{(641)^2}{60}$$

$$SS_{rows} = 1{,}085.65$$

$$SS_{conditions \times rows} = SS_{tots} - SS_{conditions} - SS_{rows}$$

$$SS_{conditions \times rows} = 1{,}498.98 - 242.23 - 1{,}085.65$$

$$SS_{conditions \times rows} = 171.10$$

analysis. Note that the F value for conditions is obtained by dividing the mean square for conditions by the mean square for the conditions-by-rows interaction. An F value for the row effect is not computed. There are only three observations in each row, and each of these three was obtained under different conditions. The main concern is whether the conditions produced a significant effect, not whether the row effect is significant. A significant F ratio for rows would only tell you that subjects differ in performance of the

TABLE 11–5

The Analysis of Variance Table for the Experiment in Which the Effectiveness of Two Treatment Conditions, Relative to a Control, for Reducing the Incidence of Smoking Was Assessed

Source	df	SS	MS	F
Conditions (C)	2	242.23	121.12	26.92
Rows (R)	19	1,085.65	57.14	
$C \times R$	38	171.10	4.5	
Total	59	1,498.98		

task. Since it is well known that subjects differ in ability, the F value for rows is of little interest.

Although there is no question that the conditions effect is of major interest, the reader may wonder why the F value for this effect is obtained by dividing the mean square for conditions by the mean square for the conditions-by-rows interaction. In order to gain an intuitive understanding of why the interaction is used, it is necessary to consider briefly what determines the size of the mean square for conditions and the mean square for the conditions-by-rows interaction. The obtained F value is evaluated in exactly the same way as they are for between-subject designs. In this case the degrees of freedom for the conditions effect are two and thirty-eight.

The Conditions-by-Rows Interaction

Obtaining an Estimate of Chance Fluctuation. The obtained difference between the treatments in the smoking example may be due solely to chance effects or to both chance and treatment effects. The estimate of chance variation is obtained differently here than it is for a between-subject design. In the present case, it is necessary to obtain a measure of chance variation for subjects with similar smoking histories. If a within-subject instead of a matched-groups design were used, it would be necessary to obtain a measure of chance variation within subjects, i.e., the extent to which a subject's performance varies over time if only chance is operating.

The estimate of chance variation is the mean square for the conditions-by-rows interaction. If a within-subject design were used, the conditions-by-rows interaction would be called the conditions-by-subjects interaction since each row total would represent the performance of a single subject. If the null hypothesis is true, the mean square for conditions and the mean square for the conditions-by-rows interaction should both be due to chance variation.

If the treatment actually has an effect then the mean square for conditions should exceed the mean square for the conditions-by-rows interaction.

Suitability of the Conditions-by-Rows Estimate. The use of the mean square for the conditions-by-rows interaction as a measure of chance variation only is not without risks. The major difficulty is, of course, that the interaction may be due to more than just chance. Perhaps the treatment effect depends on the particular subject considered.

Note that it is possible to obtain an estimate of the effect of the treatment manipulation by considering each row separately. If a within-subject design were used there would only be one subject in each row so it would be possible to assess the effect for each subject separately. If the effect is the same for all subjects (within-subject design), or rows (matched-groups design), then the conditions-by-rows (subject) interaction provides an estimate of chance variation within subjects, or between similar subjects. Therefore, this variance estimate can be used to assess the treatment effect.

An important issue is whether it is reasonable to assume that the mean square for the conditions-by-rows (subject) interaction represents chance variation only. In some cases there will be ample evidence that the effect of the treatment does not depend on the type of subject manipulation so one can be confident that the conditions-by-rows (subject) interaction is due to chance. This evidence can be obtained by using other designs (e.g., a between-subject design in which type of subject and treatments are manipulated factorially). If it is known that the effect of the treatment manipulation depends on the type of subject, then it would be unwise to use a matched-groups or within-subject design unless the results could be analyzed separately for the different kinds of subjects. Such an analysis could be done if a combination between- and within-subject design were used.

Conditions-by-Subjects Interactions and Experimental Design. The importance of matched-groups and within-subject designs relative to between-subject designs is likely to depend on the particular problem area being investigated. If there is little reason to be concerned about interactions between subject and nonsubject variables, then the matched-groups and within-subject designs can be extremely useful. In many research areas (e.g., perception, learning, memory) there is little support for the view that normal members of the same species function differently. An investigator who is concerned about the differential effect of treatments on different subjects can, of course, combine subject variable with nonsubject variable manipulations to determine if the two kinds of variables interact.

If it is assumed that there is no conditions-by-rows (subject) interaction and, in fact, there is, it still may be correct to use the statistical analysis presented. However, it is necessary to apply a mixed-effects statistical model. The appropriateness of the model and the statistical analysis presented will be determined by the symmetry of the variance-covariance matrix. If the matrix is not symmetrical the critical values in the F table will be too low. Thus the probability of committing a Type 1 error is slightly greater than the significance level adopted. A consideration of these topics is beyond the scope of this text.

Manipulating Versus Matching a Variable

A situation may arise in which an investigator would like to control for the effect of some variable such as smoking history but is afraid to do so because the variable to be used in matching may interact with the independent variable. In this case it may be more reasonable to manipulate than to match on the variable. For example, subjects could be classified as light or heavy smokers. Type of smoker could be manipulated as one variable and the treatments for smoking as the other. Thus, a between-subject design with two independent variables — one subject variable and one nonsubject variable — would be used. The subjects could be randomly assigned to conditions such that the same number of light and heavy smokers were assigned to each. This design is presented in Table 11-6. Note that there is nothing new about

TABLE 11-6

The Mean Daily Decrease in the Number of Cigarettes Smoked Each Day for the Subjects in the Six Groups (fictitious data)

	Treatment					
	Control		*Verbal*		*Shock*	
	Smokers		*Smokers*		*Smokers*	
	Light	*Heavy*	*Light*	*Heavy*	*Light*	*Heavy*
	7	8	11	15	12	11
	4	18	5	20	7	16
	3	11	8	22	6	16
	6	15	10	17	12	14
	0	14	7	13	4	15
	5	15	10	25	11	19
	2	10	5	13	7	8
	6	6	10	14	7	11
	7	8	9	17	12	13
	7	10	13	16	9	9
ΣX	47	115	88	172	87	132
ΣX^2	273	1455	834	3102	833	1850

TABLE 11-7

The Analysis of Variance Computation and the Analysis of Variance Table for the Results Presented in Table 11-6

$$SS_{tot} = \Sigma\Sigma X^2 - \frac{(T)^2}{N}$$

$$SS_{tot} = 8347 - \frac{(641)^2}{60}$$

$$SS_{tot} = 1{,}498.98$$

$$SS_{bg} = \Sigma \frac{(group\ total)^2}{n} - \frac{(T)^2}{N}$$

$$SS_{bg} = \frac{(47)^2 + (115)^2 + (88)^2 + (172)^2 + (87)^2 + (132)^2}{10} - \frac{(641)^2}{60}$$

$$SS_{bg} = 927.48$$

$$SS_{wg} = SS_{tot} - SS_{bg}$$

$$SS_{wg} = 1{,}498.98 - 927.48$$

$$SS_{wg} = 571.50$$

$$SS_{smoking} = \Sigma \frac{(group\ total)^2}{n} - \frac{(T)^2}{N}$$

$$SS_{smoking} = \frac{(222)^2 + (419)^2}{30} - \frac{(641)^2}{60}$$

$$SS_{smoking} = 646.81$$

$$SS_{treatment} = \Sigma \frac{(group\ total)^2}{n} - \frac{(T)^2}{N}$$

$$SS_{treatment} = \frac{(162)^2 + (260)^2 + (219)^2}{20} - \frac{(641)^2}{60}$$

$$SS_{treatment} = 242.23$$

$$SS_{smoking \times treatment} = SS_{bg} - SS_{smoking} - SS_{treatment}$$

$$SS_{smoking \times treatment} = 927.48 - 646.81 - 242.23$$

$$SS_{smoking \times treatment} = 38.44$$

Source	df	SS	MS	F
Smoking (*S*)	1	646.81	646.81	61.14
Treatment (*T*)	2	242.23	121.12	11.45
$S \times T$	2	38.44	19.22	1.82
Within-groups	54	571.50	10.58	
Total	59	1498.98		

this design; it was considered in Chapter 10. It is mentioned again to point out that the effects of a variable can be controlled by manipulating as well as by matching.

The analysis of variance computation and table for this version of the experiment are presented in Table 11-7. Note that this procedure is an effective way to control for the effects of prior smoking history. If smoking history had not been manipulated, a larger mean square for within groups would have been obtained and, therefore, the chances of obtaining a statistically significant treatment effect would have been decreased. Moreover, this design makes it possible to assess whether there is a treatment-condition-by-type-of-smoker interaction.

SUMMARY

The statistical tests discussed in this chapter are appropriate for within-subject designs and for matched-groups designs if the matching is done on a subject by subject basis. The Cochran Q Test is appropriate for nominal data, the Friedman Test for ordinal data, and the analysis of variance for interval data. The steps involved in using the Cochran Q and Friedman Tests are relatively straightforward. The obtained values are evaluated by comparing them with the values in the Chi Square table with the appropriate degrees of freedom.

Using the analysis of variance to analyze experiments with matched-groups or within-subject designs is quite similar to using it with between-subject designs. The major difference is that fluctuations within subjects or within matched sets of subjects are used to evaluate the effect of the independent variable. This estimate of chance fluctuation is the conditions-by-rows interaction if a matched-groups design with a subject by subject matching procedure is used, or the conditions-by-subjects interaction if a within-subject design is used.

QUESTIONS

1. An experiment was conducted to assess the effects of two treatments. A within-subject design was used and nominal data were obtained. Perform the appropriate statistical test to determine if the treatments differed in effectiveness. A score of 1 indicates that the treatment was successful, and a score of 0 indicates failure. The presentation order of the conditions was counterbalanced so that half the subjects were given Treatment A first and the other half were given Treatment B first.

Subject	*Treatment A*	*Treatment B*
a	0	0
b	0	1
c	0	1
d	1	1
e	0	1
f	0	1
g	1	1
h	0	1
i	1	0
j	0	1
k	0	1
l	0	1
m	0	1
n	1	1
o	0	1
p	1	0

2. An experiment was conducted to assess the effect of three treatments. A within-subject design was used and the three treatment conditions were ranked for effectiveness for each subject. The score of 1 indicates that the treatment was most effective; the score of 3 indicates that it was least effective. Do an analysis to determine whether the three treatments differed in effectiveness. The order of treatments was counterbalanced.

Subject	*Treatment A*	*Treatment B*	*Treatment C*
a	1	2	3
b	1	2	3
c	2	1	3
d	2	3	1
e	1	3	2
f	1	2	3
g	2	3	1
h	1	3	2
i	1	3	2
j	1	2	3
k	1	3	2
l	3	1	2

3. An experiment was conducted in which a within-subject design was used. Subjects were tested under Condition A and Condition B. The dependent measure was whether subjects were successful or unsuccessful under each testing condition. They were given a score of 0 if they were unsuccessful and a score of 1 if successful (see p. 236). Do the appropriate analysis to determine if the condition manipulation had any effect. In this case, you should treat the success versus failure categorization as an instance of a nominal classification.

Subject	*Condition A*	*Condition B*
1	0	0
2	1	0
3	1	0
4	1	0
5	1	0
6	1	0
7	1	1
8	0	1
9	1	0

4. Assume that the same experiment was conducted as in Question 3, but that interval data were obtained. Do the appropriate analysis.

Subject	*Condition A*	*Condition B*
1	24	19
2	23	18
3	31	23
4	18	14
5	29	22
6	20	16
7	26	31
8	17	19
9	12	10

5. An experiment was conducted to assess the effect of three treatments. A within-subject design was used and interval data obtained. Each subject obtained a score for each of three treatment conditions. A high score indicates good performance. Do an analysis to determine whether the three treatments differed in effectiveness. The order of the treatments was counterbalanced.

Subject	*Treatment A*	*Treatment B*	*Treatment C*
a	23	18	45
b	26	23	41
c	25	17	38
d	27	19	42
e	31	24	35
f	28	28	29
g	24	21	33
h	22	17	39
i	27	25	32
j	26	35	38
k	25	21	41
l	41	32	55
m	18	11	42
n	28	33	43

6. Analyze the results obtained in the above experiment as if a between-subject design had been used. That is, imagine that fourteen different subjects were tested in each of the three conditions and the above scores obtained. Do you expect to obtain a higher F value for the treatment manipulation with the between-subject or the within-subject analysis? Why?

12 evaluating and reporting results

The first section of the chapter is a discussion of the steps in reevaluating the psychological significance of a research finding. The result of this reevaluation is the major factor determining whether the results of the research should be reported. The second section deals with reporting research findings. Topics discussed include: the decision to report the findings; factors to consider before writing; writing the introduction, method, results, and discussion sections; general comments about writing; and preparing the manuscript for publication.

In this chapter we will examine some of the difficulties encountered in evaluating and reporting results. Our task is to consider whether the results are worth reporting and, if they are, where and how they should be reported. This is not easy. There is no accepted standard for evaluating research, no prescribed place to send the manuscript, and no single set of principles to follow in writing the report. The experimenter has to make a set of decisions. Deciding whether his results are worth reporting means that he will have to consider their psychological significance.

THE PSYCHOLOGICAL SIGNIFICANCE OF RESULTS

Statistical versus Psychological Significance

It is important to distinguish between statistical and psychological significance. Statistical significance refers to the likelihood that an event can be attributed to chance effects. Psychological significance refers to whether or not a particular finding is a contribution to knowledge. The fact that a result is statistically significant does not mean, necessarily, that it is of psychological significance. For example, an experimenter who conducts a learning experiment should be able to obtain a significant F value for practice, indicating that subjects improve with practice. Although the effect is statistically significant, it is of little psychological significance because it has been known for a very long time. If it were possible to demonstrate the "mechanism" by which people learn, the finding would have great psychological significance since the learning process is still not understood. The psychological significance of a study is determined by the quality of the idea, the adequacy of the test, and the clarity of the results. All three are important.

In order to evaluate the results for psychological significance, the research idea should be reconsidered. It is true that the merit of the idea was evaluated at length before the experiment was conducted, but it is likely that a lot of time has passed since the earlier evaluation. Probably you are now a wiser, though perhaps sadder, person. You may have insights that you lacked previously.

Evaluating the Quality of Ideas

Investigators have different standards for determining the worth of ideas. In general, it is counterproductive to adopt standards that are markedly higher or lower than those adopted by most other members of the scientific community. If an investigator's standards are lower, he is likely to have his articles rejected by journal editors. If his standards are higher and he is unwilling to publish his results, then other researchers may be denied findings of interest. Therefore, there is some advantage to having standards consistent with those of the rest of the scientific community. These standards can be determined by examining the findings presented in refereed scientific journals. Articles in such journals are evaluated for their contribution to knowledge, and only those meeting the standards of the referees are accepted.

Adequacy of the Test

If the idea passes the quality evaluation, the next step is to consider the adequacy of the test. Did the experimental manipulation provide a fair test of the prediction? Were there any confounding variables? Could the results have turned out in such a way that the idea would have been proved incorrect? An adequate test of an idea is obtained only if the results can refute as well as support the assertions to be tested.

Sometimes an experimental design fails to yield an adequate test of the idea owing to unforeseen problems. For example, an investigator may decide to test the effectiveness of different learning strategies by manipulating the strategy instructions to each group. If differences are obtained between the groups, there is no problem. However, if differences are not obtained, it will be very difficult to determine whether the strategies actually do not differ in effectiveness or the subjects simply failed to use the strategy they were told to use. If the test is inadequate, then there is little choice but to start over by devising a better test. If the test is adequate, the next task is to consider the clarity of the results.

Definitiveness of the Results

Evaluating the results for clarity involves both statistical and nonstatistical considerations. If statistically significant, easily interpreted results are obtained, the investigator is very fortunate. Interpretational problems arise when the results are not as clear as the experimenter would have liked. For example, when two predictions are made and one is clearly supported and the other is not, then there will be interpretational problems. If both predictions follow from the theoretical view, the investigator is likely to be ambivalent about the results. In evaluating the clarity of results, one should consider whether it is possible to draw firm conclusions from the findings. If the predictions received firm support, and the experiment was a fair test of the predictions, and the research idea was equal to or better than ideas already reported in refereed scientific journals, then it is fair to conclude that the findings are psychologically significant.

Let us assume that the results are not clear or that the experiment was not a particularly good test of the idea. At this point the investigator may be very discouraged. He has spent a lot of time and energy on an insignificant result. Clearly, he has reason to be discouraged, but it may be incorrect to conclude that he gained nothing but a few more gray hairs and a higher hostility level. He may now be in a good position to redesign the experiment and conduct it properly, having discovered some of the pitfalls in conducting research.

It is not uncommon for an investigator to make mistakes which invalidate the results of the experiment. The task is to decide whether the test was inadequate or the idea was wrong. If the test was inadequate, then the experimenter may have some firm notions about how a better test could be made. If the idea was wrong, then perhaps an alternative theoretical notion is now worthy of test. The point is that experimenters should not be surprised if their first attempts at research do not come out as well as they had hoped. The fact of life is that many research projects do not yield the anticipated results. Let us assume, however, that the results are clear and important. The next task is to report the findings.

REPORTING THE FINDINGS

The Decision to Report Research Findings

Importance of the Findings. It would appear that the only factor in deciding whether to report research findings is their psychological significance. If you have something important to report, you are likely to be eager to have it in print. If you have rather uninteresting results, then there is usually little reason to bother reporting them. However, there may be situations which make it necessary to report insignificant results. For example, an instructor may insist that his students report the less-than-exciting results of a laboratory experiment in order to gain skill in making and evaluating reports. √√ YES YES

Graphic Phobia. There is at least one additional factor which may influence the decision on whether to report findings. For lack of a better term, let us label this factor *graphic phobia,* i.e., fear of writing. In some cases anxiety about writing may be related to the lack of psychologically significant findings. Yet, many people experience anxiety about writing even when they are convinced that the finding should be reported or even when they have excellent "external justification" (e.g., being required to report a laboratory experiment). You can expect to be a little anxious about reporting the findings because writing can be both a reinforcing and a punishing experience. This point requires further elaboration.

We have said before that one should attempt to find a research problem of genuine personal interest. An experimenter is not likely to derive much satisfaction from research unless it is intrinsically rewarding. Let us assume that you did find a problem of personal interest. You generated an idea that you believe to be excellent, designed an experiment to test it, and obtained statistically significant results. You evaluate all that you have done and conclude that the findings are psychologically significant. You are extremely excited by this chain of events. Now it is time to report the findings so that others can evaluate the work.

If the experiment required a large commitment, you will undoubtedly want the finished manuscript to reflect this. Perhaps friends and relatives know that you have been conducting a research project, and they are interested in learning the results. How, you may ask, can one possibly communicate all the excitement, frustration, confusion, depression, and insight that went into the research project? The answer is that one cannot, and should not, as this would detract from the major goal of reporting the findings. Perhaps the objective approach that investigators convey on the printed page has led some students to conclude that scientists are a cool, unemotional lot. However, the reader who has experienced some of the rewards and punishments of doing research should know better. In short, don't be overly concerned if you sweat a little while preparing the manuscript.

Factors to Consider Before Writing

Selecting the Audience. If the findings are worth reporting, the next task is to consider what audience to reach and how to reach it. There are scores of journals which publish research findings about behavior and mental activity. The task is to select the most appropriate journal or other medium. In order to determine the proper audience, it is necessary to assess the extent to which the finding is of general interest.

If the finding is of broad significance, it may be reasonable to inform the major communications networks. If it is likely to be of interest to scientists in other disciplines, a journal should be selected that is widely read among scientists (e.g., *Science* and *Scientific American*). If it is of interest mainly to psychologists, then a psychological journal should be selected. If it is of interest to psychologists working on a particular problem only, then a specialized psychological journal would be appropriate. If the finding is unimportant, it may only be necessary to notify the one other person in the world who is interested. You accomplish this by calling your mother.

It is important to take care in selecting the place to submit the manuscript because if an inappropriate journal is chosen, your time and that of the journal editor will be wasted. The manuscript will be returned, and you will be advised to send it elsewhere. Since the format varies for different journals, it will then be necessary to make changes in the manuscript so that it conforms to the style of a second journal. Investigators often decide where they want to submit their articles by the time they are ready to start writing. If you have not familiarized yourself with the journals that publish articles in your area of interest, you should do so before starting to write.

Following the Correct Format. After you have selected a journal, you should study recent issues to learn the particular style used. Often there will be instructions for investigators who plan to submit manuscripts to the journal. It is also a good idea to obtain a copy of the style manual published by the American Psychological Association (1200 Seventeenth Street, N.W., Washington, D.C., 20036). This manual provides useful information for preparing a manuscript. It is still necessary to examine recent issues of the journal you are interested in, however, because each journal usually has slight deviations from the general style.

Now let us turn to general problems encountered in manuscript preparation. We will examine the four major sections of a research article: introduction, method, results, and discussion.

The Introduction Section

The four major sections of the manuscript correspond roughly to the four major stages of experimentation. One can conceptualize experimentation as involving an idea stage in which the problem area is selected and testable ideas generated, a testing stage in which data are collected, a results stage in which the effects are determined and evaluated for statistical significance, and an overall evaluation stage in which the possible value of the finding to the state of knowledge in the field is considered.

The introduction corresponds to the idea stage. The goal in the introduction should be to familiarize the reader with the problem, the insights for problem solution, and the procedure for testing the insights. One should say why the predictions, if supported, will be of psychological significance. The task of writing an introduction is usually more difficult than it first appears, often because of poor organization and a failure to assess accurately how much background information is needed.

Selecting the Relevant Prior Research. The amount of background information needed will depend on the nature of the problem, the audience, and the journal. Obviously, if the readers of the journal already know a great deal about the problem it is not necessary to present much background information in the introduction. To do so would be to waste journal space and the reader's time. Yet, the investigator does have an obligation to consider the earlier work most directly related to his study. He should recognize that it is extremely unlikely that the idea is completely new. The chances are that someone investigated a similar idea but not in quite the same way or in the same context or for the same purpose. Thus, at the very least the reader should be informed about the previous work that is most closely related to the study to be reported. Planning the organization of the introduction should be relatively easy after a decision has been made about how much background information to provide.

Organizing the Introduction. At the risk of laboring the obvious, it should be pointed out that one should plan the introduction before writing it. In many cases, unfortunately, little or no thought goes into planning. One needs to consider how much background material to present, the order in which to present it if there is more than one relevant study, the specific problem, the solution, and how the solution is to be tested. If the reader does not learn from the introduction what is going to be done and why, then it has not been written properly.

Indicating the Importance of the Problem. The introduction is the place to persuade the reader of the importance of the experiment. If you are ashamed of your idea, you should not bother to report the study. If you are not ashamed of it, then you should talk about its psychological significance in the introduction. The reader should be told the basic plan for testing the idea, the results to be expected, and how the results will support or refute the predictions. The specific details of the testing procedure, however, should be left for the method section.

The Method Section

The major task in the method section is to explain how the predictions were tested. If elaborate equipment or complicated materials were used it may be helpful to discuss this in a special subsection. If the experiment was extremely simple, no subheadings may be needed. In general, however, subheadings for design and procedure are useful.

Design. The reader should be told in the design subsection what was manipulated, correlated, or observed, and what was measured. If the experimental method was used, then it is necessary to specify the independent variable(s) and dependent variable(s). In general, the method section should proceed from the more molar aspects of the experiment (e.g., independent and dependent variables) to the more specific procedures employed. After reading the discussion of design, the reader should have a clear view of what was manipulated and the type of design used to test the predictions. The specific procedures used in making the tests are reported in the procedure subsection.

Procedure. The task in the discussion of procedure is to tell exactly how the experiment was conducted so that the reader could repeat the experiment in essentially the same way. After writing the procedure subsection, you should ask yourself if the experiment could be completed by referring only to the information presented in the method section. The reader has to be told how subjects were obtained, how they were assigned to conditions, what materials were used, how much time was needed for each phase of the experiment, what the subjects were told, how the dependent measure was obtained, and so on. One way to present this information is to describe the procedure used to test the subjects in each of the conditions. It is a good idea to study the method sections of published journal articles to see how this is done. After the procedure is presented, the next step is to consider the results of the experiment.

The Results Section

It is important to plan the results section before starting to write it. When you have completed all the statistical analyses, you should have a clear notion of what aspects of the results are interesting and what aspects are not. For example, if there are two or more independent variables and only one produced a statistically significant effect, this variable, all things being equal, is going to be more interesting than the others. It is also important to double-check calculations to be sure that the reported results are identical to the obtained results.

Organizing the Results. The major task is to lead the reader through the results, pointing out what is significant and what is not. Your role is like that of a guide taking visitors through a museum. Make sure that the reader is made aware of the important results. The results have to be organized in such a way that the reader is not confronted with a large mass of data. The task is to give a simple, clear, and reasonably complete account of the results. Although the specific organization will depend on the particular study considered, there are a few points that need to be emphasized.

Presenting Data. There is usually no reason to present the raw data to the reader. You should simplify the data by presenting descriptive measures (e.g., measures of central tendency such as the mean) for each group. You may have to decide whether it would be better to present the descriptive measures in the text, in a figure, or in a table. There is no rule that can be applied in all circumstances. However, if there are many numbers to present (say, ten or more), probably a table or figure should be used. Often a figure cannot be used because there are too many means to present. In such a case the tabular presentation should be preferred. The choice between a table and a figure will often depend on the nature of the data.

If you are unsure of which way to present the measures of central tendency, frequency, or whatever, prepare them in different forms. Then it may become clear which mode of presentation is best. If you are still unsure which method is the clearest for the reader, ask a few friends or colleagues to judge. Do not present the same measures in two different ways in the manuscript as this may tend to confuse or insult the reader.

Leading the Reader Through the Results. A very common mistake experimenters make in reporting results is to present a measure of central tendency in a figure or table and then leave the readers to their own devices. This is analogous to an unguided trip through a museum. If the results are simply presented in a table and the reader is expected to decide which values are important and which are unimportant, the investigator is not assuming the responsibilities of the guide. After all, by the time you report the results you should have thought about them for a long time, and should be in a good position to point out what is important.

Amount of Data Presented. You should avoid, if possible, presenting a large amount of data. If you have an exceptionally interesting study in which there are many important measures, there is little choice but to present a great deal of information. However, if a large amount of data is to be reported, the burden of the guide is increased. In most cases there is not a great deal of data that is interesting. If an investigator has one major measure and a few minor measures, and the minor measures did not yield results of statistical or psychological significance, this fact can be stated without boring the reader with a number of uninteresting tables and figures.

You should accept the fact that you are in a better position than the reader is to judge the importance of your data and should organize the results section to emphasize what is important. It is reasonable to ignore completely or just give passing notice to unimportant results. As long as your view of what is important is reasonably consistent with what others think, you should have little difficulty with instructors, journal editors, or readers.

After presenting the basic descriptive measures, you need to indicate what comparisons the reader should consider and whether they are statistically significant. If a complex analysis of variance was conducted, you may decide to present the analysis of variance table. However, it is generally better to present the F values of interest without bothering to present the entire table. Once again, the task is to decide which method of presentation is easier for the reader. The plan of the results section, then, is to present the basic descriptive measures, point out the important comparisons, and indicate whether the differences between conditions are statistically significant.

Discussing the Results. Another question is how much discussion of the results is desirable in the results section. Some investigators prefer to present the bare results and save all discussion of them for the discussion section. Others prefer to say more about them in the results section. The nature of the experiment, as well as the preferences of the investigator, may influence the choice. If it would be clearer to discuss each finding right after presenting it, then it would be better to combine the discussion section with the results section.

Let us assume, however, that you do not want to eliminate the separate discussion section because it is necessary to provide an overall evaluation of the present findings and relate them to previous research. Yet, you would still like to say something about each finding immediately after presenting it. Is it permissible to do so? The answer is *yes,* if the discussion does not take you too far afield. In general, you should avoid comparing your results with the results of earlier work as this may tend to confuse the reader. It is usually best to concentrate on making concise remarks about the interesting aspects of *your* results. A consideration of the relationship of the findings to other findings, their psychological significance, and the overall state of the problem is usually best left for the discussion section.

The Discussion Section

The discussion section is similar to the introduction in that it is a place to consider the broader problem area of interest. The introduction can be regarded as the *before* and the discussion section as the *after*. In the introduction the state of the art prior to the investigation was examined. In the discussion section you should consider the state of the art after the investigation, i.e., how the investigation influenced knowledge about the phenomenon in question. The introduction offered the idea or insight which was expected to further the understanding of a particular phenomenon or produce a particular result. The insight is testable since certain predictions follow from it. In the discussion section, presented after the reader has been informed about the accuracy of the prediction, all the cards are on the table so it is time to assess the degree of success or failure.

Reporting an Important Finding. The ease of writing the discussion section will be determined in large part by the psychological significance of the findings. If the understanding of a particular phenomenon has changed drastically because of your contribution, then, of course, you will want to emphasize the impact of your finding. The discussion section should be very enjoyable to write. Perhaps the finding has implications for further research, or perhaps it makes possible the reinterpretation of earlier work within a different theoretical framework. If the finding has practical application, this may be emphasized in the discussion. The specific nature of the discussion will depend, of course, on the particular contribution.

Reporting a Finding of Some Interest. Another possibility is that the results, although clear, are not entirely consistent with earlier findings. The task, therefore, is to compare your findings with those of other investigators and try to resolve the differences. Since you have the most recent evidence bearing on a particular problem, you should be in a good position to evaluate the current state of knowledge. The experiment may provide evidence which suggests that one view is to be preferred over the others. It may be difficult to write this kind of discussion because it may be necessary to spend a lot of time studying the results of other investigators in an attempt to integrate the results. Yet, the attempt at integration may result in additional insights which can be tested experimentally. That is, though in most cases the results will not provide a complete solution to the problem of interest, they may suggest avenues for additional research.

Reporting Findings of Little Interest. Another possibility is that the results did essentially nothing to clarify the problem, but you still have to report the findings in order to gain experience. This kind of discussion is painful to write. It is not feasible to concentrate on the extent of your contribution because this would only depress you. You cannot concentrate on a comparison of your results with those of other investigators because yours were not sufficiently clear to warrant the comparison. Thus, there is little choice but to admit that your predictions were not supported and consider the possible reasons for the failure. The state of knowledge is the same as it was before your "contribution" except that you may be convinced that one idea, yours, is not a particularly useful insight. You have the relatively unpleasant task of considering a problem for which you were unable to offer a good solution. However, since you probably learned a great deal about the problem, or at least thought a great deal about it, you may have a number of new ideas to present in the discussion section. If you can generate sufficiently interesting ideas you may wish to put them to an experimental test.

General Comments About Writing

After you have completed a draft of the four major sections, you may be tempted to decide on a title, write an abstract or summary as required, prepare the tables or figures, list the references, and then type the manuscript for publication. This would be a mistake. There is almost no chance that the first draft would measure up to the standards of a refereed journal. It is necessary to polish the manuscript. You polish it by recasting unclear statements, eliminating redundancy, correcting faulty organization, and remedying any other defects you can find. After you believe the manuscript is in fine shape, it is a good idea to ask someone to read it and make criticisms. One has to be very careful in choosing a critic.

It is important to find someone who will criticize constructively. You are likely to be ego-involved in your work and, therefore, somewhat reluctant to accept even constructive criticism. If you are offered nonconstructive criticism (e.g., "I can't believe you passed Freshman English!"), the only thing you gain is animosity toward the critic. There is also the danger of finding a critic who is so picayune that you doubt the value of the criticism. On the other hand, there is the danger of finding someone who is unwilling to make any criticism for fear of offending. What is needed is someone who will discreetly tell you if you have literary "bad breath." It may be difficult to find such a person. Hopefully, you know at least one individual who qualifies.

Once you have found this rare person you need to treat him with extreme care. It is important to take his comments seriously. If he says a statement is unclear, you have to be willing to clarify it. It is irrelevant that the statement is clear to you. The important thing is that it be clear to others. After all, your purpose is to communicate your findings.

You may be frustrated by the criticism. You would probably prefer the critic to say that the manuscript is in excellent shape so that you could prepare it for publication. Task completion is usually a rewarding state of affairs so anything that delays it may be frustrating. Yet, it is necessary to fight the urge to get the job over with at any cost. Once a manuscript is published there is no way to change it.

Preparing the Manuscript for Publication

As we have said, you should check recent issues of the journal you have in mind and any instructions for authors — such as instructions on the inside covers of the journal or in the publication manual of the American Psychological Association — before preparing the manuscript for publication. Unless you have special drawing talents, you should find a professional draftsman to prepare the figures. The manuscript should be typed according to the specifications of the journal and the appropriate number of copies made. Then it is important to proofread carefully. After any errors are eliminated, the manuscript is sent to the journal editor along with a covering letter asking that it be considered for the journal. After a reasonable length of time (in some cases an unreasonable length of time), you will receive a reply from the editor. The manuscript will be accepted as is, accepted subject to certain revisions, or rejected.

Let us assume that your manuscript has been accepted. Except for checking the printer's proofs, the task is completed. You have generated an idea, devised a test for it, executed the test, determined the results, evaluated them, and published the findings. If you have been able to complete the entire cycle, you should be very proud of yourself. Obviously, a tremendous amount of thought and effort is needed to conduct a successful research project. If you enjoyed testing your idea, you may want to give serious thought to a research career. There is a need for people who can generate and test important ideas.

SUMMARY

It is important to distinguish between statistical and psychological significance. Statistical significance refers to the likelihood that an event can be attributed to chance effects. Psychological significance refers to whether a finding is a contribution to knowledge. The psychological significance of a study is determined by the quality of the idea tested, the adequacy of the test, and the clarity of the results.

The decision to report research findings should be based solely on their importance, but other factors frequently enter in. Some people are reluctant to report their findings because writing makes them "nervous." One should expect to experience some anxiety while preparing a manuscript because research usually involves a tremendous personal commitment.

The four major sections of the manuscript correspond roughly to the four major stages of experimentation. The introduction corresponds to the idea stage, the method section to the testing stage, the results section to the evaluation of the obtained findings, and the discussion section to the overall evaluation.

The problems in writing the introduction are selecting the relevant prior research, organizing the introduction, and explaining why the proposed idea is a contribution to knowledge. The reader should be told in the method section about how the idea was tested. It should be possible to repeat the experiment by referring only to the information presented in the method section. The problems in writing the results section include organizing the results and deciding what to present and how to present it. The nature of the discussion section will be influenced by whether the finding is of little interest, some interest, or great interest.

APPENDIX

WEAPONS AS AGGRESSION-ELICITING STIMULI

Leonard Berkowitz and Anthony LePage

University of Wisconsin

Abstract

An experiment was conducted to test the hypothesis that stimuli commonly associated with aggression can elicit aggressive responses from people ready to act aggressively. 100 male university students received either 1 or 7 shocks, supposedly from a peer, and were then given an opportunity to shock this person. In some cases a rifle and revolver were on the table near the shock key. These weapons were said to belong, or not to belong, to the available target person. In other instances there was nothing on the table near the shock key, while for a control group 2 badminton racquets were on the table near the key. The greatest number of shocks was given by the strongly aroused <u>Ss</u> (who had received 7 shocks) when they were in the presence of the weapons. The guns had evidently elicited strong aggressive responses from the aroused men.

Reprinted by permission of the senior author and publisher from the *Journal of Personality and Social Psychology,* vol. 7 (1967), pp. 202–207.

WEAPONS AS AGGRESSION-ELICITING STIMULI[1]

Leonard Berkowitz and Anthony LePage

University of Wisconsin

General statement

Human behavior is often goal directed, guided by strategies and ✓ influenced by ego defenses and strivings for cognitive consistency. There clearly are situations, however, in which these purposive considerations are relatively unimportant regulators of action. Habitual behavior patterns become dominant on these occasions, and the person responds relatively automatically to the stimuli impinging upon him. Any really complete psychological system must deal with these stimulus-elicited, impulsive reactions as well as with more complex behavior patterns. More than this, we should also be able to specify the conditions under which the various behavior determinants increase or decrease in importance.

The senior author has long contended that many aggressive actions are controlled by the stimulus properties of the available targets rather than by anticipations of ends that might be served (Berkowitz, 1962, 1964, 1965). Perhaps because strong emotion results in an increased utilization of only the central cues in the immediate situation (Easterbrook, 1959; Walters & Parke, 1964), anger arousal can lead to impulsive aggressive responses which, for a short time at least, may be relatively free of cognitively mediated inhibitions against aggression or, for that matter, purposes and strategic considerations. This impulsive action is not necessarily pushed out by the anger, however. Berkowitz has suggested that appropriate cues must be present in the situation if aggressive responses are actually to occur. While there is still considerable uncertainty as to just what characteristics define aggressive cue properties, the association of a stimulus with aggression evidently can enhance the aggressive cue value of this stimulus. A variety of observations can be cited in support of this reasoning (cf. Berkowitz, 1965).

Direct evidence for the present formulation can be found in a study conducted by Loew (1965). His subjects, in being required to learn a concept, either aggressive or neutral words, spoke either 20 aggressive or 20 neutral words aloud. Following this "learning task," each subject was to give a peer in an adjacent room an electric shock whenever this person made a mistake in his learning problem. Allowed to vary the intensity of the shocks they administered over a 10-point continuum, the subjects who had uttered the aggressive words gave shocks of significantly greater intensity than did the subjects who had spoken the neutral words. The aggressive words had evidently evoked implicit aggressive responses from the subjects, even though they had not been angered beforehand, which then led to the stronger attacks upon the target person in the next room when he supposedly made errors.

Cultural learning shared by many members of a society can also associate external objects with aggression and thus affect the objects' aggressive cue value. Weapons are a prime example. For many men (and probably women as well) in our society, these objects are closely associated with aggression. Assuming that the weapons do not produce inhibitions that are stronger than the evoked aggressive reactions (as would be the case, e.g., if the weapons were labeled as morally "bad"), the presence of the aggressive objects should generally lead to more intense attacks upon an available target than would occur in the presence of a neutral object.

The present experiment was designed to test this latter hypothesis. At one level, of course, the findings contribute to the current debate as to the desirability of restricting sales of firearms. Many arguments have been raised for such a restriction. Thus, according to recent statistics, Texas communities having virtually no prohibitions against firearms have a much higher homicide rate than other American cities possessing stringent firearm regulations, and J. Edgar Hoover has maintained in *Time* magazine that the availability of firearms is an important factor in murders (Anonymous, 1966). The experiment reported here seeks to determine how this influence may come about. The availability of weapons obviously makes it easier for a person who wants to commit murder to do so. But, in addition, we ask whether weapons can serve as aggression-eliciting stimuli, causing an angered individual to display stronger violence than he would have shown in the absence of such weapons. Social significance aside, and at a more general theoretical level, this research also attempts to demonstrate that situational stimuli can exert "automatic" control over socially relevant human actions.

Method

Subjects

The subjects were 100 male undergraduates enrolled in the introductory psychology course at the University of Wisconsin who volunteered for the experiment (without knowing its nature) in order to earn points counting toward their final grade. Thirty-nine other subjects had also been run, but were discarded because they suspected the experimenter's confederate (21), reported receiving fewer electric shocks than was actually given them (7), had not attended to information given them about the procedure (9), or were run while there was equipment malfunctioning(2).

Procedure

General design. Seven experimental conditions were established, six organized in a 2 x 3 factorial design, with the seventh group serving essentially as a control. Of the men in the factorial design, half were made to be angry with the confederate, while the other subjects received a friendlier treatment from him. All of the subjects were then given an opportunity to administer electric shocks to the confederate, but for two-thirds of the men there were weapons lying on the table near the shock apparatus. Half of these people were informed the weapons belonged to the confederate in order to test the hypothesis that aggressive stimuli which also were associated with the anger instigator would evoke the strongest aggressive reaction from the subjects. The other people seeing the weapons were told the weapons had been left by a previous experimenter. There was nothing on the table except the shock key when the last third of the subjects in both the angered and nonangered conditions gave the shocks. Finally, the seventh group consisted of angered men who gave shocks with two badminton racquets and shuttlecocks lying near the shock key. This condition sought to determine whether the presence of *any* object near the shock apparatus would reduce inhibitions against aggression, even if the object were not connected with aggressive behavior.

Experimental manipulations. When each subject arrived in the laboratory, he was informed that two men were required for the experiment and that they would have to wait for the second subject to appear. After a 5-minute wait, the experimenter, acting annoyed, indicated that they had to begin because of his other commitments. He said he would have to look around outside to see if he could find another person who might serve as a substitute for the missing subject. In a few minutes the experimenter returned with the confederate. Depending upon the condition, this person was introduced as either a psychology student who had been about to sign up for another experiment or as a student who had been running another study.

The subject and confederate were told the experiment was a study of physiological reactions to stress. The stress would be created by mild electric shocks, and the subjects could withdraw, the experimenter said, if they objected to these shocks. (No subjects left.) Each person would have to solve a problem knowing that his performance would be evaluated by his partner. The "evaluations" would be in the form of electric shocks, with one shock signifying a very good rating and 10 shocks meaning the performance was judged as very bad. The men were then told what their problems were. The subject's task was to list ideas a publicity agent might employ in order to better a popular singer's record sales and public image. The other person (the confederate) had to think of things a used-car dealer might do in order to increase sales. The two were given 5 minutes to write their answers, and the papers were then collected by the experimenter who supposedly would exchange them.

Following this, the two were placed in separate rooms, supposedly so that they would not influence each other's galvanic skin response (GSR) reactions. The shock electrodes were placed on the subject's right forearm, and GSR electrodes were attached to fingers on his left hand, with wires trailing from the electrodes to the next room. The subject was told he would be the first to receive electric shocks as the evaluation of his problem solution. The experimenter left the subject's room saying he was going to turn on the GSR apparatus, went to the room containing the shock machine and the waiting confederate, and only then looked at the schedule indicating whether the subject was to be angered or not. He informed the confederate how many shocks the subject was to receive, and 30 seconds later the subject was given seven shocks (angered condition) or one shock (nonangered group). The experimenter then went back to the subject, while the confederate quickly arranged the table holding the shock key in the manner appropriate for the subject's condition. Upon entering the subject's room, the experimenter asked him how many shocks he had received and provided the subject with a brief questionnaire on which he was to rate his mood. As soon as this was completed, the subject was taken to the room holding the shock machine. Here the experimenter told the subject it was his turn to evaluate his partner's work. For one group in both the angered and nonangered conditions the shock key was alone on the table (no-object groups). For two other groups in each of these angered and non-angered conditions, however, a 12-guage shotgun and a .38-caliber revolver were lying on the table near the key (aggressive-weapon conditions). One group in both the angered and nonangered conditions was informed the weapons belonged to the subject's partner. The subjects given this treatment had been told earlier that their partner was a student who had been conducting an experiment. They now were reminded of this, and the experimenter said the weapons were being used in some way by this person in his research (associated-weapons condition); the guns were to be disregarded. The other men were told simply the weapons "belong to someone else" who "must have been doing an experiment in here" (unassociated-weapons group), and they too were asked to disregard the guns. For the last treatment, one group of angered men found two badminton racquets and shuttlecocks lying on the table near the shock key, and these people were also told the equipment belonged to someone else (badminton-racquets group).

Immediately after this information was provided, the experimenter showed the subject what was supposedly his partner's answer to his assigned problem. The subject was reminded that he was to give the partner shocks as his evaluation and was informed that this was the last time shocks would be administered in the study. A second copy of the mood questionnaire was then completed by the subject after he had delivered the shocks. Following this, the subject was asked a number of oral questions about the experiment, including what, if any, suspicions he had. (No doubts were voiced about the presence of the weapons.) At the conclusion of this interview the experiment was explained, and the subject was asked not to talk about the study.

Results

Effectiveness of Arousal Treatment

Analyses of variance of the responses to each of the mood scales following the receipt of the partner's evaluation indicate the prior-shock treatment succeeded in creating differences in anger arousal. The subjects getting seven shocks rated themselves as being significantly angrier than the subjects receiving only one shock, $F(1,84) = 20.65$, $p < .01$). There were no reliable differences among the groups within any one arousal level.

Aggression Toward Partner

The mean number of shocks administered in each experimental condition are given in Table 1. The hypothesis guiding the present study receives good support. The strongly provoked men delivered more frequent electrical attacks upon their tormentor in the presence of a weapon than when non-

---

Insert Table 1 about here

---

aggressive objects (the badminton racquets and shuttle-cocks) were present or when only the shock key was on the table. An analysis of variance of the shock data for the six groups in the 3 x 2 factorial design (i.e., exclude the badminton racquets condition) revealed two significant effects. The subjects who received seven shocks delivered more shocks to the confederate than the subjects who received one shock $\underline{F}(1,84) = 104.62$, $\underline{p} < .001$. And, the Number of Shocks by Weapons Association interaction was significant, $\underline{F}(2,84) = 5.02$, $\underline{p} < .01$. The significant interaction means that the effect of the presence of the weapons on the dependent measure was influenced by whether subjects were given one or seven shocks.

Discussion

Common sense, as well as a good deal of personality theorizing, both influenced to some extent by an egocentric view of human behavior as being caused almost exclusively by motives within the individual, generally neglect the type of weapons effect demonstrated in the present study. If a person holding a gun fires it, we are told either that he wanted to do so (consciously or unconsciously) or that he pulled the trigger "accidentally." The findings summarized here suggest yet another possibility: The presence of the weapon might have elicited an intense aggressive reaction from the person with the gun, assuming his inhibitions against aggression were relatively weak at the moment. Indeed, it is altogether conceivable that many hostile acts which supposedly stem from unconscious motivation really arise because of the operation of aggressive cues. Not realizing how these situational stimuli might elicit aggressive behavior, and not detecting the presence of these cues, the observer tends to locate the source of the action in some conjectured underlying, perhaps repressed, motive. Similarly, if he is a Skinnerian rather than a dynamically oriented clinician, he might also neglect the operation of aggression-eliciting stimuli by invoking the concept of operant behavior, and thus sidestep the issue altogether. The sources of the hostile action, for him, too, rest within the individual, with the behavior only steered or permitted by discriminative stimuli.

Alternative explanations must be ruled out, however, before the present thesis can be regarded as confirmed. One obvious possibility is that the subjects in the weapons condition reacted to the demand characteristics of the situation as they saw them and exhibited the kind of behavior they thought was required of them. ("These guns on the table mean I'm supposed to be aggressive, so I'll give many shocks.") Several considerations appear to negate this explanation. First, there are the subject's own verbal reports. None of the subjects voiced any suspicions of the weapons and, furthermore, when they were queried generally denied that the weapons had any effect on them. But even those subjects who did express any doubts about the experiment typically acted like the other subjects.

Setting this aside, moreover, it is not altogether certain from the notion of demand characteristics that only the angered subjects would be inclined to act in conformity with the experimenter's supposed demands. The nonangered men in the weapons group did not display a heightened number of attacks on their partner. Would this have been predicted beforehand by researchers interested in demand characteristics? The last finding raises one final observation. Recent unpublished research by Allen and Bragg indicates that awareness of the experimenter's purpose does not necessarily result in an increased display of the behavior the experimenter supposedly desires. Dealing with one kind of socially disapproved action (conformity), Allen and Bragg demonstrated that high levels of experimentally induced awareness of the experimenter's interests generally produced a decreased level of the relevant behavior. Thus, if the subjects in our study had known the experimenter was interested in observing their *aggressive* behavior, they might well have given less, rather than more, shocks, since giving shocks is also socially disapproved. This type of phenomenon was also not observed in the weapons conditions.

Nevertheless, any one experiment cannot possibly definitely exclude all of the alternative explanations. Scientific hypotheses are only probability statements, and further research is needed to heighten the likelihood that the present reasoning is correct.

References

Anonymous. A gun-toting nation. _Time_, August 12, 1966.

Berkowitz, L. _Aggression: A social psychological analysis_. New York: McGraw-Hill, 1962.

Berkowitz, L. Aggressive cues in aggressive behavior and hostility catharsis. _Psychological Review_, 1964, _71_, 104-122.

Berkowitz, L. The concept of aggressive drive: Some additional considerations. In L. Berkowitz (Ed.), _Advances in experimental social psychology_. Vol.2. New York: Academic Press, 1965, pp. 301-329.

Easterbrook, J. A. The effect of emotion on cue utilization and the organization of behavior. _Psychological Review_, 1959, _66_, 183-201.

Loew, C. A. Acquisition of a hostile attitude and its relationship to aggressive behavior. Unpublished doctoral dissertation, State University of Iowa, 1965.

Walters, R. H., & Parke, R. D. Social motivation, dependency, and susceptibility to social influence. In L. Berkowitz (Ed.), _Advances in Experimental Social Psychology_. Vol.1. New York: Academic Press, 1964, pp. 231-276.

Footnotes

1. The present experiment was conducted by Anthony LePage under Leonard Berkowitz' supervision as part of a research program sponsored by Grant G-23988 from the National Science Foundation to the senior author.

Table 1

Mean Number of Shocks Given

in Each Condition

Condition	Shocks received	
	1	7
Associated weapons	2.60	6.07
Unassociated weapons	2.20	5.67
No object	3.07	4.67
Badminton racquets	----	4.60

appendix: proofs and examples

1. *Probability*
2. *Proof That Two Independent Estimates of Population Variance Can Be Obtained If the Null Hypothesis Is True*
3. *Proof That the* $SS_{tot} = SS_{bg} + SS_{wg}$
4. *Computation of the Analysis of Variance with the Deviation Formulae*
5. *Proof That the Deviation and Computation Formulae for the Analysis of Variance Are Mathematically Equivalent*

1. PROBABILITY

In Chapter 4 the probability of an event was defined as the ratio of favorable events divided by the total possible events. For example, the probability of drawing a heart from a standard deck of playing cards is .25 since there are thirteen favorable events and fifty-two total possible events. In this example it is easy to determine the number of favorable events and the total number of events. But as the number of possible events and favorable events increases, or the complexity of the events increases, the task of determining the probability of an outcome becomes more difficult. For example, determining the probability of a particular sequence of events is usually more difficult than assessing the probability of a single event. Fortunately, in some instances it is possible to use rules to calculate the probability of events if the complexity or number of events precludes determining the probability directly by dividing the number of favorable events by the total number of possible events.

Multiplication Rule

The multiplication rule is useful because in many instances the probability of two independent events is known (e.g., the probability of obtaining heads when tossing a coin and the probability of obtaining a 4 with one roll of a die). The probability of obtaining both events in succession is calculated by multiplying the probabilities of the separate events. For example, the probability of tossing a head and then obtaining a 4 by rolling a die is .083 since the probability of obtaining a head is .50 and the probability of obtaining a 4 is .167. Thus, the probability of a *complex* outcome can be determined if the probability of the *components* of the event is known. It is only necessary to multiply the probabilities of the components. It is assumed that the components are discrete, independent events. For example, the toss of the coin should not influence the roll of the die. Or, stated differently, if the probability of the joint occurrence of two events is equal to the probability of the occurrence of one event times the probability of the occurrence of the other event, the events are independent.

Permutations

In many instances it is useful to know the number of ways that objects or events can be arranged. An ordered arrangement is called a *permutation*. The total number of permutations of N objects or events is $N!$. The symbol ! is called *factorial*. $N!$ is the product of all successive integers from N to 1. For example, if an investigator has six different conditions and desires to counterbalance them completely, the number of permutations of the six conditions is 6! or $6 \times 5 \times 4 \times 3 \times 2 \times 1$ or 720. After determining the number of permutations, it is likely that the investigator will decide against complete counterbalancing of the six conditions.

The reader who does not believe there are 720 different orders of six objects or events can generate all possible orders. In generating the first order, the reader will find that there are six possible conditions for the first position, five for the second position, four for the third position, three for the fourth position, two for the fifth position, and only one for the sixth position. The reader who notes this relationship will only have to generate one order to realize that the number of possible permutations is $N!$. It is assumed that each condition can be used once and only once in each sequence.

In some cases it is not feasible or desirable to arrange the entire set of N objects or events. Instead, it is necessary to determine the number of ways of selecting and arranging a *portion* of the N objects. If r is equal to the number of objects selected and r is equal to or less than N, then the number of permutations of r objects selected from among N distinct objects is equal to:

$$\frac{N!}{(N-r)!}.$$

For example, if an investigator could only test three of six possible conditions in each session, then r would equal 3 and N would equal 6. The number of permutations of the three conditions selected from the six conditions would be

$$\frac{6!}{(6-3)!}$$

or $6 \times 5 \times 4$ or 120.

In short, the number of possible arrangements of events can be determined by using the permutation formulae. If the total number of permutations is known, then it is a relatively simple task to assess whether an obtained sequence is a rare or common event. However, for many purposes it is not important to consider the order of events but only the number of ways that r events can be selected from N events. If the ordering is not important then a way is needed to compute the number of combinations of N events taken r at a time. For permutations the order of the events is important. For combinations the order of the events is irrelevant.

Combinations

The number of ways of selecting r distinct combinations of N objects can be calculated by the formula

$$\frac{N!}{r!\,(N-r)!}.$$

For example, assume that an investigator wants to select four subjects, at random without replacement, from a group of ten subjects. How many ways could four subjects be selected from among the ten subjects? In this case $r = 4$ and $N = 10$. The number of combinations of ten things taken four at a time is equal to

$$\frac{10!}{4!\,6!} = 210.$$

Thus, the probability of obtaining any particular set of four subjects is 1/210 or .0047.

The use of the combination formula makes it possible to determine the probability of relatively complex events. For example, the combination formula can be used to calculate the probability of being dealt a flush (all five cards of the same suit) in a game of stud poker. There are thirteen cards in each suit so it is necessary to determine the number of ways of selecting five distinct combinations of thirteen objects. That is, it is necessary to determine the number of different ways one can get a flush in each suit. The number of combinations is

$$\frac{13!}{5!\,(13-5)!} = 1287.$$

Since there are four different suits there are 5,148 different ways that one can be dealt a flush in stud poker. Thus, there are 5,148 favorable events. The total number of possible events is calculated by determining the number of possible poker hands that one can be dealt. This is determined by computing the number of combinations of fifty-two cards taken five at a time. The number of combinations is

$$\frac{52!}{5!\,(47)!} = 2{,}598{,}960.$$

Thus, the probability of being dealt a flush in a game of stud poker is 5,148/2,598,960 or slightly less than .002.

2. PROOF THAT TWO INDEPENDENT ESTIMATES OF POPULATION VARIANCE CAN BE OBTAINED IF THE NULL HYPOTHESIS IS TRUE

The following set of symbols are used in the proofs in Appendix A. It is assumed that there are the same number of scores in each condition or group.

$n =$ number of scores in each group
$X =$ any score
$\overline{X}_j =$ mean of group j
$\overline{X}. =$ mean for all groups combined or the grand mean
$\sigma^2 =$ population variance
$s^2 =$ sample variance
$s =$ standard deviation of the sample
$s_{\overline{x}} =$ standard error of the sample

Within-Group Estimate of Population Variance

The first step is to prove that the SS_{wg} divided by its degrees of freedom is equal to the sample variance. Remember that sample variance is the best estimate of population variance. The task, therefore, is to obtain two independent ways to compute s^2. If there is only one sample or group, the best estimate of population variance is the sample variance or

$$\frac{\Sigma (X - \overline{X}_j)^2}{n - 1}.$$

If there is more than one sample, the best estimate is obtained by pooling the k different estimates of population variance by summing them and dividing by k. Thus the best estimate of population variance is:

$$\frac{\Sigma\Sigma\ (X - \overline{X}_j)^2}{k(n - 1)} = s^2.$$

The double summation sign means that the values obtained by performing the indicated operations on the scores in each group are summed over groups.

The symbol s^2 is used since the obtained value is an estimate of population variance and not the actual population variance. An examination of the left side of the equation reveals that the numerator is equal to the SS_{wg} (i.e., the sum of the squared deviations of each score from its group mean) and the denominator is equal to the degrees of freedom for within groups. The number of scores that are free to vary in each group is equal to $n - 1$. Since there are k groups, the degrees of freedom for within groups is equal to $k(n - 1)$. In short, the SS_{wg} divided by its degrees of freedom provides one estimate of population variance.

Between-Groups Estimate of Population Variance

The next task is to demonstrate that the SS_{bg} divided by its degrees of freedom also provides an estimate of population variance if the null hypothesis is true. In order to do this it is necessary to know that the standard deviation of the null hypothesis sampling distribution is called the *standard error.* Any time there is more than one group, the different groups comprise a sampling distribution, i.e., a distribution of samples. If the independent variable does not have an effect, the distribution can be considered a null hypothesis sampling distribution.

The standard error is equal to the standard deviation divided by the square root of n (i.e., $s_{\bar{x}} = \frac{s}{\sqrt{n}}$). Since it is necessary to work with the variance instead of the standard deviation, each side of the equation is squared. This gives equation 1.

$$s_{\bar{x}}^2 = \frac{s^2}{n} \tag{1}$$

If each side of equation 1 is multiplied by n, an estimate of population variance is obtained since s^2 is an estimate of population variance.

$$ns_{\bar{x}}^2 = s^2 \tag{2}$$

Since

$$s_{\bar{x}}^2 = \frac{\Sigma(\overline{X}_j - \overline{X}.)^2}{k - 1}$$

the right hand value in this equation can be inserted in equation 2 to give equation 3.

$$\frac{\Sigma\ n(\overline{X}_j - \overline{X}.)^2}{k - 1} = s^2 \tag{3}$$

Note that the numerator of the left term in equation 3 is equal to the SS_{bg} and the denominator is equal to the degrees of freedom for the SS_{bg}. Therefore, the SS_{bg} divided by its degrees of freedom provides an estimate of population variance when the null hypothesis is true. Since the SS_{bg} divided by its degrees of freedom and the SS_{wg} divided by its degrees of freedom provide independent estimates of population variance when the null hypothesis is true, these estimates can be compared in order to assess whether the null hypothesis is true. This point has already been discussed under the heading "Logic of Analysis of Variance."

3. PROOF THAT THE $SS_{tot} = SS_{bg} + SS_{wg}$

Once again, it is assumed that there are the same number of scores for each condition or group. The symbol notation is the same as the notation used in Appendix A-2. The first step is to show that the grand mean subtracted from any score is equal to the difference between the score and the group mean plus the difference between the group mean and the grand mean. This equation is obtained by simply adding and subtracting the group mean from the right side of the equation.

$$(X - \overline{X}.) = (X - \overline{X}_j) + (\overline{X}_j - \overline{X}.) \tag{1}$$

Equation 1 applies to any score. Since the SS_{tot} is obtained by considering all scores, it is necessary to obtain the sum of the values obtained by performing the operation on every score in each group and for all groups. The double summation sign indicates that the values obtained by considering all the scores in each group and all the groups are added. Each side of equation 2 is also squared since it is necessary to consider squared deviations from the mean. Equation 3 is obtained by expanding the right side of equation 2. Equation 3 reduces to equation 4,

$$\Sigma\Sigma(X - \overline{X}.)^2 = \Sigma\Sigma[(X - \overline{X}_j) + (\overline{X}_j - \overline{X}.)]^2 \tag{2}$$

$$\Sigma\Sigma(X - \overline{X}.)^2 = \Sigma\Sigma(X - \overline{X}_j)^2 + \Sigma\Sigma(\overline{X}_j - \overline{X}.)^2 + 2\Sigma\Sigma(X - \overline{X}_j)(\overline{X}_j - \overline{X}.) \tag{3}$$

$$\Sigma\Sigma(X - \overline{X}.)^2 = \Sigma\Sigma(X - \overline{X}_j)^2 + \Sigma\Sigma(\overline{X}_j - \overline{X}.)^2 \tag{4}$$

$$SS_{tot} = SS_{wg} + SS_{bg} \tag{5}$$

since the deviations that are not squared sum to zero. That is, the last term in equation 3 is equal to zero. The first term in equation 4 is equal to the SS_{tot}; the second term is equal to the SS_{wg}; and the third term is equal to the SS_{bg}.

4. COMPUTATION OF THE ANALYSIS OF VARIANCE WITH THE DEVIATION FORMULAE

The hypothetical experiment was designed to investigate the influence of alcohol on motor performance. The independent variable was the amount of alcohol: 0, 1, 2, or 3 shots. The dependent variable was the number of total errors for each of the twenty-four players for a four game series.

Number of Errors

	0 Condition	1 Condition	2 Condition	3 Condition
	1	2	4	5
	2	3	5	6
	3	4	6	7
	1	2	4	5
	2	3	5	6
	3	4	6	7
Total	12	18	30	36
$\overline{X}$	2	3	5	6

Grand Mean equal to 4

$$SS_{tot} = \Sigma\Sigma(X - \overline{X}.)^2$$
$$SS_{tot} = (9 + 4 + 1 + 9 + 4 + 1) + (4 + 1 + 0 + 4 + 1 + 0) + (0 + 1 + 4 + 0 + 1 + 4) + (1 + 4 + 9 + 1 + 4 + 9)$$
$$SS_{tot} = 28 + 10 + 10 + 28$$
$$SS_{tot} = 76$$

$$SS_{bg} = \Sigma n(\overline{X}_j - \overline{X}.)^2$$
$$SS_{bg} = 6[(2)^2 + (1)^2 + (1)^2 + (2)^2]$$
$$SS_{bg} = 6\ [10]$$
$$SS_{bg} = 60$$

$$SS_{wg} = SS_{tot} - SS_{bg}$$
$$SS_{wg} = 76 - 60$$
$$SS_{wg} = 16$$
or
$$SS_{wg} = \Sigma\Sigma[X - \overline{X}_j]^2$$
$$SS_{wg} = [(1^2 + 0^2 + 1^2 + 1^2 + 0^2 + 1^2) + (1^2 + 0^2 + 1^2 + 1^2 + 0^2 + 1^2) + (1^2 + 0^2 + 1^2 + 1^2 + 0^2 + 1^2) + (1^2 + 0^2 + 1^2 + 1^2 + 0^2 + 1^2)]$$
$$SS_{wg} = 4 + 4 + 4 + 4$$
$$SS_{wg} = 16$$

Analysis of Variance Table

Source	*df*	*SS*	*MS*	*F*
bg	3	60	20	25.00
wg	20	16	.80	
tot	23	76		

5. PROOF THAT THE DEVIATION AND COMPUTATIONAL FORMULAE FOR THE ANALYSIS OF VARIANCE ARE MATHEMATICALLY EQUIVALENT

Once again, it is assumed that there are an equal number of subjects in each condition. The symbol notation is the same as the notation used in Appendix A-2.

In order to demonstrate that the deviation formulae are equivalent to the computational formulae, the computational formulae are derived from the deviation formulae. That is, the plan is to start with the deviation formulae and by a series of algebraic steps end up with the computational formulae. The student who has a weak background in algebra may elect to skip this proof. Another "proof" can be obtained by computing the analysis of variance in Appendix A-4 by using the computational formulae.

The SS_{tot}

$$SS_{tot} = \Sigma\Sigma(X - \bar{X}.)^2 = \Sigma\Sigma(X^2 - 2\bar{X}.X + \bar{X}.^2) \qquad (1)$$

$$SS_{tot} = \Sigma\Sigma X^2 - 2\bar{X}.\Sigma\Sigma X + \bar{X}.^2\Sigma n$$

$$SS_{tot} = \Sigma\Sigma X^2 - \frac{2\Sigma\Sigma X(\Sigma\Sigma X)}{\Sigma n} + \frac{(\Sigma\Sigma X)^2\Sigma n}{(\Sigma n)^2}$$

$$SS_{tot} = \Sigma\Sigma X^2 - \frac{2(\Sigma\Sigma X)^2}{\Sigma n} + \frac{(\Sigma\Sigma X)^2}{\Sigma n}$$

$$SS_{tot} = \Sigma\Sigma X^2 - \frac{(\Sigma\Sigma X)^2}{N}$$

$$SS_{tot} = \Sigma\Sigma X^2 - \frac{(T)^2}{N} \qquad (2)$$

In equation 2, T is equal to the sum of all the scores and N is equal to the number of different scores.

The SS_{bg}

$$SS_{bg} = \Sigma n(\bar{X}_j - \bar{X}.)^2 \qquad (3)$$

$$SS_{bg} = \Sigma n(\bar{X}_j^2 - 2\bar{X}_j\bar{X}. + \bar{X}.^2)$$

$$SS_{bg} = \Sigma n\bar{X}_j^2 - 2\bar{X}.\Sigma n\bar{X}_j + \bar{X}.^2\Sigma n$$

$$SS_{bg} = \frac{\Sigma(\Sigma X)^2}{n} - \frac{2(\Sigma\Sigma X)}{\Sigma n} \times \frac{\Sigma n(\Sigma X)}{n} + \frac{(\Sigma\Sigma X)^2}{\Sigma n}$$

$$SS_{bg} = \frac{\Sigma(\Sigma X)^2}{n} - \frac{2(\Sigma\Sigma X)^2}{\Sigma n} + \frac{(\Sigma\Sigma X)^2}{\Sigma n}$$

$$SS_{bg} = \frac{\Sigma(\Sigma X)^2}{n} - \frac{(\Sigma\Sigma X)^2}{N}$$

$$SS_{bg} = \frac{\Sigma(group\ total)^2}{n} - \frac{(T)^2}{N} \qquad (4)$$

The SS_{wg}

$$SS_{wg} = SS_{tot} - SS_{bg}$$

appendix: research topics

Topic 1. The Lost Letter Technique
Topic 2. Correlation of Abilities
Topic 3. Mnemonic Systems
Topic 4. Information Processing
Topic 5. Aggression
Topic 6. The Cocktail Party Phenomenon
Topic 7. Interhemispheric Differences in Functioning
Topic 8. Reading
Topic 9. Machiavellianism
Topic 10. The Prisoner's Dilemma

The purpose of this appendix is to present a small number of research topics which can be used as starting points for further research. Suggestions for research are made for each of the topics, but the task of selecting, planning, and executing a project is left for the student. Planning and executing your own research project is an excellent way to gain an understanding of the various stages of experimentation and the relationships among them. Moreover, the student who becomes actively involved in a research project which is of personal interest is likely to find that research can be fun. The student who does not find a topic to his liking in this appendix is encouraged to examine the journals which report research findings in psychology and the other social sciences. The topics in this appendix are not representative of the research areas investigated by social scientists because it was necessary to exclude those topics which require special skills, equipment, or an extensive knowledge of the area. Instructors who elect to emphasize a particular content area can offer alternative research topics.

TOPIC 1. THE LOST LETTER TECHNIQUE

Milgram (1969) describes a technique that can be used to assess public opinion and that avoids some of the problems inherent in the survey technique. The survey technique typically entails selecting a representative sample from a larger population and then questioning each subject in the sample. Its success is demonstrated by the fact that political polls tend to predict accurately the outcome of elections. The survey technique is a reactive measure, of course, because the person being interviewed is aware that some sort of "evaluation" is occurring.

The lost letter technique yields a nonreactive measure. The subjects are not aware, presumably, that their performance is being assessed, because the investigator does not select or make direct contact with them. The only contact between the investigator and the subjects is through a "lost letter." The investigator plants a number of self-addressed, stamped letters at various locations. The dependent measure is the number of letters that are mailed by the people who find them. Thus, the lost letter technique differs from the survey technique in that it assesses the willingness of individuals to carry out a particular act — to mail or not mail a letter — instead of assessing opinion directly.

In one of Milgram's studies, four hundred letters were addressed in exactly the same way (to the same address in New Haven, Connecticut) except that they were directed either to Mr. Walter Carnap, to the Friends of the Communist Party, to the Friends of the Nazi Party, or to the Medical Research Associates. The words "Attention: Mr. Walter Carnap" were typed at the lower left on each of the three hundred envelopes addressed to one of the organizations. The contents of every letter were the same. Walter Carnap was told that the plans for the meeting had changed because the speakers could not arrive in time. The letter was straightforward but suggestive in light of the organization involved. That is, the reader would be likely to infer that the sender (Max Thuringer) and addressee (Walter Carnap) were actively involved in the affairs of the organization, particularly in the recruitment of new members. The envelopes were distributed in various locations (sidewalks, shops, telephone booths) in ten preselected districts of New Haven. In addition, each envelope had been sealed so that, provided the letter was posted, the investigator would be able to determine whether it had been opened.

The results were striking. The percentage of the 100 letters posted was very high for the letters to the Medical Research Associates (72 percent) and for the personal letters (71 percent), but very low (25 percent) for letters to the other two organizations. There was a greater tendency to open the letters addressed to the organizations, particularly the Communist (40 percent) and Nazi (32 percent) ones, than the personal letters (10 percent).

There are a number of ways the Milgram technique can be used. It can be used to assess public opinion on a controversial issue by varying the name of the organization that is placed on the lost letters. If the issue is one about which people tend to be highly emotional, it may be interesting to compare the results of the lost letter technique with the results obtained wih a survey technique. Or, the technique could be used to study how subject variables or location variables influence whether individuals will carry out a particular act. For example, if you lost a textbook which was clearly marked with your name, address, and telephone number, do you believe the probability of having it returned would be influenced by whether it was left in a chapel, dormitory, or classroom?

Reference

Milgram, S. The lost-letter technique. *Psychology Today,* 1969, June.

TOPIC 2. CORRELATION OF ABILITIES

Many problems can be investigated only by correlational and observational techniques. For example, beginning in 1921, Terman and his associates studied over 1,500 children who had I.Q.'s of 140 or above. The progress of the children was followed through the middle years of their adult lives. The major finding was that the gifted children were above average in characteristics other than intelligence. That is, there is a positive correlation between intelligence and health, social adaptability, and leadership. In general, the gifted children continued to be superior to their own generation as they grew older.

The student is encouraged to design a correlational study which would yield data of personal interest. For example, you may be interested in whether performance in a methodology course is related to performance in nonmethodology courses, whether quantitative abilities are related to verbal abilities, or whether the amount of study time is related to course performance. Or, you could select a test of ability such as the Remote Associates Test (Mednick and Mednick, 1967), a memory test, or a vocabulary test and correlate performance on the test with another variable of interest.

The Remote Associates Test can be described as a search task. Each item consists of three stimulus words. The subject's task is to find a word which is related to all three of the stimulus words. For example, *party* is an acceptable solution to the stimulus triad of *line, birthday,* and *surprise.* A remote associates test similar to the Mednick test is published in the paperback entitled *Involvement in Psychology Today*. There are a number of ways to construct a memory test. For example, you could select a list of twenty-five common nouns, read it aloud to subjects at the rate of one word every five seconds, and then have them recall as many words as they can from the list in any order. A vocabulary test can be constructed by selecting words which differ in degree of difficulty. It is important to select enough words of intermediate difficulty so that individual differences among the subjects will be detected.

After the test has been constructed, the next step is to establish the reliability of the measure. Reliability can be assessed by correlating the performance of subjects on even-numbered items with their performance on odd-numbered items, by correlating the scores obtained by testing each subject twice with a time lag between the two testing sessions, or by correlating the performance of subjects on two comparable tests. For example, for the memory test, you could select fifty common nouns and randomly assign each noun to List 1 or List 2 with the restriction that there be twenty-five nouns in each list. Then you could test each subject on both lists. Half the subjects would receive List 1 and then List 2 and the other half the reverse order. The performance for each subject on the two lists could then be correlated.

The reader who has attempted to establish the reliability of a test is likely to appreciate the fact that it is not a simple matter to construct a reliable test. A number of attempts may be necessary. After a reliable test has been constructed, it is reasonable to question whether test performance is related to other measures. Keep in mind that there should be logical or theoretical grounds for correlating variables. For example, one might ask whether performance on a memory test can predict performance in a course which requires extensive memorization. Unfortunately, it is still not uncommon for psychologists to construct a test and then correlate it with everything in sight. On the positive side, it should be noted that psychologists have developed very sophisticated correlational techniques. These techniques, which are beyond the scope of this text, allow investigators to "explain" correlations. And, if it is possible to obtain correlations between measures at different points in a subject's life, such data can be used to assess whether variables are causally related.

References

Crano, W. D., Kenny, D. A., & Campbell, D. T. Does intelligence cause achievement? A cross-lagged panel analysis. *Journal of Educational Psychology,* 1972, 63, 258–275.

Involvement in Psychology Today. Del Mar, California: CRM Books, 1970.

Mednick, S. A., & Mednick, M. T. *Examiner's Manual: Remote Associates Test.* Boston: Houghton-Mifflin, 1967.

Oden, M. H. The fulfillment of promise: forty year follow up of the Terman gifted group. *Genetic Psychology Monographs,* 1968, 77, 3–93.

Terman, L. M., & Oden, M. H. *The Gifted Child Grows Up*. Stanford, California: Stanford Univ. Press, 1947.

TOPIC 3. MNEMONIC SYSTEMS

There are slight variations among different mnemonic systems, but the basic components are essentially the same. The first phase of most systems involves the memorization of a series of "pegs." Generally, words are used as pegs and each word is numbered, with associations between numbers and words. A frequently used peg list is: 1-bun, 2-shoe, 3-tree, 4-door, 5-hive, 6-stick, 7-heaven, 8-gate, 9-line, 10-hen. Following the memorization of the peg words, new words can be memorized by using bizarre imagery to connect the new words to the peg words. For example, given that *automobile* is the first to-be-recalled word, the task is to conjure up a bizarre image connecting the first peg, *bun,* and *automobile.* A possible image might be a five-foot bun driving an automobile. The same principle is used for the remaining to-be-recalled words. At recall, the peg words, which are accessible because they have been well memorized, are presumed to elicit the visual images formed during the study trial and thus make the to-be-recalled words accessible.

The effectiveness of providing subjects with a plan for improving memory can be demonstrated by performing an experiment. The experimental subjects are given the list of peg words to memorize. It is important that they have the list extremely well memorized. Then they are told to use the peg list items to recall new items by linking each peg word with a to-be-recalled word by conjuring up a bizarre image of the two words. The control subjects do not receive a peg list. They are told to study the words so that they can recall them during the subsequent recall trial. The list of to-be-recalled words is read to subjects at a rate of one word every five seconds. Concrete words such as *automobile, paper, tiger,* and *football* are used. The typical finding (e.g., Bugelski, Kidd, and Segman, 1968) is that the experimental subjects perform much better than controls.

A number of experiments can be conducted using this basic procedure. For example, one could assess whether young children, who tend to have better imagery (at least eidetic imagery) than adults, can use a peg system effectively. Or, one could assess the effects of imagery instructions, the bizarreness of the images, or the concreteness or abstractness of the list of words.

References

Bower, G. H. Analysis of a mnemonic device. *American Scientist,* 1970, 58, 496–510.

Bugelski, B. R., Kidd, E., & Segman, J. Image as a mediator in one-trial paired-associate learning. *Journal of Experimental Psychology,* 1968, 76, 69–73.

Wood, G. Mnemonic systems in recall. *Journal of Educational Psychology,* 1967, 58 (6, Pt. 2), 1–27.

TOPIC 4. INFORMATION PROCESSING

If you have thought about the acquisition of skills you have probably noted that voluntary control is required during the early stages of skill acquisition. For example, in the early stages of learning to type one has to think about the letters that are being typed. As greater proficiency is developed it is no longer necessary to think about each individual letter. In fact, thinking about individual letters tends to result in more mistakes and a slower rate of typing. One explanation for this phenomenon is that the skilled typist processes units larger than single letters (e.g., words or phrases). It may only appear that the processing is controlled by involuntary mechanisms because the use of larger units does not require all the capacity of the voluntary processing system.

It is possible to study the size of the unit or the nature of the unit that the skilled typist processes. Suppose, for example, that you were interested in determining whether a typist processes the meaning of the material to be typed. That is, you are interested in determining whether meaning units or nonmeaning units are processed. One way to answer this question is, of course, simply to ask skilled typists whether they pay attention to the meaning of the passage they are typing. Or, you could select two passages of equal difficulty and change the ordering of the nouns so that the meaning is disrupted without affecting the syntax and grammar. The normal and distorted versions of each passage are used equally often. Each typist receives the distorted version of one passage and the normal version of the other. The distortion should have a negative effect on typing performance only if the typist is processing the meaning of the passage being typed. If this manipulation has such an effect, then it is possible to conclude that meaning units are being processed.

The size of the units being processed can be studied by taking a passage and varying the presentation order of its parts. For one condition the passage could be presented without any changes. For a second condition the sentences could be presented in a random order. For a third condition the sentences and the phrases within each sentence could be presented in a random order. For a fourth condition all the words could be ordered randomly. For a fifth condition the letters of each word could be scrambled. The effect of the various disruptions can then be used to determine the size of the unit that the typist is processing. For example, if there are no differences between the first four conditions and the fifth condition is the poorest, it is possible to conclude that the typist is processing word units.

References

Annett, J. Acquisition of skill. *British Medical Bulletin,* 1971, 27, 266–271.

TOPIC 5. AGGRESSION

There are a number of studies of aggression in which nonhumans are used as subjects. Animals have a strong tendency to attack each other if they are shocked on the feet (Ulrich and Azrin, 1962) or if a positive reinforcer is withdrawn (Azrin, Hutchinson, and Hake, 1966). In the Azrin, et al., study pigeons were trained to peck a disk, in a schedule which included both reinforcement and extinction. For the reinforcement periods food was delivered as a reward for pecking. For the extinction periods no food was delivered when the pigeons pecked the disk. When the two periods of reinforcement and extinction were alternated, the investigators found that the pigeons would attack a nearby pigeon during the extinction periods. Some of the pigeons attacked even when the "bystander" pigeon was a stuffed model.

The length of the attack on the other pigeon decreased as the length of the time since the last reinforcement increased, and it increased as the number of prior reinforcements increased. It was necessary to alternate reinforcement with extinction in order to get attack, and attack was produced only if the food delivered during the reinforcement period was eaten. That is, satiated pigeons were less likely to attack. The extinction-produced-attack effect was not attributable to a past history of aggression because the effect was also obtained with socially deprived pigeons. The authors concluded that the change from food reinforcement to extinction produced aggression. The reader who has recently been denied an anticipated reward should empathize with the pigeons in the Azrin, et al., study. Yet, it is difficult to demonstrate that the findings obtained with lower animals are applicaple to the understanding of human aggression.

Aggression in humans cannot readily be studied through procedures comparable to those used with lower animals because of practical and ethical considerations. Investigators have demonstrated that human subjects tend to be aggressive after witnessing an aggressive act (e.g., Bandura, Ross, and Ross, 1963), but it is difficult to determine whether these effects are long lasting or applicable to more "real life" situations. The student who is interested in studying human aggression in natural situations is limited primarily to observational and correlational techniques. There are at least two problems that may be of interest. One is determining the level of aggression. Another is determining the antecedents of aggressive behavior.

The investigator who wants to assess the level of aggression can use a number of approaches. One approach is to obtain the incidence of violent crimes per 100,000 population over a period of years. It should be easy to obtain this data since law enforcement agencies keep records of violent crimes. If these records can be accepted as accurate (e.g., if there is no reason to believe the relationship between *actual* and *reported* crimes varied from year to year) *and* there is a trend toward more or less violence, the incidence of crime can be used as a starting point for determining the antecedent conditions. For example, if there is an increase in actual violence as inferred from police records and an increase in the incidence of violence in magazines, newspapers, movies, and television, it is reasonable to ask whether the relationship between depicted and actual violence is causal. If it is possible to obtain measures on actual and depicted violence at various points in time, it is possible to use correlational techniques which allow a cause-effect interpretation. The reader who is interested in this approach can refer to Eron, Huesmann, Lefkowitz, and Walder's (1972) article on television violence and aggression.

The suggestions made above are not realistic for the student who is interested in studying aggression but does not have the time or resources for an elaborate project. Instead, he may elect to study aggression using an observational technique. For example, one could design a questionnaire or interview people to assess attitudes toward violence. Why do some people enjoy watching movies which depict beatings, rapes, killings, shootouts, and slaughters? Is watching violence a novel experience? Is it a safety valve that allows people to release violence rather than commit violent acts? Do people learn to like violence? Another procedure would be to assess individual differences in preference for violence. How do people who enjoy watching violence differ from those people who do not? Or, one could assess whether people are satiated quickly on violence. For example, one could determine whether the repeat rate (people who see a particular movie more than once) is greater for violent or nonviolent movies.

References

Ardrey, R. *The Territorial Imperative.* New York: Atheneum, 1966.

Azrin, N. H., Hutchinson, R. R., & Hake, D. F. Extinction-induced aggression. *Journal of the Experimental Analysis of Behavior,* 1966, 9, 191–204.

Bandura, A., Ross, D., & Ross, S. A. Imitation of film mediated aggressive models. *Journal of Abnormal and Social Psychology,* 1963, 66, 3–11.

Berkowitz, L. Experimental investigations of hostility catharsis. *Journal of Consulting and Clinical Psychology,* 1970, 35, 1–7.

Eron, L. D., Huesmann, L. R., Lefkowitz, M. M., & Walder, L. O. Does television violence cause aggression? *American Psychologist,* 1972, 27, 253–263.

Lorenz, K. *On Aggression.* New York: Harcourt Brace Jovanovich, 1966.

Smith, D., King, M., & Hoebel, B. Lateral hypothalamic control of killing: Evidence for a cholinoceptive mechanism. *Science,* 1970, 167, 900–901.

Ulrich, R. E., & Azrin, N. H. Reflexive fighting in response to aversive stimulation. *Journal of the Experimental Analysis of Behavior,* 1962, 5, 511–520.

Zimbardo, P. G., The human choice: Individuation, reason, and order versus deindividuation, impulse, and chaos. *Nebraska Symposium on Motivation, 1969,* 1970, 18, 237–307.

TOPIC 6. THE COCKTAIL PARTY PHENOMENON

The cocktail party phenomenon (Cherry, 1957) is the label given to the observation that it is possible to select a message to listen to and ignore other messages. Thus, at a cocktail party you can eavesdrop on the conversation behind you or attend to a different conversation, but not both. It is possible to switch back and forth between the two conversations but very difficult to comprehend both if the level of discourse is complex. The phenomenon of selective attention can be investigated using earphones which make it possible to send one message to one ear and a different message to the other ear. The subject has to repeat (shadow) the message in one ear. The message to be shadowed must be sufficiently difficult so that full attention is required. This can usually be accomplished by presenting the material to be shadowed at a relatively fast rate.

The shadowing procedure makes it possible to study some interesting aspects of selective attention. One can consider whether subjects process any of the unattended message by varying the relationship between the attended and unattended message (Treisman, 1964) and by presenting high priority information (e.g., the subject's name) in the unattended message (Moray, 1959). The results of these studies reveal that subjects do process some of the unattended message.

The study of selective attention is usually performed with special equipment which makes it possible to control the messages presented to each ear, but elaborate equipment is not essential for all studies of selective attention. The student can study selective attention by presenting two messages simultaneously to both ears and requiring subjects to attend to only one. This is similar to the situation faced by the student who wants to study while a roommate is playing the stereo. A similar procedure could be used to investigate whether the ability to attend selectively is influenced greatly by the similarity of the two messages. For example, are some kinds of music more disruptive of reading than others? Does music interfere with ability to work mathematical problems? Is it more difficult to attend selectively to one message when both messages are in the same modality (verbal) than when they are in different modalities (one verbal and one visual)? Are there other variables which influence a subject's ability to attend selectively?

One such variable is prior attention habits. The effect of trying to ignore well-learned habits can be demonstrated by constructing a task similar to one developed by Stroop (1935). Pens or pencils with different color inks or leads — say, red, black, green, yellow, and brown — are used to print the words *red, black, green, yellow,* and *brown* in rows. Each word should appear once in each row and the order of the words in each row should be random. Each word is printed in a color other than the color for which it is the label. For example, the word *red* could be printed in black, green, yellow, or brown, but not in red. The color for each word is changed each time the word is presented. The task for the subject is to name the color of each word (i.e., the color of the ink) as quickly as possible. The amount of time needed to complete the task can be the performance measure. The student who performs this task is likely to notice the interference. The interference results from the fact that there is a very strong tendency to respond (attend) to the word instead of to the color of the word. A test of this nature may be used to investigate selective attention.

References

Cherry, C. *On Human Communication.* New York: Science Editions, 1957.

Howarth, C. I., & Bloomfield, J. R. Search and selective attention. *British Medical Bulletin,* 1971, 27, 253–257.

Lindsay, P. H., & Norman, D. A. *Human Information Processing: An Introduction to Psychology.* New York: Academic Press, 1972.

Moray, N. Attention in dichotic listening: Affective cues and the influence of instructions. *Quarterly Journal of Experimental Psychology,* 1959, 11, 56–60.

Stroop, J. R. Studies of interference in serial verbal reactions. *Journal of Experimental Psychology,* 1935, 18, 643–662.

Treisman, A. M. Monitoring and storage of irrelevant messages in selective attention. *Journal of Verbal Learning and Verbal Behavior,* 1964, 3, 449–459.

TOPIC 7. INTERHEMISPHERIC DIFFERENCES IN FUNCTIONING

There is considerable evidence to support the view that the two cerebral hemispheres have markedly different functions in humans. The evidence comes from clinical reports of brain damage, from dichotic listening studies in which different messages are presented simultaneously to each ear, and from studies of patients who have had the connections between the two cerebral hemispheres severed in order to control epileptic seizures. If the connections between the two hemispheres are severed it is possible for the two to function independently. One would not, of course, sever the cerebral commissures in humans solely to study hemispheric differences.

The evidence indicates that for most right-handed subjects and many left-handed subjects language is controlled by the left hemisphere, and nonverbal cognitive functioning appears to be controlled primarily by the right hemisphere. Milner (1971) reports a particularly interesting set of experiments performed on subjects who had had their cerebral commissures severed to control epileptic seizures. The results of her studies reveal that subjects perform nonverbal tasks better with the left hand, which is controlled by the right hemisphere, than with the right hand, which is controlled by the left hemisphere.

The results of experiments with split-brain subjects clearly demonstrate that there is marked asymmetry in the functioning of the two hemispheres. A question of considerable interest is whether one can demonstrate asymmetry effects in subjects with undamaged cerebral commissures. If right-handed subjects are used, it is highly likely that their "language centers" will be represented in the left hemisphere. If the intact cerebral commissures eliminate any asymmetry effects, then it should not make any difference whether information is fed directly to the right or left hemisphere. (Information can be sent directly to the left hemisphere if it is presented only in the right visual field, and vice versa.) The fact that differences in performance can be obtained by presenting information directly to the right or left hemisphere of normal subjects reveals that the presence of connections between the hemispheres does not make them functionally equal. For example, letters exposed for a brief interval are recognized better if the information is sent directly to the left hemisphere than directly to the right hemisphere (Kimura, 1966; McKeever and Huling, 1971). Thus, it appears that normal subjects function like split-brain subjects to some extent.

There are a number of experiments that the reader can do to study asymmetry effects in normal subjects. If equipment is available for presenting stimuli for a brief duration or if there is time to make the necessary equipment, then it is possible to investigate hemispheric differences in visual recognition. For example, is recognition performance for verbal items better when the information is fed directly to the left hemisphere or the right hemisphere? The same question can be asked about nonverbal items.

Another possibility, which does not require special equipment, is to have subjects perform two tasks simultaneously. One task could be to balance a stick with the left or right hand. The other task could be a verbal or nonverbal mental task. In general, the left hemisphere controls the right part of the body and the right hemisphere controls the left part of the body. Therefore, one might expect that it would be more difficult to balance a stick with the right hand while performing a verbal task than while performing a nonverbal mental task. The reverse should be true when the balancing is done with the left hand. In short, there should be an interaction between the hand manipulation (right versus left) and the type of mental task (verbal versus nonverbal).

It is important that the verbal and nonverbal tasks be such that the subjects can perform them successfully. That is, the experimenter "controls" the level of performance on one task and looks for differences in performance on the other. For example, the experimenter could have the subject repeat a verbal message at the same rate that it is presented (i.e., shadow a verbal message) and count the number of times the stick falls while the subject is trying to balance it.

Another possibility is to consider hemispheric differences as a subject variable manipulation. Bakan (1971) argues that a person's psychological functioning may be tied to hemispheric dominance. Bakan provides a test to select people who fit into two categories, right movers or left movers. To administer the test, the investigator looks directly at the subject and asks a question like, "How many letters are in the word Washington?" Subjects who consistently (e.g., 80 percent of the time) look to their right while answering are labeled right movers. Subjects who consistently look to their left are labeled left movers. Subjects who are not consistent can be excused from the experiment. Bakan finds that right movers tend to have higher quantitative ability and left movers have higher verbal ability. It follows, therefore, that an experiment with the type of task (verbal versus quantitative) as one independent variable and the type of subject (right movers versus left movers) as the second independent variable should yield a significant interaction. The reader may want to test this prediction. If a significant interaction is obtained, does this finding add information that was not already available from Bakan's finding that there is a correlation between hemispheric dominance, as defined by the Bakan procedure, and quantitative ability?

References

Bakan, P. The eyes have it. *Psychology Today,* 1971, April.

Gazzaniga, M. S. The split brain in man. *Scientific American,* 1967, 217, 24–29.

Kimura, D. Dual functional asymmetry of the brain in visual perception. *Neuropsychologia,* 1966, 4, 275–289.

McKeever, R., & Huling, J. Bilateral tachistoscopic word recognition as a function of hemisphere stimulated and interhemispheric transmission time. *Neuropsychologia,* 1971, 9, 281–288.

Milner, B. Interhemispheric differences in the localization of psychological processes in man. *British Medical Bulletin,* 1971, 27, 272–277.

Storandt, M. Recognition across visual fields and age. *Journal of Gerontology,* 1972, 27, 482–486.

TOPIC 8. READING

Reading is obviously a very important and, unfortunately, a very complicated phenomenon to understand. One important question concerns the size of the units that one processes while reading. Do you attend to individual letters, to syllables, to words, or to phrases each time your eyes fixate on the material to be read? Miller (1962) argues that the unit must be larger than single syllables because there is not time to process individual syllables and still read as fast as we do. Miller suggests that we make one decision about every second while reading and, therefore, we probably read phrases rather than smaller units.

A number of experiments can be performed to investigate reading. For example, one could vary the difficulty of the material and note the effect on reading rate. The difficulty of the material can be influenced by manipulating the style or content of the passage. One could also investigate performance on the difficult and easy passages by requiring subjects to read the passage upside down. Is the effect of the difficulty manipulation greater when the passage is presented right side up or upside down? What is the effect of allowing the subjects to read the passage once before attempting to read it upside down? What does this effect tell you about reading?

References

Kohler, P. A. Experiments in reading. *Scientific American,* 1972, 227, 84–91.

Miller, G. A. Decision units in the perception of speech. *I. R. E. Trans.* Information Theory, 1962, IT–8, 81–83.

Slobin, D. I. *Psycholinguistics.* Glenview, Ill.: Scott, Foresman, 1971.

Vernon, M. D. *Reading and Its Difficulties: A Psychological Study.* Cambridge, England: Cambridge Univ. Press, 1971.

TOPIC 9. MACHIAVELLIANISM

It is possible to administer a test to assess whether an individual has a Machiavellian view of others (Christie, 1970). A Machiavellian is someone who believes that people are no good so it is permissible to use guile and deceit to influence and control them. The items in the test are designed to assess how the individual views others (e.g., as good, honest, and kind, or as selfish, vicious, and dishonest). The results of the research reported by Christie revealed that people who score high on the Machiavellian scale are more likely to be young, male, from urban environments, and members of professions that manipulate people (lawyers, psychiatrists, and behavioral scientists, as opposed to accountants, surgeons, and natural scientists). The scores were not related to intelligence, personality variables, authoritarianism, occupational status, education, marital status, or birth order.

Christie reported a study conducted by Dorothea Braginsky in which children were given a Machiavellianism test designed for elementary school children. The children who had high scores on the test were compared with children who had low scores. The task was to persuade children who had middle scores to eat crackers soaked in quinine. As you probably know, crackers soaked in quinine have a very bitter taste. The subjects who were to be the persuaders were told they would receive one nickel for every quinine-soaked cracker their subject (victim?) ate. The high Machiavellian persuaders out-performed the low Machiavellian persuaders.

There are a number of possible experiments that the student could perform to study Machiavellianism. For example, it is possible to assess the effect of flattery on behavior to determine whether it "pays" to be a Machiavellian. Or, Machiavellianism could be studied by using factorial experiments in which Machiavellianism (a subject variable) and a nonsubject variable are manipulated. For example, one could manipulate the reasons subjects are given for complying with a request. In one case the reasons are subject based (i.e., gains for the subject) and in the other case the reasons are altruistic (i.e., gains for others). The effect of the reasons manipulation can be expected to be different for high and low Machiavellians. For example, the experimenter could manipulate the reasons given for donating blood (money versus an altruistic appeal). The effectiveness of the two appeals should depend on whether high or low Machiavellians are asked to donate blood. The reader may be able to think of other nonsubject variables which will interact with Machiavellianism.

References

Christie, R. The Machiavellis among us. *Psychology Today,* 1970, November.

Geis, F., & Christie, R. (Eds.). *Studies in Machiavellianism.* New York: Academic Press, 1970.

TOPIC 10. THE PRISONER'S DILEMMA

The prisoner's dilemma game has been used to study conflict and conflict resolution. The name of the game is believed to be based on the conflict situation that two individuals could face when picked up on suspicion of committing a crime (see Lindsay and Norman, 1972). The district attorney can interrogate each suspect separately and offer each a special deal for confessing. He may promise that the person who confesses will be set free and the person who does not will be prosecuted on the maximum charge. If both confess, then they will be prosecuted on a lesser charge. If neither confesses, then the district attorney will not have a good case so the probability of either of the suspects being convicted is quite small. In this case the most reasonable procedure is for neither suspect to confess. This poses a dilemma, however, in that it is necessary for the two suspects to trust each other for this strategy to work.

The game is played by two players. Each player has to select one of two alternatives on each trial. They have to choose simultaneously, usually by writing their choices on pieces of paper, so that neither player knows what the other will do. The amount that one player gains or loses is determined both by his own choice and the choice of the other player. This can be seen by examining a typical payoff matrix presented in Table B-1. If both players choose B, they both receive

TABLE B–1

A Payoff Matrix for the Prisoner's Dilemma Game

		Player 1	
		Selects A	*Selects B*
Player 2	*Selects A*	+10¢ / +10¢	+50¢ / −5¢
	Selects B	−5¢ / +50¢	+1¢ / +1¢

only one cent. If they both choose A, they both receive ten cents. If Player 2 chooses B and Player 1 chooses A, then Player 2 receives fifty cents and Player 1 loses five cents. The reverse is true if Player 1 chooses B and Player 2 chooses A. The game is usually played for a number of trials.

A number of variables can be studied with the prisoner's dilemma game. For example, one could compare choices when subjects are playing for keeps or when they have to return the money. One could look at performance over different stages of practice. That is, do the players arrive at a cooperative strategy or not? A confederate of the experimenter could be one of the players so that the choices of one player (the confederate) could be manipulated. The effect of the confederate's strategy on the selections of the subject could then be systematically investigated. A questionnaire could be given at the end of the experiment to determine how the subjects view each other; the actual subject would not know, of course, that the other "subject" is actually a confederate of the experimenter.

References

Lindsay, P. H., & Norman, D. A. *Human Information Processing: An Introduction to Psychology*. New York: Academic Press, 1972.

Wrightsman, L. S., O'Connor, J., & Baker, N. J. (Eds.). *Cooperation and Competition: Readings on Mixed-Motive Games*. Belmont, California: Brook/Cole, 1972.

appendix: tables

1. *Number Tables for Random Assignment*
2. *Table of* χ^2
3. *Critical Values of* T *in the Wilcoxon-Mann-Whitney Sum of Ranks Test*
4. F *Distribution*
5. *Distribution of* F_{max} *Statistic*
6. *Critical Values of* r_s *(Rank-Order Correlation Coefficient)*
7. *Critical Values of* r *(Pearson Product-Moment Correlation)*
8. *Table of Squares and Square Roots*

1. NUMBER TABLES FOR RANDOM ASSIGNMENT

1	2	3	4	5	6	7	8	9	10	11	12	13	14	15	16	17	18	19	20
3	2	8	2	4	6	4	5	5	1	7	6	4	6	1	5	2	8	1	8
1	5	7	4	5	4	1	2	7	3	4	2	8	7	3	2	3	6	7	6
4	8	2	8	8	8	8	3	1	4	6	5	7	5	2	6	1	3	4	4
2	6	1	5	7	1	5	1	3	7	8	1	2	2	6	4	5	1	6	7
8	4	6	7	1	3	6	8	2	6	5	8	1	3	5	1	7	2	3	3
6	3	4	1	3	5	7	4	8	5	1	4	5	1	7	3	8	7	2	5
7	1	3	3	6	7	3	6	6	8	2	7	3	4	8	7	4	4	8	1
5	7	5	6	2	2	2	7	4	2	3	3	6	8	4	8	6	5	5	2

21	22	23	24	25	26	27	28	29	30	31	32	33	34	35	36	37	38	39	40
1	6	3	4	5	1	3	5	5	7	8	2	1	6	1	7	7	1	6	4
3	8	1	6	6	3	6	3	7	1	3	8	3	8	4	6	1	5	3	2
7	4	4	3	8	5	5	8	2	8	2	7	4	7	5	2	5	8	1	6
6	2	7	2	3	2	4	2	6	3	5	6	5	3	7	5	6	4	4	8
2	3	6	7	4	4	8	6	3	2	7	1	8	5	6	3	3	2	5	3
4	7	8	5	2	7	7	7	1	4	6	4	7	2	3	8	4	6	7	7
5	1	5	8	1	8	1	1	8	5	1	3	2	1	2	1	2	7	8	5
8	5	2	1	7	6	2	4	4	6	4	5	6	4	8	4	8	3	2	1

41	42	43	44	45	46	47	48	49	50	51	52	53	54	55	56	57	58	59	60
2	3	3	2	5	1	8	3	2	6	4	7	5	5	2	2	7	8	7	7
7	6	4	1	3	4	6	7	3	1	6	3	6	7	5	3	1	7	6	5
1	8	8	4	4	6	3	4	8	3	3	8	2	4	4	4	5	6	3	6
5	2	1	8	7	8	4	6	1	2	2	5	8	3	1	7	8	4	1	3
6	5	2	7	2	3	5	2	5	8	7	2	4	2	6	8	2	2	8	1
3	4	6	6	6	7	7	1	6	4	1	4	1	8	3	1	4	1	4	2
8	7	7	5	1	2	2	8	7	5	5	6	7	6	7	6	6	3	5	8
4	1	5	3	8	5	1	5	4	7	8	1	3	1	8	5	3	5	2	4

61	62	63	64	65	66	67	68	69	70	71	72	73	74	75	76	77	78	79	80
4	4	2	8	5	7	5	7	2	1	8	4	7	1	8	3	3	5	5	2
5	8	1	5	2	2	6	6	5	3	2	7	5	7	5	8	5	6	2	4
8	7	4	1	7	6	8	3	6	2	5	5	2	4	6	7	8	3	3	8
6	3	3	2	6	5	7	2	7	5	7	1	3	8	7	2	2	4	6	7

7	5	6	6	3	4	2	4	3	8	3	2	6	2	3	4	4	7	7	1
2	1	7	4	1	3	1	1	1	6	4	6	4	6	4	5	6	2	4	3
3	2	5	3	8	1	3	5	8	4	6	3	1	5	2	6	7	1	1	6
1	6	8	7	4	8	4	8	4	7	1	8	3	8	1	1	1	8	8	5
81	*82*	*83*	*84*	*85*	*86*	*87*	*88*	*89*	*90*	*91*	*92*	*93*	*94*	*95*	*96*	*97*	*98*	*99*	*100*
5	8	1	2	2	6	3	8	7	1	2	7	2	2	3	2	1	2	5	4
8	5	3	1	5	2	8	5	6	4	4	8	7	3	2	6	8	5	7	2
2	3	2	5	6	8	5	6	2	3	6	6	6	6	7	1	2	8	8	1
6	2	8	6	3	1	2	7	5	8	5	2	8	1	6	5	6	3	2	3
7	4	7	4	1	3	4	2	3	5	1	1	3	7	4	8	4	6	1	5
1	1	4	7	8	7	7	1	8	6	3	4	1	4	1	4	7	4	4	6
4	6	5	8	7	4	6	4	4	2	8	3	5	5	8	7	5	1	3	7
3	7	6	3	4	5	1	3	1	7	7	5	4	8	5	3	3	7	6	8
101	*102*	*103*	*104*	*105*	*106*	*107*	*108*	*109*	*110*	*111*	*112*	*113*	*114*	*115*	*116*	*117*	*118*	*119*	*120*
7	5	1	6	8	3	1	3	4	2	3	6	8	3	6	7	3	2	1	2
3	1	2	4	3	1	2	6	8	1	8	5	6	8	4	8	6	8	3	4
8	3	6	5	4	7	3	4	6	8	4	8	2	2	8	4	4	6	2	3
1	2	5	1	7	4	7	5	5	4	1	1	7	4	2	6	1	7	5	8
6	7	7	2	2	6	8	8	1	7	7	4	5	7	7	2	8	1	4	7
2	8	4	3	5	8	6	1	3	3	6	7	3	6	5	3	7	3	6	1
4	6	8	7	1	2	4	7	2	5	2	3	1	1	3	1	2	5	8	6
5	4	3	8	6	5	5	2	7	6	5	2	4	5	1	5	5	4	7	5
121	*122*	*123*	*124*	*125*	*126*	*127*	*128*	*129*	*130*	*131*	*132*	*133*	*134*	*135*	*136*	*137*	*138*	*139*	*140*
6	2	5	2	7	8	7	5	2	4	1	4	6	3	2	7	7	2	5	5
8	3	1	8	6	1	5	2	7	8	7	7	7	2	6	4	1	7	3	6
3	1	2	3	4	6	6	8	5	7	8	3	5	7	3	8	3	3	2	7
2	7	6	4	3	4	2	4	4	6	6	8	8	4	8	3	8	4	7	8
7	6	8	1	5	2	4	7	3	2	4	2	3	6	5	1	6	1	6	4
5	4	4	5	8	3	8	6	8	5	5	5	4	5	7	2	5	6	4	1
4	8	7	7	2	7	1	1	6	1	3	6	1	8	4	5	2	8	1	3
1	5	3	6	1	5	3	3	1	3	2	1	2	1	1	6	4	5	8	2

141	142	143	144	145	146	147	148	149	150	151	152	153	154	155	156	157	158	159	160
2	6	7	2	4	5	2	7	2	6	3	8	1	3	6	1	4	6	7	2
4	4	6	4	8	7	7	1	7	8	4	3	2	5	2	7	7	5	4	6
7	5	1	7	5	6	5	8	3	3	5	7	6	1	1	2	1	7	1	7
5	3	4	5	2	1	6	4	5	2	1	2	8	8	7	5	3	8	3	3
3	7	2	6	3	2	3	2	8	5	7	5	3	7	4	8	6	3	8	1
8	8	5	1	6	3	8	3	4	4	6	6	4	2	3	3	8	2	6	5
1	2	3	8	7	8	4	6	6	1	8	1	5	6	8	4	5	1	2	4
6	1	8	3	1	4	1	5	1	7	2	4	7	4	5	6	2	4	5	8

161	162	163	164	165	166	167	168	169	170	171	172	173	174	175	176	177	178	179	180
7	8	8	4	3	4	6	4	1	5	3	7	6	8	6	2	6	3	7	3
3	7	2	7	1	5	2	3	2	4	1	2	4	5	5	1	4	1	6	7
4	4	6	8	8	6	1	1	4	7	5	1	2	7	3	6	2	2	8	4
6	2	3	3	5	8	4	6	7	6	8	6	3	4	2	7	5	4	5	2
1	3	1	1	6	3	8	7	5	8	4	4	7	2	7	5	1	5	4	6
8	6	4	6	2	2	5	5	8	3	7	8	1	1	4	4	7	7	1	8
5	5	5	2	7	1	7	8	6	2	6	5	5	3	8	8	3	6	2	1
2	1	7	5	4	7	–	2	3	1	2	3	8	6	1	3	8	8	3	5

181	182	183	184	185	186	187	188	189	190	191	192	193	194	195	196	197	198	199	200
1	8	2	5	7	4	5	2	4	7	6	8	8	5	7	1	4	6	5	7
5	3	6	6	6	5	8	8	1	8	5	5	5	3	6	2	5	1	1	5
6	7	7	3	3	6	4	4	7	2	7	1	6	7	1	4	7	4	8	8
2	6	4	4	5	1	6	6	3	6	8	7	3	4	5	3	3	3	6	4
4	2	1	7	1	8	3	3	2	5	1	4	4	8	2	8	2	5	4	3
7	4	3	2	2	2	7	7	5	3	4	3	2	2	8	6	8	8	7	2
3	5	8	1	4	7	2	1	6	4	2	6	7	1	4	5	6	2	6	1
8	1	5	8	8	3	1	5	8	1	3	2	1	6	3	7	1	7	3	6

201	202	203	204	205	206	207	208	209	210	211	212	213	214	215	216	217	218	219	220
5	4	8	2	6	7	1	8	4	2	3	2	5	2	7	6	6	5	4	8
1	1	2	3	3	4	8	2	8	3	1	3	4	1	6	5	1	4	2	2
2	7	5	4	1	5	7	3	7	1	5	1	7	7	1	1	7	8	8	6
4	3	7	8	8	3	2	1	6	5	7	6	2	6	8	4	4	7	5	4

7	5	4	7	5	2	6	7	3	4	8	5	3	8	2	2	5	1	1	7
3	8	1	5	4	6	4	4	2	8	2	7	6	5	4	8	3	2	7	3
6	6	6	6	2	1	5	5	1	7	4	8	1	4	3	7	2	6	3	5
8	2	3	1	7	8	3	6	5	6	6	4	8	3	5	3	8	3	6	1

221	*222*	*223*	*224*	*225*	*226*	*227*	*228*	*229*	*230*	*231*	*232*	*233*	*234*	*235*	*236*	*237*	*238*	*239*	*240*
7	4	4	3	5	3	6	4	7	6	8	6	5	1	2	6	3	4	6	5
5	2	8	8	1	4	4	3	1	7	4	5	8	4	8	3	2	2	3	4
2	7	7	1	4	2	1	5	6	8	7	2	6	5	6	2	5	7	1	7
6	8	2	6	6	8	7	2	2	2	5	7	1	7	3	1	8	6	7	8
3	1	5	4	7	6	3	7	8	1	3	4	3	8	4	7	1	5	4	3
4	3	1	7	3	7	8	1	4	4	2	1	7	6	5	5	7	1	5	2
8	5	3	2	8	1	5	8	3	5	1	8	2	3	7	4	6	8	2	1
1	6	6	8	2	5	2	6	5	3	6	3	4	2	1	8	4	3	8	6

241	*242*	*243*	*244*	*245*	*246*	*247*	*248*	*249*	*250*	*251*	*252*	*253*	*254*	*255*	*256*	*257*	*258*	*259*	*260*
8	3	7	4	1	1	8	5	1	1	4	5	6	7	5	3	2	7	4	7
4	6	8	1	8	6	1	4	4	4	1	3	3	8	7	7	4	8	1	5
3	8	3	3	2	3	5	2	5	7	5	6	5	6	6	1	5	5	8	2
6	1	4	2	7	2	3	6	6	2	7	7	8	3	1	5	3	2	2	6
5	5	2	8	6	5	4	7	3	6	6	4	2	2	8	8	7	6	7	3
1	4	5	5	5	7	7	8	8	8	3	1	1	1	3	2	8	3	3	1
2	2	6	6	4	8	2	1	7	5	8	2	4	4	2	4	6	4	5	4
7	7	1	7	3	4	6	3	2	3	2	8	7	5	4	6	1	1	6	8

261	*262*	*263*	*264*	*265*	*266*	*267*	*268*	*269*	*270*	*271*	*272*	*273*	*274*	*275*	*276*	*277*	*278*	*279*	*280*
7	1	5	4	2	2	3	4	5	2	2	6	2	7	2	8	1	4	3	3
8	6	7	1	6	7	7	8	1	5	3	2	8	3	7	7	8	2	6	2
4	8	3	6	5	6	5	2	4	7	6	8	3	4	8	3	7	1	7	7
3	2	8	5	4	8	1	3	7	6	7	3	4	6	5	6	6	7	4	8
6	3	1	8	6	4	6	1	8	8	8	2	1	1	1	4	4	5	8	1
2	4	6	7	7	3	2	6	3	3	1	7	6	2	4	2	2	3	2	4
1	5	4	2	1	5	8	5	6	4	4	4	7	8	3	1	5	8	1	6
5	7	2	3	3	1	4	7	2	1	5	1	5	5	6	5	3	6	5	5

281	282	283	284	285	286	287	288	289	290	291	292	293	294	295	296	297	298	299	300
5	8	3	6	2	7	5	5	4	2	4	6	3	8	4	1	3	1	2	3
3	2	7	8	5	4	6	8	5	3	5	3	5	6	8	4	6	2	8	6
6	3	2	2	6	3	8	1	3	5	6	7	4	7	2	8	7	7	6	2
2	7	1	3	1	2	2	2	8	7	8	4	1	2	7	2	2	4	4	8
7	6	4	7	4	5	3	3	7	8	1	5	6	5	3	7	4	6	3	4
8	1	5	5	3	1	4	6	2	4	3	2	7	1	5	6	8	5	1	7
1	5	6	4	8	6	7	4	1	6	2	1	8	3	6	5	5	8	7	1
4	4	8	1	7	8	1	7	6	1	7	8	2	4	1	3	1	3	5	5

301	302	303	304	305	306	307	308	309	310	311	312	313	314	315	316	317	318	319	320
7	6	2	7	6	6	1	8	6	1	2	7	3	6	4	5	4	1	5	4
3	8	3	5	4	3	2	2	2	3	5	8	2	4	5	6	5	2	7	3
8	5	1	1	3	4	6	1	5	4	1	6	4	2	3	7	2	6	8	8
6	2	7	3	5	7	4	5	3	7	7	2	7	5	6	2	3	4	2	6
2	4	6	6	8	2	8	6	8	8	6	4	1	3	2	4	1	7	3	2
5	7	4	4	1	5	3	7	1	2	8	3	8	8	7	3	8	8	1	5
4	3	8	8	7	8	7	4	4	6	4	5	6	7	8	8	7	5	6	7
1	1	5	2	2	1	5	3	7	5	3	1	5	1	1	1	6	3	4	1

321	322	323	324	325	326	327	328	329	330	331	332	333	334	335	336	337	338	339	340
4	8	5	8	2	6	3	7	5	2	2	2	1	4	3	4	2	1	3	6
6	2	6	4	6	3	4	3	4	1	7	4	8	7	2	1	7	5	1	7
7	7	2	3	5	4	2	1	3	8	8	8	2	1	4	5	3	3	2	5
3	6	3	6	3	2	5	2	2	6	5	1	6	5	1	8	8	8	4	4
1	5	7	7	1	1	6	5	8	3	3	7	3	2	7	2	5	7	5	1
2	1	8	1	8	7	1	6	1	5	1	5	4	6	6	3	1	6	8	8
5	4	1	5	7	5	7	8	7	4	6	3	5	3	5	7	4	4	7	2
8	3	4	2	4	8	8	4	6	7	4	6	7	8	8	6	6	2	6	3

341	342	343	344	345	346	347	348	349	350	351	352	353	354	355	356	357	358	359	360
6	1	1	3	7	5	5	3	6	7	5	3	1	7	8	1	1	2	4	1
3	6	7	8	5	4	4	7	1	5	3	5	5	6	5	6	7	5	1	6
5	4	2	7	6	1	7	1	4	1	1	7	6	8	3	2	5	3	2	2
1	3	4	2	1	7	6	5	3	8	2	6	3	1	1	5	6	6	5	3
8	5	3	5	3	3	8	2	5	4	8	2	4	4	4	8	8	7	3	8
2	8	5	1	4	2	1	6	8	3	4	4	2	3	6	3	4	8	8	4

4	2	8	4	2	8	2	4	2	6	7	1	8	2	2	7	3	4	6	5
7	7	6	6	8	6	3	8	7	2	6	8	7	5	7	4	2	1	7	7

361	*362*	*363*	*364*	*365*	*366*	*367*	*368*	*369*	*370*	*371*	*372*	*373*	*374*	*375*	*376*	*377*	*378*	*379*	*380*
2	7	5	3	6	2	7	3	8	1	6	3	5	4	7	5	2	8	3	8
3	1	3	5	3	7	3	8	5	3	8	1	7	5	4	4	8	4	6	6
4	4	7	8	4	1	6	6	2	6	2	8	6	7	3	6	7	3	5	7
8	5	2	6	5	3	5	7	7	5	5	5	8	6	5	8	6	2	2	4
5	2	1	1	2	6	4	5	4	2	1	6	1	3	2	3	4	7	4	3
7	8	4	2	1	5	1	1	6	7	7	7	4	8	8	7	5	6	1	2
1	6	6	4	8	8	2	4	1	4	3	2	2	1	6	1	3	1	7	5
6	3	8	7	7	4	8	2	3	8	4	4	3	2	1	2	1	5	8	1

381	*382*	*383*	*384*	*385*	*386*	*387*	*388*	*389*	*390*	*391*	*392*	*393*	*394*	*395*	*396*	*397*	*398*	*399*	*400*
8	2	4	1	8	4	1	3	2	5	5	5	5	1	6	7	3	4	7	2
6	7	1	8	6	3	2	6	8	1	1	7	2	8	3	2	4	3	2	8
4	1	6	4	5	2	5	8	6	4	8	2	6	4	1	1	5	8	3	3
5	3	8	6	7	7	8	2	1	7	3	4	7	5	4	5	7	1	8	7
2	6	3	7	3	6	3	7	5	6	7	6	1	7	7	8	1	2	5	4
3	5	5	2	2	8	6	1	4	2	2	1	3	2	2	6	8	6	4	6
7	8	7	5	1	1	7	4	3	3	6	3	8	6	5	4	2	7	6	5
1	4	2	3	4	5	4	5	7	8	4	8	4	3	8	3	6	5	1	1

401	*402*	*403*	*404*	*405*	*406*	*407*	*408*	*409*	*410*	*411*	*412*	*413*	*414*	*415*	*416*	*417*	*418*	*419*	*420*
2	8	6	6	8	1	6	6	2	4	8	4	5	3	7	7	4	8	7	7
7	4	4	4	6	2	5	4	6	8	4	1	8	2	2	2	2	3	3	1
6	1	1	1	5	4	1	1	7	1	2	8	6	1	3	8	5	6	6	6
5	2	8	3	7	8	4	5	8	6	6	5	2	5	6	3	7	1	1	8
4	6	7	2	3	7	8	7	5	7	3	7	1	7	8	5	8	2	4	3
8	7	5	5	1	5	3	3	3	5	7	6	7	4	5	1	1	5	5	5
1	3	3	7	4	6	2	8	1	2	1	3	3	6	1	6	3	4	8	2
3	5	2	8	2	3	7	2	4	3	5	2	4	8	4	4	6	7	2	4

421	*422*	*423*	*424*	*425*	*426*	*427*	*428*	*429*	*430*	*431*	*432*	*433*	*434*	*435*	*436*	*437*	*438*	*439*	*440*
2	4	4	7	8	5	4	4	2	2	1	2	1	6	1	2	8	2	7	7
8	5	8	2	6	4	8	3	1	3	2	6	4	5	8	8	7	6	4	5
5	3	5	3	7	6	7	1	6	4	4	7	8	3	6	4	3	8	6	1

421	422	423	424	425	426	427	428	429	430	431	432	433	434	435	436	437	438	439	440
7	1	3	6	2	2	6	5	8	6	5	5	6	8	3	1	6	7	5	2
4	8	7	1	3	1	1	7	3	8	6	1	5	2	5	6	5	4	3	4
3	7	1	4	1	3	3	6	5	7	3	4	3	1	7	7	2	1	8	6
1	6	6	8	5	7	2	8	4	5	8	8	2	4	2	5	1	3	1	3
6	2	2	5	4	8	5	2	7	1	7	3	7	7	4	3	4	5	2	8

441	442	443	444	445	446	447	448	449	450	451	452	453	454	455	456	457	458	459	460
5	7	2	8	6	6	3	6	4	8	6	7	6	2	3	3	7	7	5	2
6	1	4	1	4	3	4	1	1	7	3	2	5	3	8	6	6	8	1	5
7	4	7	5	8	2	2	8	7	1	1	5	4	4	7	1	2	4	6	4
4	2	1	3	1	4	6	3	5	2	7	8	8	1	4	2	5	1	7	3
2	3	8	6	2	5	7	7	8	4	8	4	1	6	5	4	1	6	4	7
8	5	5	7	7	7	1	5	3	3	2	1	3	5	1	7	4	3	8	8
1	6	6	4	3	8	5	4	6	6	4	3	2	7	2	8	8	2	2	6
3	8	3	2	5	1	8	2	2	5	5	6	7	8	6	5	3	5	3	1

461	462	463	464	465	466	467	468	469	470	471	472	473	474	475	476	477	488	489	490
1	8	8	3	1	4	8	5	4	5	7	8	8	6	1	2	5	5	8	1
5	7	7	1	6	8	1	4	1	7	3	5	6	5	2	5	4	8	1	4
7	1	5	8	8	2	7	2	5	6	5	4	1	4	5	6	1	1	5	8
3	3	6	7	5	1	5	1	3	8	1	7	4	8	4	7	7	7	7	5
4	5	3	6	2	6	4	7	8	2	8	1	3	2	3	8	8	6	2	6
8	2	2	4	3	7	3	8	7	4	4	2	5	7	8	4	3	4	6	3
2	6	4	5	7	5	2	6	2	3	6	3	7	3	7	1	6	2	4	7
6	4	1	2	4	3	6	3	6	1	2	6	2	1	6	3	2	3	3	2

481	482	483	484	485	486	487	488	489	490	491	492	493	494	495	496	497	498	499	500
2	8	4	5	8	4	2	2	8	3	6	4	6	4	1	5	5	1	2	1
5	4	2	4	5	7	8	7	4	1	5	2	5	6	2	4	7	8	3	5
8	7	7	6	6	5	7	4	7	4	1	7	1	1	6	6	4	6	5	6
1	6	5	1	2	3	6	5	2	7	4	8	8	5	8	3	6	2	4	8
7	1	6	7	4	6	5	1	1	8	3	5	3	2	3	1	1	4	7	4
6	5	8	2	3	2	4	3	6	6	8	1	7	8	7	7	2	5	6	3
4	3	3	8	1	1	3	8	5	5	2	3	2	3	4	2	3	7	8	2
3	2	1	3	7	8	1	6	3	2	7	6	4	7	5	8	8	3	1	7

2. TABLE OF CHI SQUARES*

Degrees of Freedom df	*Two-tail levels*			
	p = *.10*	*.05*	*.02*	*.01*
1	2.706	3.841	5.412	6.635
2	4.605	5.991	7.824	9.210
3	6.251	7.815	9.837	11.341
4	7.779	9.488	11.668	13.277
5	9.236	11.070	13.388	15.086
6	10.645	12.592	15.033	16.812
7	12.017	14.067	16.622	18.475
8	13.362	15.507	18.168	20.090
9	14.684	16.919	19.679	21.666
10	15.987	18.307	21.161	23.209
11	17.275	19.675	22.618	24.725
12	18.549	21.026	24.054	26.217
13	19.812	22.362	25.472	27.688
14	21.064	23.685	26.873	29.141
15	22.307	24.996	28.259	30.578
16	23.542	26.296	29.633	32.000
17	24.769	27.587	30.995	33.409
18	25.989	28.869	32.346	34.805
19	27.204	30.144	33.687	36.191
20	28.412	31.410	35.020	37.566
21	29.615	32.671	36.343	38.932
22	30.813	33.924	37.659	40.289
23	32.007	35.172	38.968	41.638
24	33.196	36.415	40.270	42.980
25	34.382	37.652	41.566	44.314
26	35.563	38.885	42.856	45.642
27	36.741	40.113	44.140	46.963
28	37.916	41.337	45.419	48.278
29	39.087	42.557	46.693	49.588
30	40.256	43.773	47.962	50.892

*This table is taken from Tables III and VI of Fischer: *Statistical Methods for Research Workers,* and Fischer and Yates: *Statistical Tables for Biological, Agricultural and Medical Research,* published by Oliver and Boyd, Edinburgh. Reprinted by permission of the authors and publishers.

3. CRITICAL VALUES OF T IN THE WILCOXON-MANN-WHITNEY SUM OF RANKS TEST*

a. Two-tailed test, $p = .10$; one-tailed test, $p = .05$

	N_1 (Smaller sample)																			
N_2	1	2	3	4	5	6	7	8	9	10	11	12	13	14	15	16	17	18	19	20
3			6																	
4			6	11																
5		3	7	12	19															
6		3	8	13	20	28														
7		3	8	14	21	29	39													
8		4	9	15	23	31	41	51												
9		4	9	16	24	33	43	54	66											
10		4	10	17	26	35	45	56	69	82										
11		4	11	18	27	37	47	59	72	86	100									
12		5	11	19	28	38	49	62	75	89	104	120								
13		5	12	20	30	40	52	64	78	92	108	125	142							
14		5	13	21	31	42	54	67	81	96	112	129	147	166						
15		6	13	22	33	44	56	69	84	99	116	133	152	171	192					
16		6	14	24	34	46	58	72	87	103	120	138	156	176	197	219				
17		6	15	25	35	47	61	75	90	106	123	142	161	182	203	225	249			
18		7	15	26	37	49	63	77	93	110	127	146	166	187	208	231	255	280		
19	1	7	16	27	38	51	65	80	96	113	131	150	171	192	214	237	262	287	313	
20	1	7	17	28	40	53	67	83	99	117	135	155	175	197	220	243	268	294	320	348

*This table is taken from Table L in Tate, M. W., and Clelland, R. C.: *Non-Parametric and Short-Cut Statistics* (1957). Reprinted by permission of The Interstate Printers and Publishers, Danville, Illinois.

b. Two-tailed test, $p = .05$; one-tailed test, $p = .025$

N_2	N_1 (Smaller sample) 1	2	3	4	5	6	7	8	9	10	11	12	13	14	15	16	17	18	19	20
3																				
4				10																
5			6	11	17															
6			7	12	18	26														
7			7	13	20	27	36													
8		3	8	14	21	29	38	49												
9		3	8	14	22	31	40	51	62											
10		3	9	15	23	32	42	53	65	78										
11		3	9	16	24	34	44	55	68	81	96									
12		4	10	17	26	35	46	58	71	84	99	115								
13		4	10	18	27	37	48	60	73	88	103	119	136							
14		4	11	19	28	38	50	62	76	91	106	123	141	160						
15		4	11	20	29	40	52	65	79	94	110	127	145	164	184					
16		4	12	21	30	42	54	67	82	97	113	131	150	169	190	211				
17		5	12	21	32	43	56	70	84	100	117	135	154	174	195	217	240			
18		5	13	22	33	45	58	72	87	103	121	139	158	179	200	222	246	270		
19		5	13	23	34	46	60	74	90	107	124	143	163	182	205	228	252	277	303	
20		5	14	24	35	48	62	77	93	110	128	147	167	188	210	234	258	283	309	337

c. Two-tailed test, $p = .01$; one-tailed test, $p = .005$

	N_1 (Smaller sample)																			
N_2	1	2	3	4	5	6	7	8	9	10	11	12	13	14	15	16	17	18	19	20
3																				
4																				
5					15															
6				10	16	23														
7				10	16	24	32													
8				11	17	25	34	43												
9			6	11	18	26	35	45	56											
10			6	12	19	27	37	47	58	71										
11			6	12	20	28	38	49	61	73	87									
12			7	13	21	30	40	51	63	76	90	105								
13			7	14	22	31	41	53	65	79	93	109	125							
14			7	14	22	32	43	54	67	81	96	112	129	147						
15			8	15	23	33	44	56	69	84	99	115	133	151	171					
16			8	15	24	34	46	58	72	86	102	119	136	155	175	196				
17			8	16	25	36	47	60	74	89	105	122	140	159	180	201	223			
18			8	16	26	37	49	62	76	92	108	125	144	163	184	206	228	252		
19		3	9	17	27	38	50	64	78	94	111	129	147	168	189	210	234	258	283	
20		3	9	18	28	39	52	66	81	97	114	132	151	172	193	215	239	263	289	315

4. *F* DISTRIBUTION*

df *for denom.*	p	df *for numerator* 1	2	3	4	5	6	7	8	9	10
1	.05	161	200	216	225	230	234	237	239	241	242
2	.05	18.5	19.0	19.2	19.2	19.3	19.3	19.4	19.4	19.4	19.4
	.01	98.5	99.0	99.2	99.2	99.3	99.3	99.4	99.4	99.4	99.4
3	.05	10.1	9.55	9.28	9.12	9.10	8.94	8.89	8.85	8.81	8.79
	.01	34.1	30.8	29.5	28.7	28.2	27.9	27.7	27.5	27.3	27.2
4	.05	7.71	6.94	6.59	6.39	6.26	6.16	6.09	6.04	6.00	5.96
	.01	21.2	18.0	16.7	16.0	15.5	15.2	15.0	14.8	14.7	14.5
5	.05	6.61	5.79	5.41	5.19	5.05	4.95	4.88	4.82	4.77	4.74
	.01	16.3	13.3	12.1	11.4	11.0	10.7	10.5	10.3	10.2	10.1
6	.05	5.99	5.14	4.76	4.53	4.39	4.28	4.21	4.15	4.10	4.06
	.01	13.7	10.9	9.78	9.15	8.75	8.47	8.26	8.10	7.98	7.87
7	.05	5.59	4.74	4.35	4.12	3.97	3.87	3.79	3.73	3.68	3.64
	.01	12.2	9.55	8.45	7.85	7.46	7.19	6.99	6.84	6.72	6.62
8	.05	5.32	4.46	4.07	3.84	3.69	3.58	3.50	3.44	3.39	3.35
	.01	11.3	8.65	7.59	7.01	6.63	6.37	6.18	6.03	5.91	5.81
9	.05	5.12	4.26	3.86	3.63	3.48	3.37	3.29	3.23	3.18	3.14
	.01	10.6	8.02	6.99	6.42	6.06	5.80	5.61	5.47	5.35	5.26
10	.05	4.96	4.10	3.71	3.48	3.33	3.22	3.14	3.07	3.02	2.98
	.01	10.0	7.56	6.55	5.99	5.64	5.39	5.20	5.06	4.94	4.85
11	.05	4.84	3.98	3.59	3.36	3.20	3.09	3.01	2.95	2.90	2.85
	.01	9.65	7.21	6.22	5.67	5.32	5.07	4.89	4.74	4.63	4.54

df for denom.	p	df for numerator 1	2	3	4	5	6	7	8	9	10
12	.05	4.75	3.89	3.49	3.26	3.11	3.00	2.91	2.85	2.80	2.75
	.01	9.33	6.93	5.95	5.41	5.06	4.82	4.64	4.50	4.39	4.30
13	.05	4.67	3.81	3.41	3.18	3.03	2.92	2.83	2.77	2.71	2.67
	.01	9.07	6.70	5.74	5.21	4.86	4.62	4.44	4.30	4.19	4.10
14	.05	4.60	3.74	3.34	3.11	2.96	2.85	2.76	2.70	2.65	2.60
	.01	8.86	6.51	5.56	5.04	4.69	4.46	4.28	4.14	4.03	3.94
15	.05	4.54	3.68	3.29	3.06	2.90	2.79	2.71	2.64	2.59	2.54
	.01	8.68	6.36	5.42	4.89	4.56	4.32	4.14	4.00	3.89	3.80
16	.05	4.49	3.63	3.24	3.01	2.85	2.74	2.66	2.59	2.54	2.49
	.01	8.53	6.23	5.29	4.77	4.44	4.20	4.03	3.89	3.78	3.69
17	.05	4.45	3.59	3.20	2.96	2.81	2.70	2.61	2.55	2.49	2.45
	.01	8.40	6.11	5.18	4.67	4.34	4.10	3.93	3.79	3.68	3.59
18	.05	4.41	3.55	3.16	2.93	2.77	2.66	2.58	2.51	2.46	2.41
	.01	8.29	6.01	5.09	4.58	4.25	4.01	3.84	3.71	3.60	3.51
19	.05	4.38	3.52	3.13	2.90	2.74	2.63	2.54	2.48	2.42	2.38
	.01	8.18	5.93	5.01	4.50	4.17	3.94	3.77	3.63	3.52	3.43
20	.05	4.35	3.49	3.10	2.87	2.71	2.60	2.51	2.45	2.39	2.35
	.01	8.10	5.85	4.94	4.43	4.10	3.87	3.70	3.56	3.46	3.37
22	.05	4.30	3.44	3.05	2.82	2.66	2.55	2.46	2.40	2.34	2.30
	.01	7.95	5.72	4.82	4.31	3.99	3.76	3.59	3.45	3.35	3.26
24	.05	4.26	3.40	3.01	2.78	2.62	2.51	2.42	2.36	2.30	2.25
	.01	7.82	5.61	4.72	4.22	3.90	3.67	3.50	3.36	3.26	3.17

26	.05	4.23	3.37	2.98	2.74	2.59	2.47	2.39	2.32	2.27	2.22
	.01	7.72	5.53	4.64	4.14	3.82	3.59	3.42	3.29	3.18	3.09
28	.05	4.20	3.34	2.95	2.71	2.56	2.45	2.36	2.29	2.24	2.19
	.01	7.64	5.45	4.57	4.07	3.75	3.53	3.36	3.23	3.12	3.03
30	.05	4.17	3.32	2.92	2.69	2.53	2.42	2.33	2.27	2.21	2.16
	.01	7.56	5.39	4.51	4.02	3.70	3.47	3.30	3.17	3.07	2.98
40	.05	4.08	3.23	2.84	2.61	2.45	2.34	2.25	2.18	2.12	2.08
	.01	7.31	5.18	4.31	3.83	3.51	3.29	3.12	2.99	2.89	2.80
60	.05	4.00	3.15	2.76	2.53	2.37	2.25	2.17	2.10	2.04	1.99
	.01	7.08	4.98	4.13	3.65	3.34	3.12	2.95	2.82	2.72	2.63
120	.05	3.92	3.07	2.68	2.45	2.29	2.17	2.09	2.02	1.96	1.91
	.01	6.85	4.79	3.95	3.48	3.17	2.96	2.79	2.66	2.56	2.47
200	.05	3.89	3.04	2.65	2.42	2.26	2.14	2.06	1.98	1.93	1.88
	.01	6.76	4.71	3.88	3.41	3.11	2.89	2.73	2.60	2.50	2.41
∞	.05	3.84	3.00	2.60	2.37	2.21	2.10	2.01	1.94	1.88	1.83
	.01	6.63	4.61	3.78	3.32	3.02	2.80	2.64	2.51	2.41	2.32

*This table is taken from Table 18 in Pearson, E. S. and Hartley, H. O.: *Biometrika Tables for Statisticians,* vol. 1, 2nd. Ed. (New York: Cambridge University Press, 1958). Reprinted by permission of Dr. E. S. Pearson.

5. DISTRIBUTION OF F_{max} STATISTICS*[a]

	k = *Number of variances*								
n-*1*	*2*	*3*	*4*	*5*	*6*	*7*	*8*	*9*	*10*
4	9.60	15.5	20.6	25.2	29.5	33.6	37.5	41.4	44.6
5	7.15	10.8	13.7	16.3	18.7	20.8	22.9	24.7	26.5
6	5.82	8.38	10.4	12.1	13.7	15.0	16.3	17.5	18.6
7	4.99	6.94	8.44	9.70	10.8	11.8	12.7	13.5	14.3
8	4.43	6.00	7.18	8.12	9.03	9.78	10.5	11.1	11.7
9	4.03	5.34	6.31	7.11	7.80	8.41	8.95	9.45	9.91
10	3.72	4.85	5.67	6.34	6.92	7.42	7.87	8.28	8.66
12	3.28	4.16	4.79	5.30	5.72	6.09	6.42	6.72	7.00
15	2.86	3.54	4.01	4.37	4.68	4.95	5.19	5.40	5.59
20	2.46	2.95	3.29	3.54	3.76	3.94	4.10	4.24	4.37
30	2.07	2.40	2.61	2.78	2.91	3.02	3.12	3.21	3.29
60	1.67	1.85	1.96	2.04	2.11	2.17	2.22	2.26	2.30
∞	1.00	1.00	1.00	1.00	1.00	1.00	1.00	1.00	1.00

*This table is taken from Table 31 in Pearson, E. S. and Hartley, H. O.: *Biometrika Tables for Statistics,* vol. 1, 2nd. Ed. (New York: Cambridge University Press, 1958). Reprinted by permission of Dr. E. S. Pearson.

[a]$p = .05$.

6. CRITICAL VALUES OF r_s (RANK-ORDER CORRELATION COEFFICIENT)*

Number of pairs	*Level of significance* .10	.05	.01
5	.900	1.000	–
6	.829	.886	1.000
7	.714	.786	.929
8	.643	.738	.881
9	.600	.683	.833
10	.564	.648	.794
12	.506	.591	.777
14	.456	.544	.715
16	.425	.506	.665
18	.399	.475	.625
20	.377	.450	.591
22	.359	.428	.562
24	.343	.409	.537
26	.329	.392	.515
28	.317	.377	.496
30	.306	.364	.478

*This table is taken from Olds, E. G.: "The 5 percent significance levels of sums of squares of rank differences and a correction," *Annals of Mathematical Statistics,* 20 (1949): 117–118, and from Olds, E. G.: "Distribution of sums of squares of rank differences for small numbers of individuals," *Annals of Mathematical Statistics,* 9 (1938): 113–148. Reprinted by permission of the Institute of Mathematical Statistics.

7. CRITICAL VALUES OF *r* (PEARSON PRODUCT-MOMENT CORRELATION)*

Number of pairs minus two	*Level of significance*		
	.10	*.05*	*.01*
1	.98769	.99692	.999877
2	.90000	.95000	.990000
3	.8054	.8783	.95873
4	.7293	.8114	.91720
5	.6694	.7545	.8745
6	.6215	.7067	.8343
7	.5822	.6664	.7977
8	.5494	.6319	.7646
9	.5214	.6021	.7348
10	.4973	.5760	.7079
11	.4762	.5529	.6835
12	.4575	.5324	.6614
13	.4409	.5139	.6411
14	.4259	.4973	.6226
15	.4124	.4821	.6055
16	.4000	.4683	.5897
17	.3887	.4555	.5751
18	.3783	.4438	.5614
19	.3687	.4329	.5487
20	.3598	.4227	.5368
25	.3233	.3809	.4869
30	.2960	.3494	.4487
35	.2746	.3246	.4182
40	.2573	.3044	.3932
45	.2428	.2875	.3721
50	.2306	.2732	.3541
60	.2108	.2500	.3248
70	.1954	.2319	.3017
80	.1829	.2172	.2830
90	.1726	.2050	.2673
100	.1638	.1946	.2540

*This table is taken from Tables III and VI of Fischer; *Statistical Methods for Research Workers,* and from Fischer and Yates: *Statistical Tables for Biological, Agricultural and Medical Research,* published by Oliver and Boyd. Reprinted by permission of the authors and publishers.

8. TABLE OF SQUARES AND SQUARE ROOTS

n	n^2	$\sqrt{n}$	$\sqrt{10n}$	n	n^2	$\sqrt{n}$	$\sqrt{10n}$
1.00	1.0000	1.00000	3.16228	1.50	2.2500	1.22474	3.87298
1.01	1.0201	1.00499	3.17805	1.51	2.2801	1.22882	3.88587
1.02	1.0404	1.00995	3.19374	1.52	2.3104	1.23288	3.89872
1.03	1.0609	1.01489	3.20936	1.53	2.3409	1.23693	3.91152
1.04	1.0816	1.01980	3.22490	1.54	2.3716	1.24097	3.92428
1.05	1.1025	1.02470	3.24037	1.55	2.4025	1.24499	3.93700
1.06	1.1236	1.02956	3.25576	1.56	2.4336	1.24900	3.94968
1.07	1.1449	1.03441	3.27109	1.57	2.4649	1.25300	3.96232
1.08	1.1664	1.03923	3.28634	1.58	2.4964	1.25698	3.97492
1.09	1.1881	1.04403	3.30151	1.59	2.5281	1.26095	3.98748
1.10	1.2100	1.04881	3.31662	1.60	2.5600	1.26491	4.00000
1.11	1.2321	1.05357	3.33167	1.61	2.5921	1.26886	4.01248
1.12	1.2544	1.05830	3.34664	1.62	2.6244	1.27279	4.02492
1.13	1.2769	1.06301	3.36155	1.63	2.6569	1.27671	4.03733
1.14	1.2996	1.06771	3.37639	1.64	2.6896	1.28062	4.04969
1.15	1.3225	1.07238	3.39116	1.65	2.7225	1.28452	4.06202
1.16	1.3456	1.07703	3.40588	1.66	2.7556	1.28841	4.07431
1.17	1.3689	1.08167	3.42053	1.67	2.7889	1.29228	4.08656
1.18	1.3924	1.08628	3.43511	1.68	2.8224	1.29615	4.09878
1.19	1.4161	1.09087	3.44964	1.69	2.8561	1.30000	4.11096
1.20	1.4400	1.09545	3.46410	1.70	2.8900	1.30384	4.12311
1.21	1.4641	1.10000	3.47851	1.71	2.9241	1.30767	4.13521
1.22	1.4884	1.10454	3.49285	1.72	2.9584	1.31149	4.14729
1.23	1.5129	1.10905	3.50714	1.73	2.9929	1.31529	4.15933
1.24	1.5376	1.11355	3.52136	1.74	3.0276	1.31909	4.17133
1.25	1.5625	1.11803	3.53553	1.75	3.0625	1.32288	4.18330
1.26	1.5876	1.12250	3.54965	1.76	3.0976	1.32665	4.19524
1.27	1.6129	1.12694	3.56371	1.77	3.1329	1.33041	4.20714
1.28	1.6384	1.13137	3.57771	1.78	3.1684	1.33417	4.21900
1.29	1.6641	1.13578	3.59166	1.79	3.2041	1.33791	4.23084
1.30	1.6900	1.14018	3.60555	1.80	3.2400	1.34164	4.24264
1.31	1.7161	1.14455	3.61939	1.81	3.2761	1.34536	4.25441
1.32	1.7424	1.14891	3.63318	1.82	3.3124	1.34907	4.26615
1.33	1.7689	1.15326	3.64692	1.83	3.3489	1.35277	4.27785
1.34	1.7956	1.15758	3.66060	1.84	3.3856	1.35647	4.28952
1.35	1.8225	1.16190	3.67423	1.85	3.4225	1.36015	4.30116
1.36	1.8496	1.16619	3.68782	1.86	3.4596	1.36382	4.31277
1.37	1.8769	1.17047	3.70135	1.87	3.4969	1.36748	4.32435
1.38	1.9044	1.17473	3.71484	1.88	3.5344	1.37113	4.33590
1.39	1.9321	1.17898	3.72827	1.89	3.5721	1.37477	4.34741
1.40	1.9600	1.18322	3.74166	1.90	3.6100	1.37840	4.35890
1.41	1.9881	1.18743	3.75500	1.91	3.6481	1.38203	4.37035
1.42	2.0164	1.19164	3.76829	1.92	3.6864	1.38564	4.38178
1.43	2.0449	1.19583	3.78153	1.93	3.7249	1.38924	4.39318
1.44	2.0736	1.20000	3.79473	1.94	3.7636	1.39284	4.40454
1.45	2.1025	1.20416	3.80789	1.95	3.8025	1.39642	4.41588
1.46	2.1316	1.20830	3.82099	1.96	3.8416	1.40000	4.42719
1.47	2.1609	1.21244	3.83406	1.97	3.8809	1.40357	4.43847
1.48	2.1904	1.21655	3.84708	1.98	3.9204	1.40712	4.44972
1.49	2.2201	1.22066	3.86005	1.99	3.9601	1.41067	4.46094

n	n^2	$\sqrt{n}$	$\sqrt{10n}$	n	n^2	$\sqrt{n}$	$\sqrt{10n}$
2.00	4.0000	1.41421	4.47214	2.50	6.2500	1.58114	5.00000
2.01	4.0401	1.41774	4.48330	2.51	6.3001	1.58430	5.00999
2.02	4.0804	1.42127	4.49444	2.52	6.3504	1.58745	5.01996
2.03	4.1209	1.42478	4.50555	2.53	6.4009	1.59060	5.02991
2.04	4.1616	1.42829	4.51664	2.54	6.4516	1.59374	5.03984
2.05	4.2025	1.43178	4.52769	2.55	6.5025	1.59687	5.04975
2.06	4.2436	1.43527	4.53872	2.56	6.5536	1.60000	5.05964
2.07	4.2849	1.43875	4.54973	2.57	6.6049	1.60312	5.06952
2.08	4.3264	1.44222	4.56070	2.58	6.6564	1.60624	5.07937
2.09	4.3681	1.44568	4.57165	2.59	6.7081	1.60935	5.08920
2.10	4.4100	1.44914	4.58258	2.60	6.7600	1.61245	5.09902
2.11	4.4521	1.45258	4.59347	2.61	6.8121	1.61555	5.10882
2.12	4.4944	1.45602	4.60435	2.62	6.8644	1.61864	5.11859
2.13	4.5369	1.45945	4.61519	2.63	6.9169	1.62173	5.12835
2.14	4.5796	1.46287	4.62601	2.64	6.9696	1.62481	5.13809
2.15	4.6225	1.46629	4.63681	2.65	7.0225	1.62788	5.14782
2.16	4.6656	1.46969	4.64758	2.66	7.0756	1.63095	5.15752
2.17	4.7089	1.47309	4.65833	2.67	7.1289	1.63401	5.16720
2.18	4.7524	1.47648	4.66905	2.68	7.1824	1.63707	5.17687
2.19	4.7961	1.47986	4.67974	2.69	7.2361	1.64012	5.18652
2.20	4.8400	1.48324	4.69042	2.70	7.2900	1.64317	5.19615
2.21	4.8841	1.48661	4.70106	2.71	7.3441	1.64621	5.20577
2.22	4.9284	1.48997	4.71169	2.72	7.3984	1.64924	5.21536
2.23	4.9729	1.49332	4.72229	2.73	7.4529	1.65227	5.22494
2.24	5.0176	1.49666	4.73286	2.74	7.5076	1.65529	5.23450
2.25	5.0625	1.50000	4.74342	2.75	7.5625	1.65831	5.24404
2.26	5.1076	1.50333	4.75395	2.76	7.6176	1.66132	5.25357
2.27	5.1529	1.50665	4.76445	2.77	7.6729	1.66433	5.26308
2.28	5.1984	1.50997	4.77493	2.78	7.7284	1.66733	5.27257
2.29	5.2441	1.51327	4.78539	2.79	7.7841	1.67033	5.28205
2.30	5.2900	1.51658	4.79583	2.80	7.8400	1.67332	5.29150
2.31	5.3361	1.51987	4.80625	2.81	7.8961	1.67631	5.30094
2.32	5.3824	1.52315	4.81664	2.82	7.9524	1.67929	5.31037
2.33	5.4289	1.52643	4.82701	2.83	8.0089	1.68226	5.31977
2.34	5.4756	1.52971	4.83735	2.84	8.0656	1.68523	5.32917
2.35	5.5225	1.53297	4.84768	2.85	8.1225	1.68819	5.33854
2.36	5.5696	1.53623	4.85798	2.86	8.1796	1.69115	5.34790
2.37	5.6169	1.53948	4.86826	2.87	8.2369	1.69411	5.35724
2.38	5.6644	1.54272	4.87852	2.88	8.2944	1.69706	5.36656
2.39	5.7121	1.54596	4.88876	2.89	8.3521	1.70000	5.37587
2.40	5.7600	1.54919	4.89898	2.90	8.4100	1.70294	5.38516
2.41	5.8081	1.55242	4.90918	2.91	8.4681	1.70587	5.39444
2.42	5.8564	1.55563	4.91935	2.92	8.5264	1.70880	5.40370
2.43	5.9049	1.55885	4.92950	2.93	8.5849	1.71172	5.41295
2.44	5.9536	1.56205	4.93964	2.94	8.6436	1.71464	5.42218
2.45	6.0025	1.56525	4.94975	2.95	8.7025	1.71756	5.43139
2.46	6.0516	1.56844	4.95984	2.96	8.7616	1.72047	5.44059
2.47	6.1009	1.57162	4.96991	2.97	8.8209	1.72337	5.44977
2.48	6.1504	1.57480	4.97996	2.98	8.8804	1.72627	5.45894
2.49	6.2001	1.57797	4.98999	2.99	8.9401	1.72916	5.46809

n	n^2	$\sqrt{n}$	$\sqrt{10n}$
3.00	9.0000	1.73205	5.47723
3.01	9.0601	1.73494	5.48635
3.02	9.1204	1.73781	5.49545
3.03	9.1809	1.74069	5.50454
3.04	9.2416	1.74356	5.51362
3.05	9.3025	1.74642	5.52268
3.06	9.3636	1.74929	5.53173
3.07	9.4249	1.75214	5.54076
3.08	9.4864	1.75499	5.54977
3.09	9.5481	1.75784	5.55878
3.10	9.6100	1.76068	5.56776
3.11	9.6721	1.76352	5.57674
3.12	9.7344	1.76635	5.58570
3.13	9.7969	1.76918	5.59464
3.14	9.8596	1.77200	5.60357
3.15	9.9225	1.77482	5.61249
3.16	9.9856	1.77764	5.62139
3.17	10.0489	1.78045	5.63028
3.18	10.1124	1.78326	5.63915
3.19	10.1761	1.78606	5.64801
3.20	10.2400	1.78885	5.65685
3.21	10.3041	1.79165	5.66569
3.22	10.3684	1.79444	5.67450
3.23	10.4329	1.79722	5.68331
3.24	10.4976	1.80000	5.69210
3.25	10.5625	1.80278	5.70088
3.26	10.6276	1.80555	5.70964
3.27	10.6929	1.80831	5.71839
3.28	10.7584	1.81108	5.72713
3.29	10.8241	1.81384	5.73585
3.30	10.8900	1.81659	5.74456
3.31	10.9561	1.81934	5.75326
3.32	11.0224	1.82209	5.76194
3.33	11.0889	1.82483	5.77062
3.34	11.1556	1.82757	5.77927
3.35	11.2225	1.83030	5.78792
3.36	11.2896	1.83303	5.79655
3.37	11.3569	1.83576	5.80517
3.38	11.4244	1.83848	5.81378
3.39	11.4921	1.84120	5.82237
3.40	11.5600	1.84391	5.83095
3.41	11.6281	1.84662	5.83952
3.42	11.6964	1.84932	5.84808
3.43	11.7649	1.85203	5.85662
3.44	11.8336	1.85472	5.86515
3.45	11.9025	1.85742	5.87367
3.46	11.9716	1.86011	5.88218
3.47	12.0409	1.86279	5.89067
3.48	12.1104	1.86548	5.89915
3.49	12.1801	1.86815	5.90762

n	n^2	$\sqrt{n}$	$\sqrt{10n}$
3.50	12.2500	1.87083	5.91608
3.51	12.3201	1.87350	5.92453
3.52	12.3904	1.87617	5.93296
3.53	12.4609	1.87883	5.94138
3.54	12.5316	1.88149	5.94979
3.55	12.6025	1.88414	5.95819
3.56	12.6736	1.88680	5.96657
3.57	12.7449	1.88944	5.97495
3.58	12.8164	1.89209	5.98331
3.59	12.8881	1.89473	5.99166
3.60	12.9600	1.89737	6.00000
3.61	13.0321	1.90000	6.00833
3.62	13.1044	1.90263	6.01664
3.63	13.1769	1.90526	6.02495
3.64	13.2496	1.90788	6.03324
3.65	13.3225	1.91050	6.04152
3.66	13.3956	1.91311	6.04979
3.67	13.4689	1.91572	6.05805
3.68	13.5424	1.91833	6.06630
3.69	13.6161	1.92094	6.07454
3.70	13.6900	1.92354	6.08276
3.71	13.7641	1.92614	6.09098
3.72	13.8384	1.92873	6.09918
3.73	13.9129	1.93132	6.10737
3.74	13.9876	1.93391	6.11555
3.75	14.0625	1.93649	6.12372
3.76	14.1376	1.93907	6.13188
3.77	14.2129	1.94165	6.14003
3.78	14.2884	1.94422	6.14817
3.79	14.3641	1.94679	6.15630
3.80	14.4400	1.94936	6.16441
3.81	14.5161	1.95192	6.17252
3.82	14.5924	1.95448	6.18061
3.83	14.6689	1.95704	6.18870
3.84	14.7456	1.95959	6.19677
3.85	14.8225	1.96214	6.20484
3.86	14.8996	1.96469	6.21289
3.87	14.9769	1.96723	6.22093
3.88	15.0544	1.96977	6.22896
3.89	15.1321	1.97231	6.23699
3.90	15.2100	1.97484	6.24500
3.91	15.2881	1.97737	6.25300
3.92	15.3664	1.97990	6.26099
3.93	15.4449	1.98242	6.26897
3.94	15.5236	1.98494	6.27694
3.95	15.6025	1.98746	6.28490
3.96	15.6816	1.98997	6.29285
3.97	15.7609	1.99249	6.30079
3.98	15.8408	1.99499	6.30872
3.99	15.9201	1.99750	6.31664

n	n^2	$\sqrt{n}$	$\sqrt{10n}$
4.00	16.0000	2.00000	6.32456
4.01	16.0801	2.00250	6.33246
4.02	16.1604	2.00499	6.34035
4.03	16.2409	2.00749	6.34823
4.04	16.3216	2.00998	6.35610
4.05	16.4025	2.01246	6.36396
4.06	16.4836	2.01494	6.37181
4.07	16.5649	2.01742	6.37966
4.08	16.6464	2.01990	6.38749
4.09	16.7281	2.02237	6.39531
4.10	16.8100	2.02485	6.40312
4.11	16.8921	2.02731	6.41093
4.12	16.9744	2.02978	6.41872
4.13	17.0569	2.03224	6.42651
4.14	17.1396	2.03470	6.43428
4.15	17.2225	2.03715	6.44205
4.16	17.3056	2.03961	6.44981
4.17	17.3889	2.04206	6.45755
4.18	17.4724	2.04450	6.46529
4.19	17.5561	2.04695	6.47302
4.20	17.6400	2.04939	6.48074
4.21	17.7241	2.05183	6.48845
4.22	17.8084	2.05426	6.49615
4.23	17.8929	2.05670	6.50384
4.24	17.9776	2.05913	6.51153
4.25	18.0625	2.06155	6.51920
4.26	18.1476	2.06398	6.52687
4.27	18.2329	2.06640	6.53452
4.28	18.3184	2.06882	6.54217
4.29	18.4041	2.07123	6.54981
4.30	18.4900	2.07364	6.55744
4.31	18.5761	2.07605	6.56506
4.32	18.6624	2.07846	6.57267
4.33	18.7489	2.08087	6.58027
4.34	18.8356	2.08327	6.58787
4.35	18.9225	2.08567	6.59545
4.36	19.0096	2.08806	6.60303
4.37	19.0969	2.09045	6.61060
4.38	19.1844	2.09284	6.61816
4.39	19.2721	2.09523	6.62571
4.40	19.3600	2.09762	6.63325
4.41	19.4481	2.10000	6.64078
4.42	19.5364	2.10238	6.64831
4.43	19.6249	2.10476	6.65582
4.44	19.7136	2.10713	6.66333
4.45	19.8025	2.10950	6.67083
4.46	19.8916	2.11187	6.67832
4.47	19.9809	2.11424	6.68581
4.48	20.0704	2.11660	6.69328
4.49	20.1601	2.11896	6.70075
4.50	20.2500	2.12132	6.70820
4.51	20.3401	2.12368	6.71565
4.52	20.4304	2.12603	6.72309
4.53	20.5209	2.12838	6.73053
4.54	20.6116	2.13073	6.73795
4.55	20.7025	2.13307	6.74537
4.56	20.7936	2.13542	6.75278
4.57	20.8849	2.13776	6.76018
4.58	20.9764	2.14009	6.76757
4.59	21.0681	2.14243	6.77495
4.60	21.1600	2.14476	6.78233
4.61	21.2521	2.14709	6.78970
4.62	21.3444	2.14942	6.79706
4.63	21.4369	2.15174	6.80441
4.64	21.5296	2.15407	6.81175
4.65	21.6225	2.15639	6.81909
4.66	21.7156	2.15870	6.82642
4.67	21.8089	2.16102	6.83374
4.68	21.9024	2.16333	6.84105
4.69	21.9961	2.16564	6.84836
4.70	22.0900	2.16795	6.85565
4.71	22.1841	2.17025	6.86294
4.72	22.2784	2.17256	6.87023
4.73	22.3729	2.17486	6.87750
4.74	22.4676	2.17715	6.88477
4.75	22.5625	2.17945	6.89202
4.76	22.6576	2.18174	6.89928
4.77	22.7529	2.18403	6.90652
4.78	22.8484	2.18632	6.91375
4.79	22.9441	2.18861	6.92098
4.80	23.0400	2.19089	6.92820
4.81	23.1361	2.19317	6.93542
4.82	23.2324	2.19545	6.94262
4.83	23.3289	2.19773	6.94982
4.84	23.4256	2.20000	6.95701
4.85	23.5225	2.20227	6.96419
4.86	23.6196	2.20454	6.97137
4.87	23.7169	2.20681	6.97854
4.88	23.8144	2.20907	6.98570
4.89	23.9121	2.21133	6.99285
4.90	24.0100	2.21359	7.00000
4.91	24.1081	2.21585	7.00714
4.92	24.2064	2.21811	7.01427
4.93	24.3049	2.22036	7.02140
4.94	24.4036	2.22261	7.02851
4.95	24.5025	2.22486	7.03562
4.96	24.6016	2.22711	7.04273
4.97	24.7009	2.22935	7.04982
4.98	24.8004	2.23159	7.05691
4.99	24.9001	2.23383	7.06399

n	n^2	$\sqrt{n}$	$\sqrt{10n}$
5.00	25.0000	2.23607	7.07107
5.01	25.1001	2.23830	7.07814
5.02	25.2004	2.24054	7.08520
5.03	25.3009	2.24277	7.09225
5.04	25.4016	2.24499	7.09930
5.05	25.5025	2.24722	7.10634
5.06	25.6036	2.24944	7.11337
5.07	25.7049	2.25167	7.12039
5.08	25.8064	2.25389	7.12741
5.09	25.9081	2.25610	7.13442
5.10	26.0100	2.25832	7.14143
5.11	26.1121	2.26053	7.14843
5.12	26.2144	2.26274	7.15542
5.13	26.3169	2.26495	7.16240
5.14	26.4196	2.26716	7.16938
5.15	26.5225	2.26936	7.17635
5.16	26.6256	2.27156	7.18331
5.17	26.7289	2.27376	7.19027
5.18	26.8324	2.27596	7.19722
5.19	26.9361	2.27816	7.20417
5.20	27.0400	2.28035	7.21110
5.21	27.1441	2.28254	7.21803
5.22	27.2484	2.28473	7.22496
5.23	27.3529	2.28692	7.23187
5.24	27.4576	2.28910	7.23878
5.25	27.5625	2.29129	7.24569
5.26	27.6676	2.29347	7.25259
5.27	27.7729	2.29565	7.25948
5.28	27.8784	2.29783	7.26636
5.29	27.9841	2.30000	7.27324
5.30	28.0900	2.30217	7.28011
5.31	28.1961	2.30434	7.28697
5.32	28.3024	2.30651	7.29383
5.33	28.4089	2.30868	7.30068
5.34	28.5156	2.31084	7.30753
5.35	28.6225	2.31301	7.31437
5.36	28.7296	2.31517	7.32120
5.37	28.8369	2.31733	7.32803
5.38	28.9444	2.31948	7.33485
5.39	29.0521	2.32164	7.34166
5.40	29.1600	2.32379	7.34847
5.41	29.2681	2.32594	7.35527
5.42	29.3764	2.32809	7.36206
5.43	29.4849	2.33024	7.36885
5.44	29.5936	2.33238	7.37564
5.45	29.7025	2.33452	7.38241
5.46	29.8116	2.33666	7.38918
5.47	29.9209	2.33880	7.39594
5.48	30.0304	2.34094	7.40270
5.49	30.1401	2.34307	7.40945

n	n^2	$\sqrt{n}$	$\sqrt{10n}$
5.50	30.2500	2.34521	7.41620
5.51	30.3601	2.34734	7.42294
5.52	30.4704	2.34947	7.42967
5.53	30.5809	2.35160	7.43640
5.54	30.6916	2.35372	7.44312
5.55	30.8025	2.35584	7.44983
5.56	30.9136	2.35797	7.45654
5.57	31.0249	2.36008	7.46324
5.58	31.1364	2.36220	7.46994
5.59	31.2481	2.36432	7.47663
5.60	31.3600	2.36643	7.48331
5.61	31.4721	2.36854	7.48999
5.62	31.5844	2.37065	7.49667
5.63	31.6969	2.37276	7.50333
5.64	31.8096	2.37487	7.50999
5.65	31.9225	2.37697	7.51665
5.66	32.0356	2.37908	7.52330
5.67	32.1489	2.38118	7.52994
5.68	32.2624	2.38328	7.53658
5.69	32.3761	2.38537	7.54321
5.70	32.4900	2.38747	7.54983
5.71	32.6041	2.38956	7.55645
5.72	32.7184	2.39165	7.56307
5.73	32.8329	2.39374	7.56968
5.74	32.9476	2.39583	7.57628
5.75	33.0625	2.39792	7.58288
5.76	33.1776	2.40000	7.58947
5.77	33.2929	2.40208	7.59605
5.78	33.4084	2.40416	7.60263
5.79	33.5241	2.40624	7.60920
5.80	33.6400	2.40832	7.61577
5.81	33.7561	2.41039	7.62234
5.82	33.8724	2.41247	7.62889
5.83	33.9889	2.41454	7.63544
5.84	34.1056	2.41661	7.64199
5.85	34.2225	2.41868	7.64853
5.86	34.3396	2.42074	7.65506
5.87	34.4569	2.42281	7.66159
5.88	34.5744	2.42487	7.66812
5.89	34.6921	2.42693	7.67463
5.90	34.8100	2.42899	7.68115
5.91	34.9281	2.43105	7.68765
5.92	35.0464	2.43311	7.69415
5.93	35.1649	2.43516	7.70065
5.94	35.2836	2.43721	7.70714
5.95	35.4025	2.43926	7.71362
5.96	35.5216	2.44131	7.72010
5.97	35.6409	2.44336	7.72658
5.98	35.7604	2.44540	7.73305
5.99	35.8801	2.44745	7.73951

n	n^2	$\sqrt{n}$	$\sqrt{10n}$	n	n^2	$\sqrt{n}$	$\sqrt{10n}$
6.00	36.0000	2.44949	7.74597	6.50	42.2500	2.54951	8.06226
6.01	36.1201	2.45153	7.75242	6.51	42.3801	2.55147	8.06846
6.02	36.2404	2.45357	7.75887	6.52	42.5104	2.55343	8.07465
6.03	36.3609	2.45561	7.76531	6.53	42.6409	2.55539	8.08084
6.04	36.4816	2.45764	7.77174	6.54	42.7716	2.55734	8.08703
6.05	36.6025	2.45967	7.77817	6.55	42.9025	2.55930	8.09321
6.06	36.7236	2.46171	7.78460	6.56	43.0336	2.56125	8.09938
6.07	36.8449	2.46374	7.79102	6.57	43.1649	2.56320	8.10555
6.08	36.9664	2.46577	7.79744	6.58	43.2964	2.56515	8.11172
6.09	37.0881	2.46779	7.80385	6.59	43.4281	2.56710	8.11788
6.10	37.2100	2.46982	7.81025	6.60	43.5600	2.56905	8.12404
6.11	37.3321	2.47184	7.81665	6.61	43.6921	2.57099	8.13019
6.12	37.4544	2.47386	7.82304	6.62	43.8244	2.57294	8.13634
6.13	37.5769	2.47588	7.82943	6.63	43.9569	2.57488	8.14248
6.14	37.6996	2.47790	7.83582	6.64	44.0896	2.57682	8.14862
6.15	37.8225	2.47992	7.84219	6.65	44.2225	2.57876	8.15475
6.16	37.9456	2.48193	7.84857	6.66	44.3556	2.58070	8.16088
6.17	38.0689	2.48395	7.85493	6.67	44.4889	2.58263	8.16701
6.18	38.1924	2.48596	7.86130	6.68	44.6224	2.58457	8.17313
6.19	38.3161	2.48797	7.86766	6.69	44.7561	2.58650	8.17924
6.20	38.4400	2.48998	7.87401	6.70	44.8900	2.58844	8.18535
6.21	38.5641	2.49199	7.88036	6.71	45.0241	2.59037	8.19146
6.22	38.6884	2.49399	7.88670	6.72	45.1584	2.59230	8.19756
6.23	38.8129	2.49600	7.89303	6.73	45.2929	2.59422	8.20366
6.24	38.9376	2.49800	7.89937	6.74	45.4276	2.59615	8.20975
6.25	39.0625	2.50000	7.90569	6.75	45.5625	2.59808	8.21584
6.26	39.1876	2.50200	7.91202	6.76	45.6976	2.60000	8.22192
6.27	39.3129	2.50400	7.91833	6.77	45.8329	2.60192	8.22800
6.28	39.4384	2.50599	7.92465	6.78	45.9684	2.60384	8.23408
6.29	39.5641	2.50799	7.93095	6.79	46.1041	2.60576	8.24015
6.30	39.6900	2.50998	7.93725	6.80	46.2400	2.60768	8.24621
6.31	39.8161	2.51197	7.94355	6.81	46.3761	2.60960	8.25227
6.32	39.9424	2.51396	7.94984	6.82	46.5124	2.61151	8.25833
6.33	40.0689	2.51595	7.95613	6.83	46.6489	2.61343	8.26438
6.34	40.1956	2.51794	7.96241	6.84	46.7856	2.61534	8.27043
6.35	40.3225	2.51992	7.96869	6.85	46.9225	2.61725	8.27647
6.36	40.4496	2.52190	7.97496	6.86	47.0596	2.61916	8.28251
6.37	40.5769	2.52389	7.98123	6.87	47.1969	2.62107	8.28855
6.38	40.7044	2.52587	7.98749	6.88	47.3344	2.62298	8.29458
6.39	40.8321	2.52784	7.99375	6.89	47.4721	2.62488	8.30060
6.40	40.9600	2.52982	8.00000	6.90	47.6100	2.62679	8.30662
6.41	41.0881	2.53180	8.00625	6.91	47.7481	2.62869	8.31264
6.42	41.2164	2.53377	8.01249	6.92	47.8864	2.63059	8.31865
6.43	41.3449	2.53574	8.01873	6.93	48.0249	2.63249	8.32466
6.44	41.4736	2.53772	8.02496	6.94	48.1636	2.63439	8.33067
6.45	41.6025	2.53969	8.03119	6.95	48.3025	2.63629	8.33667
6.46	41.7316	2.54165	8.03741	6.96	48.4416	2.63818	8.34266
6.47	41.8609	2.54362	8.04363	6.97	48.5809	2.64008	8.34865
6.48	41.9904	2.54558	8.04984	6.98	48.7204	2.64197	8.35464
6.49	42.1201	2.54755	8.05605	6.99	48.8601	2.64386	8.36062

n	n^2	$\sqrt{n}$	$\sqrt{10n}$
7.00	49.0000	2.64575	8.36660
7.01	49.1401	2.64764	8.37257
7.02	49.2804	2.64953	8.37854
7.03	49.4209	2.65141	8.38451
7.04	49.5616	2.65330	8.39047
7.05	49.7025	2.65518	8.39643
7.06	49.8436	2.65707	8.40238
7.07	49.9849	2.65895	8.40833
7.08	50.1264	2.66083	8.41427
7.09	50.2681	2.66271	8.42021
7.10	50.4100	2.66458	8.42615
7.11	50.5521	2.66646	8.43208
7.12	50.6944	2.66833	8.43801
7.13	50.8369	2.67021	8.44393
7.14	50.9796	2.67208	8.44985
7.15	51.1225	2.67395	8.45577
7.16	51.2656	2.67582	8.46168
7.17	51.4089	2.67769	8.46759
7.18	51.5524	2.67955	8.47349
7.19	51.6961	2.68142	8.47939
7.20	51.8400	2.68328	8.48528
7.21	51.9841	2.68514	8.49117
7.22	52.1284	2.68701	8.49706
7.23	52.2729	2.68887	8.50294
7.24	52.4176	2.69072	8.50882
7.25	52.5625	2.69258	8.51469
7.26	52.7076	2.69444	8.52056
7.27	52.8529	2.69629	8.52643
7.28	52.9984	2.69815	8.53229
7.29	53.1441	2.70000	8.53815
7.30	53.2900	2.70185	8.54400
7.31	53.4361	2.70370	8.54985
7.32	53.5824	2.70555	8.55570
7.33	53.7289	2.70740	8.56154
7.34	53.8756	2.70924	8.56738
7.35	54.0225	2.71109	8.57321
7.36	54.1696	2.71293	8.57904
7.37	54.3169	2.71477	8.58487
7.38	54.4644	2.71662	8.59069
7.39	54.6121	2.71846	8.59651
7.40	54.7600	2.72029	8.60233
7.41	54.9081	2.72213	8.60814
7.42	55.0564	2.72397	8.61394
7.43	55.2049	2.72580	8.61974
7.44	55.3536	2.72764	8.62554
7.45	55.5025	2.72947	8.63134
7.46	55.6516	2.73130	8.63713
7.47	55.8009	2.73313	8.64292
7.48	55.9504	2.73496	8.64870
7.49	56.1001	2.73679	8.65448

n	n^2	$\sqrt{n}$	$\sqrt{10n}$
7.50	56.2500	2.73861	8.66025
7.51	56.4001	2.74044	8.66603
7.52	56.5504	2.74226	8.67179
7.53	56.7009	2.74408	8.67756
7.54	56.8516	2.74591	8.68332
7.55	57.0025	2.74773	8.68907
7.56	57.1536	2.74955	8.69483
7.57	57.3049	2.75136	8.70057
7.58	57.4564	2.75318	8.70632
7.59	57.6081	2.75500	8.71206
7.60	57.7600	2.75681	8.71780
7.61	57.9121	2.75862	8.72353
7.62	58.0644	2.76043	8.72926
7.63	58.2169	2.76225	8.73499
7.64	58.3696	2.76405	8.74071
7.65	58.5225	2.76586	8.74643
7.66	58.6756	2.76767	8.75214
7.67	58.8289	2.76948	8.75785
7.68	58.9824	2.77128	8.76356
7.69	59.1361	2.77308	8.76926
7.70	59.2900	2.77489	8.77496
7.71	59.4441	2.77669	8.78066
7.72	59.5984	2.77849	8.78635
7.73	59.7529	2.78029	8.79204
7.74	59.9076	2.78209	8.79773
7.75	60.0625	2.78388	8.80341
7.76	60.2176	2.78568	8.80909
7.77	60.3729	2.78747	8.81476
7.78	60.5284	2.78927	8.82043
7.79	60.6841	2.79106	8.82610
7.80	60.8400	2.79285	8.83176
7.81	60.9961	2.79464	8.83742
7.82	61.1524	2.79643	8.84308
7.83	61.3089	2.79821	8.84873
7.84	61.4656	2.80000	8.85438
7.85	61.6225	2.80179	8.86002
7.86	61.7796	2.80357	8.86566
7.87	61.9369	2.80535	8.87130
7.88	62.0944	2.80713	8.87694
7.89	62.2521	2.80891	8.88257
7.90	62.4100	2.81069	8.88819
7.91	62.5681	2.81247	8.89382
7.92	62.7264	2.81425	8.89944
7.93	62.8849	2.81603	8.90505
7.94	63.0436	2.81780	8.91067
7.95	63.2025	2.81957	8.91628
7.96	63.3616	2.82135	8.92188
7.97	63.5209	2.82312	8.92749
7.98	63.6804	2.82489	8.93308
7.99	63.8401	2.82666	8.93868

n	n^2	$\sqrt{n}$	$\sqrt{10n}$	n	n^2	$\sqrt{n}$	$\sqrt{10n}$
8.00	64.0000	2.82843	8.94427	8.50	72.2500	2.91548	9.21954
8.01	64.1601	2.83019	8.94986	8.51	72.4201	2.91719	9.22497
8.02	64.3204	2.83196	8.95545	8.52	72.5904	2.91890	9.23038
8.03	64.4809	2.83373	8.96103	8.53	72.7609	2.92062	9.23580
8.04	64.6416	2.83549	8.96660	8.54	72.9316	2.92233	9.24121
8.05	64.8025	2.83725	8.97218	8.55	73.1025	2.92404	9.24662
8.06	64.9636	2.83901	8.97775	8.56	73.2736	2.92575	9.25203
8.07	65.1249	2.84077	8.98332	8.57	73.4449	2.92746	9.25743
8.08	65.2864	2.84253	8.98888	8.58	73.6164	2.92916	9.26283
8.09	65.4481	2.84429	8.99444	8.59	73.7881	2.93087	9.26823
8.10	65.6100	2.84605	9.00000	8.60	73.9600	2.93258	9.27362
8.11	65.7721	2.84781	9.00555	8.61	74.1321	2.93428	9.27901
8.12	65.9344	2.84956	9.01110	8.62	74.3044	2.93598	9.28440
8.13	66.0969	2.85132	9.01665	8.63	74.4769	2.93769	9.28978
8.14	66.2596	2.85307	9.02219	8.64	74.6496	2.93939	9.29516
8.15	66.4225	2.85482	9.02774	8.65	74.8225	2.94109	9.30054
8.16	66.5856	2.85657	9.03327	8.66	74.9956	2.94279	9.30591
8.17	66.7489	2.85832	9.03881	8.67	75.1689	2.94449	9.31128
8.18	66.9124	2.86007	9.04434	8.68	75.3424	2.94618	9.31665
8.19	67.0761	2.86182	9.04986	8.69	75.5161	2.94788	9.32202
8.20	67.2400	2.86356	9.05539	8.70	75.6900	2.94958	9.32738
8.21	67.4041	2.86531	9.06091	8.71	75.8641	2.95127	9.33274
8.22	67.5684	2.86705	9.06642	8.72	76.0384	2.95296	9.33809
8.23	67.7329	2.86880	9.07193	8.73	76.2129	2.95466	9.34345
8.24	67.8976	2.87054	9.07744	8.74	76.3876	2.95635	9.34880
8.25	68.0625	2.87228	9.08295	8.75	76.5625	2.95804	9.35414
8.26	68.2276	2.87402	9.08845	8.76	76.7376	2.95973	9.35949
8.27	68.3929	2.87576	9.09395	8.77	76.9129	2.96142	9.36483
8.28	68.5584	2.87750	9.09945	8.78	77.0884	2.96311	9.37017
8.29	68.7241	2.87924	9.10494	8.79	77.2641	2.96479	9.37550
8.30	68.8900	2.88097	9.11043	8.80	77.4400	2.96648	9.38083
8.31	69.0561	2.88271	9.11592	8.81	77.6161	2.96816	9.38616
8.32	69.2224	2.88444	9.12140	8.82	77.7924	2.96985	9.39149
8.33	69.3889	2.88617	9.12688	8.83	77.9689	2.97153	9.39681
8.34	69.5556	2.88791	9.13236	8.84	78.1456	2.97321	9.40213
8.35	69.7225	2.88964	9.13783	8.85	78.3225	2.97489	9.40744
8.36	69.8896	2.89137	9.14330	8.86	78.4996	2.97658	9.41276
8.37	70.0569	2.89310	9.14877	8.87	78.6769	2.97825	9.41807
8.38	70.2244	2.89482	9.15423	8.88	78.8544	2.97993	9.42338
8.39	70.3921	2.89655	9.15969	8.89	79.0321	2.98161	9.42868
8.40	70.5600	2.89828	9.16515	8.90	79.2100	2.98329	9.43398
8.41	70.7281	2.90000	9.17061	8.91	79.3881	2.98496	9.43928
8.42	70.8964	2.90172	9.17606	8.92	79.5664	2.98664	9.44458
8.43	71.0649	2.90345	9.18150	8.93	79.7449	2.98831	9.44987
8.44	71.2336	2.90517	9.18695	8.94	79.9236	2.98998	9.45516
8.45	71.4025	2.90689	9.19239	8.95	80.1025	2.99166	9.46044
8.46	71.5716	2.90861	9.19783	8.96	80.2816	2.99333	9.46573
8.47	71.7409	2.91033	9.20326	8.97	80.4609	2.99500	9.47101
8.48	71.9104	2.91204	9.20869	8.98	80.6404	2.99666	9.47629
8.49	72.0801	2.91376	9.21412	8.99	80.8201	2.99833	9.48156

n	n^2	$\sqrt{n}$	$\sqrt{10n}$	n	n^2	$\sqrt{n}$	$\sqrt{10n}$
9.00	81.0000	3.00000	9.48683	9.50	90.2500	3.08221	9.74679
9.01	81.1801	3.00167	9.49210	9.51	90.4401	3.08383	9.75192
9.02	81.3604	3.00333	9.49737	9.52	90.6304	3.08545	9.75705
9.03	81.5409	3.00500	9.50263	9.53	90.8209	3.08707	9.76217
9.04	81.7216	3.00666	9.50789	9.54	91.0116	3.08869	9.76729
9.05	81.9025	3.00832	9.51315	9.55	91.2025	3.09031	9.77241
9.06	82.0836	3.00998	9.51840	9.56	91.3936	3.09192	9.77753
9.07	82.2649	3.01164	9.52365	9.57	91.5849	3.09354	9.78264
9.08	82.4464	3.01330	9.52890	9.58	91.7764	3.09516	9.78775
9.09	82.6281	3.01496	9.53415	9.59	91.9681	3.09677	9.79285
9.10	82.8100	3.01662	9.53939	9.60	92.1600	3.09839	9.79796
9.11	82.9921	3.01828	9.54463	9.61	92.3521	3.10000	9.80306
9.12	83.1744	3.01993	9.54987	9.62	92.5444	3.10161	9.80816
9.13	83.3569	3.02159	9.55510	9.63	92.7369	3.10322	9.81326
9.14	83.5396	3.02324	9.56033	9.64	92.9296	3.10483	9.81835
9.15	83.7225	3.02490	9.56556	9.65	93.1225	3.10644	9.82344
9.16	83.9056	3.02655	9.57079	9.66	93.3156	3.10805	9.82853
9.17	84.0889	3.02820	9.57601	9.67	93.5089	3.10966	9.83362
9.18	84.2724	3.02985	9.58123	9.68	93.7024	3.11127	9.83870
9.19	84.4561	3.03150	9.58645	9.69	93.8961	3.11288	9.84378
9.20	84.6400	3.03315	9.59166	9.70	94.0900	3.11448	9.84886
9.21	84.8241	3.03480	9.59687	9.71	94.2841	3.11609	9.85393
9.22	85.0084	3.03645	9.60208	9.72	94.4784	3.11769	9.85901
9.23	85.1929	3.03809	9.60729	9.73	94.6729	3.11929	9.86408
9.24	85.3776	3.03974	9.61249	9.74	94.8676	3.12090	9.86914
9.25	85.5625	3.04138	9.61769	9.75	95.0625	3.12250	9.87421
9.26	85.7476	3.04302	9.62289	9.76	95.2576	3.12410	9.87927
9.27	85.9329	3.04467	9.62808	9.77	95.4529	3.12570	9.88433
9.28	86.1184	3.04631	9.63328	9.78	95.6484	3.12730	9.88939
9.29	86.3041	3.04795	9.63846	9.79	95.8441	3.12890	9.89444
9.30	86.4900	3.04959	9.64365	9.80	96.0400	3.13050	9.89949
9.31	86.6761	3.05123	9.64883	9.81	96.2361	3.13209	9.90454
9.32	86.8624	3.05287	9.65401	9.82	96.4324	3.13369	9.90959
9.33	87.0489	3.05450	9.65919	9.83	96.6289	3.13528	9.91464
9.34	87.2356	3.05614	9.66437	9.84	96.8256	3.13688	9.91968
9.35	87.4225	3.05778	9.66954	9.85	97.0225	3.13847	9.92472
9.36	87.6096	3.05941	9.67471	9.86	97.2196	3.14006	9.92975
9.37	87.7969	3.06105	9.67988	9.87	97.4169	3.14166	9.93479
9.38	87.9844	3.06268	9.68504	9.88	97.6144	3.14325	9.93982
9.39	88.1721	3.06431	9.69020	9.89	97.8121	3.14484	9.94485
9.40	88.3600	3.06594	9.69536	9.90	98.0100	3.14643	9.94987
9.41	88.5481	3.06757	9.70052	9.91	98.2081	3.14802	9.95490
9.42	88.7364	3.06920	9.70567	9.92	98.4064	3.14960	9.95992
9.43	88.9249	3.07083	9.71082	9.93	98.6049	3.15119	9.96494
9.44	89.1136	3.07246	9.71597	9.94	98.8036	3.15278	9.96995
9.45	89.3025	3.07409	9.72111	9.95	99.0025	3.15436	9.97497
9.46	89.4916	3.07571	9.72625	9.96	99.2016	3.15595	9.97998
9.47	89.6809	3.07734	9.73139	9.97	99.4009	3.15753	9.98499
9.48	89.8704	3.07896	9.73653	9.98	99.6004	3.15911	9.98999
9.49	90.0601	3.08058	9.74166	9.99	99.8001	3.16070	9.99500
				10.00	100.000	3.16228	10.0000

appendix:

answers for problems in chapters 8 through 11

CHAPTER 8

1. a. Nominal
   b. Ordinal
   c. Ordinal or interval
   d. Ratio
   e. Ratio
   f. Ordinal
2. Mode = 13, median = 12.5, mean = 12.0.
3. Mode = 14 and 16, median = 15, mean = 15.0.
4. Mode = 3, median = 4.5, mean = 8.0.
5. Mean is greater than median for 8-2A, mean is less than median for 8-2B, and mean is equal to median for 8-2C.
7. Range = 13, variance = 15.11, and standard deviation = 3.89 for problem 2. Range = 2, variance = 1.11, and standard deviation = 1.05 for problem 3. Range = 17, variance = 45.11, and standard deviation = 6.72 for problem 4.
9. The first test.
10. The means are 11.8, 13.0, and 14.6 for the Mnemonic Group and 6.8, 9.4, and 12.6 for the Control Group.
11. Rank order correlation = .806, product moment correlation = .821.
12. $R = 1.00$, no, no.
13. $R = -.95$.

CHAPTER 9

1. The expected frequencies are 25, 75, 37.5, 112.5, 37.5, and 112.5.
2. The obtained Chi Square of 9.37 exceeds the table value so the null hypothesis can be rejected.
4. Chi Square = 46.16.
5. Chi Square for males = 64.0, Chi Square for females = 1.96.
7. Chi Square for Median Test = 2.68 so you cannot reject the null hypothesis.
8. Smaller sum = 108 so you can reject the null hypothesis.

CHAPTER 10

2. $F = .80$, you cannot reject the null hypothesis.
3. $F = 11.24$, you can reject the null hypothesis.
4. $F = 3.43$, you cannot reject the null hypothesis.
5. $F = 56.63$, you can reject the null hypothesis.
6. $F = 2.84$, you cannot reject the null hypothesis for the group I versus Group

III comparison. $F = 68.49$, you can reject the null hypothesis for the Group I versus Group II comparison. $F = 98.85$, you can reject the null hypothesis for the Group II versus Group III comparison. The mean square for within groups was taken from the overall analysis.

7. $F = 1.13$ for the humanitarian versus lawyer comparison, you cannot reject the null hypothesis. $F = .41$ for the type of appeal effect, you cannot reject the null hypothesis. $F = 191.35$ for the interaction, you can reject the null hypothesis.
8. $F = .32$ for anxiety level, you cannot reject the null hypothesis. $F = 146.29$ for the type of task effect, you can reject the null hypothesis. $F = 31.65$ for the interaction, you can reject the null hypothesis.
11. Yes, the $F_{max} = 3.30$.

CHAPTER 11

1. $Q = 5.33$, you can reject the null hypothesis.
2. Friedman test yields value of 6.17, you can reject the null hypothesis.
3. $Q = 3.57$, you cannot reject the null hypothesis.
4. $F = 4.94$ for conditions, you cannot reject the null hypothesis.
5. $F = 41.50$ for treatments, you can reject the null hypothesis.
6. $F = 27.08$, you can reject the null hypothesis.

REFERENCES

Barber, T. X., & Silver, M. J. Fact, fiction, and the experimenter bias effect. *Psychological Bulletin Monograph,* 1968, 70, No. 6, Part 2, 1–29.

Beach, F. A. The snark was a boojum. *American Psychologist,* 1950, 5, 115–124.

Bennett, C. F. Marital agreement as a function of status-related agreement. *Social Forces,* 1971, 50, 249–255.

Cameron, P. Children's reactions to second-hand tobacco smoke. *Journal of Applied Psychology,* 1972, 56, 171–173.

Campbell, D. T. Blind variation and selective retention in creative thought and in other knowledge processes. *Psychological Review,* 1960, 67, 380–400.

Cavior, N., & Boblett, P. J. The physical attractiveness of dating vs. married couples. *Proceedings of the Annual Convention of The American Psychological Association,* 1972, 7 (Pt. 1), 175–176.

Cochran, W. G. The comparison of percentages in matched samples. *Biometrika,* 1950, 37, 256–266.

Cohen, M., Liebson, I. A., & Faillace, L. A. A technique for establishing controlled drinking in chronic alcoholics. *Diseases of the Nervous System,* 1972, 33, 46–49.

Crano, W. D., Kenny, D. A., & Campbell, D. T. Does intelligence cause achivement? A cross-lagged panel analysis. *Journal of Educational Psychology*, 1972, 63, 258–275.

Dabbs, J. M. Sex, setting, and reactions to crowding on sidewalks. *Proceedings of the Annual Convention of The American Psychological Association,* 1972, 7, (Pt. 1), 205–206.

Hanley, C., Personal Communication, 1969.

Hays, W. L. *Statistics for Psychologists.* New York: Holt, Rinehart, & Winston, 1963.

Johnson, D. A., Porter, R. J., & Marteljan, P. Racial discrimination in apartment rentals. *Journal of Applied Social Psychology,* 1971, 1, 364–377.

Koch, M. D., & Arnold, W. J. Effects of early social deprivation on emotionality in rats. *Journal of Comparative and Physiological Psychology,* 1972, 78, 391–399.

Kolstoe, R. H. *Introduction to Statistics for the Behavioral Sciences.* Homewood, Illinois: Dorsey, 1973.

Kruskal, W. H., & Wallis, W. A. Use of ranks in one criterion variance analysis. *Journal of American Statistical Association,* 1952, 47, 583–621.

Lockard, R. B. The albino rat: A defensible choice or a bad habit? *American Psychologist,* 1968, 23, 734–742.

Marshall, A. J., & Disney, H. J. de S. Experimental induction of the breeding season in a xerophilous bird. *Nature,* 1957, 180, 647–649.

Mednick, S. A., & Mednick, M. T. *Examiner's Manual: Remote Associates Test.* Boston: Houghton-Mifflin, 1967.

Neisser, U. *Cognitive Psychology.* New York: Appleton-Century-Crofts, 1967.

Norris, D. Crying and laughing in imbeciles. *Developmental Medicine and Child Neurology,* 1971, 13, 756–761.

Orne, M. T. The nature of hypnosis: Artifact and essence. *Journal of Abnormal and Social Psychology,* 1959, 58, 277–299.

Orne, M. T. On the social psychology of the psychological experiment: With particular reference to demand characteristics and their implications. *American Psychologist,* 1962, 17, 776–783.

Rosenthal, R. On the social psychology of the psychological experiment: The experimenter's hypothesis as unintended determinant of experimental results. *American Scientist,* 1963, 51, 268–283.

Rosenthal, R. *Experimenter Effects in Behavioral Research.* New York: Appleton-Century-Crofts, 1966.

Schusterman, R. J., & Gentry, R. L. Development of a fatted male phenomenon in California sea lions. *Developmental Psychobiology,* 1971, 4, 333–338.

Siegel, S. *Nonparametric Statistics for the Behavioral Sciences.* New York: McGraw-Hill, 1956.

Skinner, B. F. *Beyond Freedom and Dignity.* New York: Alfred A. Knopf, 1971.

Suomi, S. J., & Harlow, H. F. Social rehabilitation of isolate-reared monkeys. *Developmental Psychology,* 1972, 6, 487–496.

Tinbergen, N. The curious behavior of the stickleback. *Scientific American,* 1952, 187, 22–26.

Toman, W. Never mind your horoscope, birth order rules all. *Psychology Today,* 1970, 4, December.

Tulving, E., & Madigan, S. A. Memory and verbal learning. *Annual Review of Psychology,* 1970, 21, 437–484.

Underwood, B. J. *Experimental Psychology* (2nd Ed.). New York: Appleton-Century-Crofts, 1966.

Webb, E. J., Campbell, D. T., Schwartz, R. D., & Sechrest, L. *Unobtrusive Measures: Nonreactive Research in the Social Sciences.* Chicago: Rand McNally, 1966.

Winer, B. J. *Statistical Principles in Experimental Design* (2nd Ed.). New York: McGraw-Hill, 1971.

Wolf, M. M., & Risley, T. M. Reinforcement: Applied research. In R. Glaser (Ed.), *The Nature of Reinforcement.* New York: Academic Press, 1971.

GLOSSARY

Abscissa: the X or horizontal axis in a graph.

Alpha: in hypothesis testing, probability of rejecting the null hypothesis when the null hypothesis is true; probability of a Type 1 error; the alpha level is equal to the significance level.

Analysis of variance: a statistical test appropriate for analyzing interval data obtained with between-subject and within-subject experimental designs.

Assumption: basic tenet of a theory which is taken for granted and from which other tenets are derived; condition which must be met before certain conclusions are warranted, e.g., the assumptions of a statistical test.

Bar graph: a frequency distribution in which the height of bars is used to indicate the frequency of each score or each class of scores.

Between-group variance: a measure of the fluctuations between groups based on group means.

Between-subject design: an experimental design in which each subject is tested under only one level of each independent variable.

Chance: in probability, chance is the lack of any systematic effect influencing the outcome of an event. All events are equally likely.

Chi Square Test: a statistical test appropriate for analyzing nominal data obtained with between-subject designs.

Cochran Q Test: a statistical test appropriate for analyzing nominal data obtained with within-subject designs.

Combination: a group of r objects or events in which the order of the objects or events within the group is not important.

Confounding variable: a variable not manipulated as an independent variable which systematically varies with an independent variable so that the effect of the confounding variable and the effect of the independent variable cannot be separated.

Constant: a term in a mathematical formula which does not vary.

Control group: the group that does not receive the treatment. The performance of the no-treatment group (control) is compared to the treatment group (experimental) to assess the effect of the treatment.

Correlation: a measure of the extent to which two variables are related, not necessarily in a causal relationship. The magnitude of a correlation can vary from -1.00 to $+1.00$.

Counterbalancing: a technique used to distribute order and time-related effects over all conditions equally by systematically varying the order of the conditions within or across subjects.

Criterion: a standard used to assess the predictive validity of a test.

Data: the scores obtained on a dependent variable or performance measure.

Degrees of freedom: the number of values that are free to vary given that the sum of the values and the number of values are fixed.

Demand characteristics: those cues available to a subject in an experiment which may enable him to determine the "purpose" of the experiment; the cues which allow the subject to infer what the experimenter "expects" of him; one type of confounding variable.

Dependent variable: the variable the investigator measures to assess the effect of the independent variable; in an experiment, the variable whose level is not determined by the experimenter.

Descriptive statistics: methods for summarizing, organizing, and communicating data.

Determinism: an assumption of science asserting that events have a finite number of causes which can be discovered.

Dichotomous variable: a variable with two and only two mutually exclusive categories, e.g., male-female, yes-no.

Differential transfer: in a within-subject design, differential transfer occurs when the effect of one treatment is dependent on the treatment which preceded it; a treatment-by-order-of-treatment interaction.

Distribution: a set of values for an attribute or variable.

Double-blind: a design in which neither the subject nor the experimenter knows which subjects are in which treatment condition.

Eidetic imagery: visual image of a visual stimulus which is retained for a short period of time after the stimulus is removed. The image is almost photographic in clarity.

Equivalent groups: groups are said to be equivalent if the probability of the obtained group differences if only chance is operating is greater than the significance level.

Ethologist: a zoologist or naturalist whose main interest is in behaviors specific to a species.

Experimental design: a plan for obtaining and treating data in which the experimental method is used.

Experimental method: a method used to study phenomena in which one or more independent variables are manipulated, and performance on one or more dependent variables is measured.

Explanation: a specification of the antecedent conditions necessary to demonstrate a phenomenon.

Factorial (!): $N!$ indicates the operation of multiplying together all of the counting numbers from 1 to N. For instance, $5! = 5 \times 4 \times 3 \times 2 \times 1 = 120$.

Factorial design: an experimental design in which each level of each independent variable occurs with each level of every other independent variable.

Fixed effects model: a statistical model which necessitates that the conclusions drawn from the experiment be limited to the actual levels of the independent variable which were manipulated, because the levels manipulated have not been randomly selected from the population of possible levels.

Frequency distribution: a set of scores arranged in ascending or descending order. The number of times each score occurs is indicated.

Friedman Test: a statistical test appropriate for analyzing ordinal data obtained with within-subject designs.

F_{max} statistic: a statistical test appropriate for determining whether the probability of the obtained differences between sample variances is less than the significance level.

Generalization: in experimentation, being able to extend the results of an experiment beyond the actual sample tested to the population from which the sample was drawn. In order to generalize the results to the population, the sample must have been randomly selected from the population.

Heterogeneous: dissimilar.

Histogram: a bar graph.

Homogeneous: similar, alike.

Hypothesis: a proposed explanation for a phenomenon.

Independent variable: a variable in an experiment whose level is determined by the experimenter; a variable systematically manipulated by the experimenter in order to determine the effect of one variable on another.

Interaction: the effect of one independent variable on performance is dependent on the level of another independent variable.

Interval scale: a scale in which the scale values are related by a single, underlying, quantitative dimension and there are equal intervals between successive scale values.

Kurtosis: the degree of peakedness of a distribution.

Leptokurtic: a distribution or curve that is steep.

Linear relationship: a relationship between two variables in which an increase in one variable is always accompanied by a consant increase or is always accompanied by a constant decrease in the other.

Longitudinal study: a method in which individuals are studied over time and measurements are obtained on the individuals at various intervals.

Matched-groups design: a between-subject design in which groups are equated on the variable(s) selected for matching in an attempt to obtain equal groups or to reduce the within-group chance fluctuations.

Mean ($\overline{X}$): a descriptive measure of central tendency appropriate for interval data; the sum of all the scores divided by the number of scores.

Mean square (MS): in analysis of variance, an estimate of population variance if the null hypothesis is true.

Median: a descriptive measure of central tendency; the value which divides the distribution in half.

Median Test: a statistical test appropriate for analyzing ordinal data obtained with between-subject designs.

Mesokurtic: a curve or distribution that is neither peaked nor flat. The normal distribution is mesokurtic.

Mnemonic system: a memory improving system.

Mode: a descriptive measure of central tendency; the most frequently occurring value.

Monotonic relationship: a relationship between two variables is monotonic if an increase in one variable is always accompanied by an increase or is always accompanied by a decrease in the other variable.

Nominal measurement: placement of subjects into qualitatively different categories.

Nonreactive measure: a measure of behavior in which the subject is not aware of being observed and the subject's behavior is not changed by the observation process.

Normal distribution: a symmetric, mesokurtic, bell-shaped curve. If scores on a measure are distributed normally, the greater the difference between a score and the mean, the less the probability of obtaining the score.

Null hypothesis: the assertion that the independent variable will not have an effect on the dependent variable.

Null hypothesis sampling distribution: a distribution of sample values that can be expected if only chance is operating.

Observational techniques: a method of research based on observing behavior of organisms without the systematic manipulation of an independent variable.

One-tailed test: a procedure for testing the null hypothesis in which the entire rejection area is placed at one end of the appropriate sampling distribution.

Operational definition: a definition of a concept in terms of the operations which must be performed in order to demonstrate the concept.

Order: an assumption of science asserting that events follow each other in regular sequences.

Ordinal scale: a scale in which scale values are related by a single, underlying quantitative dimension but it is not possible to assume that the differences between successive scale values are of equal magnitude.

Ordinate: the *Y* or vertical axis in a graph.

Permutation: an ordered sequence of objects or events.

Phenomenon: a fact or event that is observable.

Placebo: a substance or treatment having no effect which is given to a control group in place of a drug or experimental treatment in order to minimize demand characteristics.

Platykurtic: a curve or distribution that is flat.

Population: the potential units for observation from which the sample to be observed is drawn.

Probability: an estimate of the likelihood that a particular event will occur; the ratio of the number of favorable events to the total number of possible events if only chance is operating.

Random assignment: a procedure used to place subjects in groups or to order events such that only chance determines the placement or ordering.

Random-groups design: a between-subject design in which random assignment is used to assign subjects to conditions.

Random sampling: a procedure used to obtain representative samples from a population. In complete random sampling, each subject in the population must have an equal chance of being selected and the selection or nonselection of one subject cannot influence the selection or nonselection of any other subject.

Range: a descriptive measure of variability; the difference score obtained by subtracting the smallest score in the distribution from the largest score in the distribution.

Ratio scale: a scale in which scale values are related by a single, underlying, quantitative dimension; there are equal intervals between scale values, and there is an absolute zero.

Reactive measure: a measure of behavior obtained under circumstances in which the observee is aware that his behavior is being observed or there is reason to believe that the observation or measurement procedures *may* influence the observee's behavior.

Reliability: consistency of a test or a measurement instrument usually determined by computing a correlation between scores obtained by the same subjects on two forms of the test, scores on the same test at two points in time, or scores obtained on each half of the test.

Research hypothesis: the assertion that the independent variable will have an effect on the dependent variable.

Rho (ρ)*:* the rank-order correlation for a population. r_s is an estimate of rho.

Sample: the group of subjects selected from the population.

Scale: a set of numbers assigned to objects or events indicating the relative amounts of some characteristic which the objects or events possess.

Scatter-plot: a plot of the scores made by the same individuals on two different variables, providing a pictorial representation of the degree of correlation between two variables.

Significance: statistical significance refers to whether the obtained results are a rare or common event if only chance is operating. Psychological significance refers to the quality of the idea, the adequacy of the test of the idea, and the clarity of the results.

Significance level: the probability that is used to define an experimental outcome as a rare event if only chance is operating and is also used to define what is meant by equivalent groups.

Skewed distribution: a nonsymmetrical distribution. In a negatively skewed distribution extreme scores are below the mean. In a positively skewed distribution extreme scores are above the mean.

Standard deviation: a descriptive measure of variability obtained by taking the square root of the variance; a unit of measurement, or a standard way of describing scores in terms of their relation to the mean.

Standard error: the standard deviation of the sampling distribution.

Stereotaxic procedure: a procedure for immobilizing and positioning the head of an organism in order to stimulate, record, or destroy brain tissue.

Subject: the object or organism on which a manipulation or observation is being made.

Subject variable: a characteristic of a subject that can be measured.

Theory: a tentative explanation for a phenomenon or set of phenomena.

Two-tailed test: A procedure for testing the null hypothesis in which the rejection area is placed at both ends of the appropriate sampling distribution.

Type 1 error: a Type 1 error occurs if the null hypothesis is rejected when it is true.

Type 2 error: a Type 2 error occurs if the null hypothesis is not rejected when it is false.

Validity: the extent to which an instrument measures what it is purported to measure.

Variable: a thing or event which can be measured or manipulated.

Variance (s^2): a descriptive measure of variability within a sample; the sum of the squared deviations of each score from the mean divided by the number of scores minus one.

Wilcoxon-Mann-Whitney Test: a statistical test appropriate for analyzing ordinal data obtained with within-subject designs.

Within-group variance: a measure of the fluctuations between subjects in the same group.

Within-subject design: an experimental design in which each subject is tested under more than one level of the independent variable.

INDEX

10:30 - 2:30

2:00

1974
1937
37
13
24

58
- 21
1936